SIR JOSEPH WHITWORTH

Sir Joseph Whitworth

'The World's Best Mechanician'

Norman Atkinson

SUTTON PUBLISHING

First published in the United Kingdom in 1996 by
Sutton Publishing Limited
Phoenix Mill · Thrupp · Stroud · Gloucestershire · GL5 2BU

Reprinted 1997

Paperback edition first published 1997

British Library Cataloguing in Publication Data
A catalogue record for this book is available from the British Library.

ISBN 0–7509–1211–1 (hardback)
ISBN 0–7509–1648–6 (paperback)

Front cover: Sir Joseph Whitworth, 1882

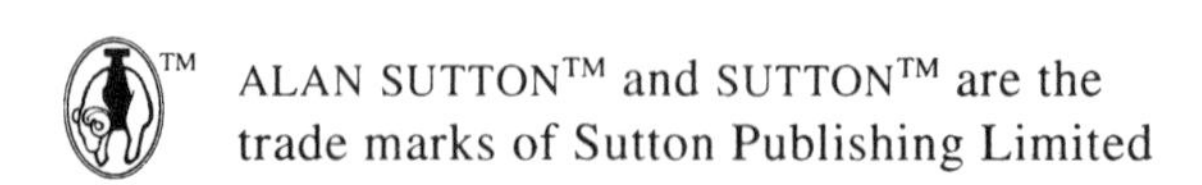

Typeset in 10/13 New Baskerville.
Typesetting and origination by
Sutton Publishing Limited.
Printed in Great Britain by
WBC Limited, Bridgend.

Contents

List of Plates

Between pages 146 and 147

Acknowledgements

As surely as darkness follows the setting sun, so surely will England recede as a manufacturing nation, unless her industrial population becomes much more conversant with science than they now are.

Dr Lyon Playfair
November 1851

Lyon Playfair was absolutely right and as the introduction to this book explains, the Victorian period of mechanical engineering is still a woefully neglected branch of our knowledge. Despite its richness, the rehabilitation of Whitworth's work would not have been so comprehensive without the unselfish effort (both past and present) of so many Whitworth devotees. I sincerely trust therefore that this book proves a competent tribute to their fact-finding and scrutiny.

One such friend from the past was the late Roy Jordeson, Chief Technician at the Simon Engineering Laboratories, who expertly demonstrated Whitworth's genius. Of the senior lecturers from the School of Engineering at Manchester, it is to John Harris FIMechE that I owe my greatest debt. His ready advice and professional expertise was so typical of the man. I am also grateful to Dr Mike Watts IMechE for letting me have sight of the work on Whitworth done at the University by S.R.E. Maddox.

Joseph Whitworth was examined endlessly as an expert engineering witness by various Parliamentary committees. Unfortunately much of this deep seam has escaped the hand of the indexer and remains difficult to get at, particularly for non-Parliamentarians. I myself left the House of Commons in 1987, therefore I am extremely grateful to Parliamentary colleagues: Jim Callaghan, Sir Patrick Cormack, Ken Eastham, Sir Robert Rhodes James, in addition to David Menhennet, the House of Commons Librarian and his expert staff. Equally expert, in equally difficult terrain, Librarians J.C. Andrews and Judithe M. Blacklaw ushered me through the MOD archive. I am correspondingly indebted to the PRO and to H.J. Woodend, the archive custodian at the RSAF Enfield. Steve Mills, TUC Librarian, also gave me invaluable help as did Christopher Barry, editor of *The Engineer.*

Naturally in a work of this kind, Mike Chrimes, the Civil Engineers' Librarian, in addition to Gordon Morrison and Keith Moore MA of IMechE, were frequently called upon. They all responded proficiently and kindly with increasing gratitude from me.

The text will show how much I am indebted to both archivists and librarians at Manchester, Stockport, Leeds, Kirklees and Cumbria local history units; David Taylor and Margaret De Motte of Manchester and Anne Brien of Stockport especially.

Anne Rowbottom of Stockport contributed much in regard to the Orrells as did Ann Boulton, prolific with her Manchester Lit. and Phil. sources. Dr Frank Stainthorp FIChemE has been expert and much appreciated. Roy Whitfield has the knack of providing answers when all seems lost – the most welcome ally any writer could wish for.

Geoffrey C. Meadowcroft, formerly of Craven Brothers, and B.C. Jarvis of NU-Type Ltd helped demystify the missing Whitworth drawings and I much appreciate their help. One of the most difficult pieces of the Whitworth jigsaw however, remains the historic sequence leading to the birth of hydraulic forging. Douglas Oldham CEng, MIMechE, an acknowledged expert in the field, generously contributed both help and advice and I am obligated and most thankful to him.

My final acknowledgements are among the most salient. Firstly to Jackie Gumpert, many thanks indeed. Over at Darley Dale, Terence Kilburn MA, ARHistS, and Iris Wagstaffe MBE are trojans in the restoration of the Whitworth heritage. The relationship between Darley Dale and Whitworth is, of course, foremost in any recall of the engineer's life and work. But I myself (in this work) and Whitworth luminaries generally, are profoundly indebted to them both for continuing their already distinguished contribution. Likewise, Kurt and Hanné Mayer in New York expertly researched every Whitworth source and it is to them I owe a particular debt. As always, my wife Irene, an absolute gem. To them all our special thanks.

Norman Atkinson
London, December 1995

Chronological Table

1803	Whitworth's parents, Charles and Sarah, are married at St Mary's Parish Church, Stockport, 14 March.
1803	Joseph Whitworth born, Stockport, 21 December.
1814	Whitworth's mother, Sarah, dies aged thirty-four, following birth of her daughter also named Sarah.
1815	Both Joseph and his brother John fostered out. Their father, Charles, enters Training College for Congregational Ministers at Idle, near Bradford. Joseph probably starts work as a 'rivet boy' or similar.
1820	Joseph absconds to Manchester. Gets job with W.J. Crighton & Co.
1824	Leaves Manchester for London.
1825	Marries Fanny Ankers at the Parish Church, Ilkeston, Derbyshire, on his way to London, 25 February.
1825	On reaching London, starts work with Maudslay.
1829	Mary Louisa Broadhurst (Whitworth's second wife) born Ardwick, Manchester, 31 August.
1831	Manchester starts to build locomotives. First one in August, class 2–2–0 named 'Manchester'.
1832	Whitworth and his wife Fanny return to Manchester. He rents small workshop in Port Street.
1833	Joseph's sister Sarah dies at Shelley, Yorkshire, aged 20.
1833	Whitworth moves to his new factory site, 44 Chorlton Street, Manchester.
1834	Applies for his first patent – a screw cutting machine.
1838	Joseph and Fanny move house to 62 Upper Brook Street, Manchester.
1842	Whitworth takes out his 12th patent – a road-sweeping machine.
1846	Whitworth purchases The Firs estate, Manchester (then known as Ardern's Place).
1851	He establishes his 'Britain's greatest mechanician' reputation at the Great Exhibition, Hyde Park, London.
1852	Engineering Masters Association Lock-out. Whitworth locks his own gates, 15 January.
1853	Appointed Royal Commissioner – visits the USA, ostensibly to study American machinery.

1854	Whitworth acquires Stancliffe Hall, Darley Dale.
1854	Employs 368 at Chorlton Street factory.
1855	Following request to manufacture rifles, Whitworth commences gun research at The Firs, Fallowfield.
1856	Elected President, Institution of Mechanical Engineers, for two years (1856–57).
1857	Reads paper to the Institution, 'On a Standard Decimal Measure of Length', 25 June.
1859	Whitworth field guns succeed at Southport Trials.
1861	American Civil War. *New York Tribune* reports that cargo aboard paddle-steamer *Bermuda* included Whitworth guns.
1866	Whitworth re-elected President IMechE, reads paper on 'Use of (gun barrel) Inside Micrometers'.
1866	Meeting to fund engineering professorship, Owens College. Whitworth made Treasurer of the fund.
1868	Education Minister accepts Whitworth's offer to found engineering scholarships.
1869	Whitworth and Fairbairn are made Baronets.
1870	Whitworth's father Charles dies at Leeds, 16 January.
1870	Joseph's wife Fanny dies, aged seventy, Forest House, Delamere, Cheshire, 28 October.
1871	Joseph marries Mary Louisa Orrell (née Broadhurst), aged forty-two, at St James's Church, Piccadilly, London, 12 April.
1874	His firm becomes a limited company, with 780 employees, 31 March.
1878	Whitworth makes application for his last patent, his 48th, Crank axles.
1880	Company starts phased move to Openshaw, Manchester.
1881	Whitworth, Bessemer and Charles Manby (ICE) set up College of Practical Engineering, Muswell Hill, London, 29 September.
1887	Sir Joseph Whitworth dies, Monaco, aged eighty-three, 22 January.
1896	Death of Lady Whitworth, St Pancras Hotel, London, 26 May.
1897	Following amalgamation, the firm becomes Sir W.G. Armstrong Whitworth & Company Limited (1,108 employees at Openshaw).
1908	Final report of Whitworth legatees, Whitworth Institute, Manchester, 29 July.
1928	Machine-tool side of business taken over by Craven Brothers of Manchester.

Introduction

> Kings, Warriors and Statesmen have heretofore monopolised not only the pages of history but almost those of biography. Surely some niche ought to be found for the mechanic, without whose skill and labour, society as it is, could not exist.
>
> Samuel Smiles, 1862

The aim of this book – apart from providing a satisfying contemporary style piece of historic scholarship – is an attempt to restore, at least in part, the illustrious engineering reputation Joseph Whitworth once enjoyed. It is a story worth telling: highly personalized, sometimes partisan but often perplexing as to why he was treated so handsomely by Louis-Napoleon yet so spitefully by the British government.

Though I suspect that many of Whitworth's distinguished laurels went down at the same time as Britain's engineering heritage, his present diminutive renown and neglected accomplishments remain a downright scandal. Indeed, until I commenced my research neither I, nor my colleagues at Manchester, fully grasped the enormity of the injustice. But as this new testimony unfolds readers will, I hope, share my unease with what has been a century-long mild form of intellectual tyranny: an anti-engineering bigotry in excess perhaps of that signified by C.P. Snow's *Two Cultures*. It is part of the rift between thinking and making and my book seeks to remedy both the injustices to Whitworth and the continual denigration of engineering.

The fact is, Whitworth *was* a giant: more, he was a colossus. With *his* record how could he be otherwise? Until Lord Nuffield (excluding Cecil Rhodes), he was Britain's most generous benefactor. His machine tool designs were so innovative that he actually pioneered a new machine tool era; he fathered flat surfaces and modern toolroom practices; he gave the western world its first one-inch standard; he taught engineers precise measurement and designed his own screw threads; he decimalized engineering measurement and came within an ace of revolutionizing military weapons with his hexagonally rifled guns; he hated street filth so he invented mechanical street sweepers; he wanted an improved steel so he developed the hydraulic forging press; he propagated the idea of mass production; he provided educational scholarships and a university engineering laboratory; he helped to promote radical newspapers and the Atlantic telegraph and much else besides – he was indefatigable.

The great bulk of this catalogue represents international firsts. What my book ventures to do is to intersperse a varied and interesting life with the history of Whitworth's technology: in short, to evaluate the debt for which we and the rest of the world are still accountable.

The first encouragement I remember, prompting me to mull over Whitworth's activities, came when the late Professor Jack Diamond, Wh.Sch., CEng., of the University of Manchester asked me if I could perhaps locate any old Whitworth machinery probably long since dumped and forgotten in any one of Lancashire's many cellar workshops. I knew most of the likely places in the north-west but discovered when I got there I was ten years too late. Vice-Admiral Sir Frank Mason, KCB, FEng, IMechE, another Whitworth devotee, took up the search and in 1965 wrote to the press appealing for information. Very little came to light. At this time, Professor Diamond was chairman of the organizing committee assembling a commemorative Whitworth exhibition at the Institution of Mechanical Engineers for summer 1966, and encouraged a whole team of Whitworth scholars to look out for memorabilia. He wanted to augment the small but impressive collection already in hand. The very humble response both he and the other searchers experienced seemed to verify this as the primary reason why so many engineer-journalists over the years abandoned their once keen ambitions to write a life of Whitworth. As Professor Diamond confessed, 'the generally difficult archival material is a problem . . . engineers seldom make good diarists'.

Two years prior to the centenary of Whitworth's death, in early 1985, a group of bookish Mancunians considered that an ideal biographer for the great engineer would have to be a writer, an ex-Manchester councillor, a machine tool draughtsman and an MP. They had in mind an engineer with access to the Parliamentary record. Their fingers pointed in my direction. I required no further persuasion.

As things turned out, it meant five years arduous research, the proliferation of worthless enquiries far outstripping the exciting new leads which occasionally dawned and made it all so worthwhile. The outcome is this first full-length biography of Whitworth and the first attempt at a meticulously weighted assessment of his contribution, based as it must be on the limited metallurgy and subordinate engineering potentialities of the period. Towards this end it was often necessary to retrace on the drawing board an actual rebuild of Whitworth's ideas and methods of construction. In consequence, my feel for his special kind of Baconian rationalism is that much richer.

Although biography is not necessarily authenticated history, one without the other is unsatisfactorily thin and deceptive. As we know only too well engineers are trained to be sceptics and for that reason even minimal reference to machine technology makes chapter and verse essential. Generally, however, I have resolved not to let dates, statistics, and excessive terminology get out of hand. My aim is to draw out and make implicit whatever relevant theoretical or empirical knowledge seems necessary and to make it stand up in its own right without invention on my part. Towards this end I have made comparisons using the work of Whitworth's contemporaries and where this appears it is pure machine historiography.

'History is bunk', said Henry Ford. It was an obvious statement for a man of the future to make, but he didn't really believe it, of course. He employed too many brilliant researchers not to have them sieve through every single piece of past engineering. Understanding yesterday helps provide tomorrow's knowledge. Ford, the archdeacon of mass production, the most famous propagator of the Whitworth message, declared 'The machine has brought actual equality between men – the critics of the machine are out of date. Instead of less machinery there will be more'. Whitworth also coined phrases like this in the mid-nineteenth century. He fervently believed that within the potential of the new machine lay the emancipation of man.

During his visit to America Whitworth studied the influence of the New York daily press. His conclusions were quite clear. Of the United States tax-free press he said 'It is a powerful agent for promoting the intelligence of the people . . . where the humblest labourer can indulge in the luxury of his daily paper; everybody reads and thought and intelligence penetrate through to the lowest grades of society'. Conversely, he considered that the restricted press in Prussia actually cancelled out any benefit they as a nation should have derived from their having the most advanced educational system in the world. It was a truly remarkable conclusion. Another equally perceptive deed: when C.P. Scott became the editor of the *Manchester Guardian*, Whitworth made available his house at Fallowfield, The Firs, which Scott occupied at a peppercorn rent for the remainder of his life.

Joseph Whitworth led a very full and interesting life. He suffered a broken marriage; his second wife was twenty-nine years younger than his first. It is a compelling story.

The Whitworth Family Tree

Charles Whitworth (1782–1870) — married Stockport Parish Church 14-3-1803 — Sarah Hulse (1780–1814)
Born 1782 Stockport
Died 16-1-1870 Leeds
Buried Leeds General Cemetery

Joseph (1803–1887)
Born Stockport 20-12-1803
Died Monte Carlo 22-1-1887
Buried Darley Dale,
Derbyshire

First marriage
Joseph married Frances Ankers (1800–70)
Ilkeston Parish Church, Derbyshire,
25-2-1825
Died Forest House, Delamere 28-10-1870
Buried Tarvin Parish Church, Cheshire.
No issue

Second marriage
Joseph married Mary Louisa Orrell 12-4-1871
St James Church, Piccadilly, London
Mary Louisa Orrell (widow) born 31-8-1829
Stockport, Cheshire
Died St Pancras Hotel, London 26-5-1896
Buried Darley Dale, Derbyshire

Mrs Mary (née Orrell) Higginbotham
Lady Louisa's daughter by her first husband,
Alfred Orrell. Married Samuel Higginbotham.
Died Sauchiehall Street, Glasgow 12-12-1889
Buried Darley Dale, Derbyshire. No issue

John – born 1805
Baptised Gee Cross Unitarian
Church, Hyde, Cheshire 1806
Married *c.* 1830 Queensland,
Australia (wife not traced)

Fanny Whitworth (1832–1908)
Born Australia 1832
Died 11 Rue de la Madeleine
Rouen, France 28-10-1908

Married

Richard Uniacke (1822–1909)
Died St Johns Wood, London
17-2-1909. No issue

Sarah – born 1813
Died 5-3-1833 (aged 20)
Buried 8-3-1833 at
base of father's pulpit
Shelley Congregational
Chapel, Shelley

Ellen Whitworth (1823–1906)
Born near Liverpool
(Exact identity of Ellen's
mother not known)

Married John Tinker McGowan
Square Chapel, Halifax
11-7-1848
Died Bournemouth
13-11-1906

Two sons, Joseph Whitworth
McGowan and William
McGowan. Two daughters,
Ellen and Elise

CHAPTER ONE

The Making of a Baconian Engineer

That reading maketh a full man

Francis Bacon, 1615

Had Joseph Whitworth the posthumous good fortune of reading his own obituaries he would have smiled contentedly: not only had he taken to his grave the well-kept secrets of his youth but also with him went a personal emnity which for a lifetime came between himself and his father, the Reverend Charles Whitworth.

The reprehensible events which had so deeply shocked young Joseph followed closely in the wake of his mother's death. He was barely twelve years of age when his father felt relieved of his family obligations and chose full-time Christian study in preference to the needs of his young children. In Joseph's opinion it was an act of utter selfishness; that his father should have fostered out both himself and his younger brother John in such uncaring conditions and that he should actually have sent their tiny sister Sarah to a Bristol orphanage was unforgivable. Indeed, as the fostering arrangements made by his father worsened so Joseph vowed never to have anything more to do with him; an ostracism he sustained throughout the remaining fifty-five years of his father's life.

This whole wretched business, stretching the length of a lifetime, ended all hope any of them had of retrieving even the feeblest of family respect. Only when the time came for Joe himself to make a will (he died a wealthy man) did he ever relent – and even then only in principle – just enough, he thought (he judged wrongly), to imply a family amnesty. Sadly, as it turned out, the small amount of money he did provide for the remaining members of his family proved wholly insignificant not only to prevent further resentment but it even failed to forestall yet another bout of prolonged acrimony in the shape of a court action – the very thing he and his lawyers had planned to avoid.

There were other such melancholic threads but Joseph himself quietly stowed them away almost without comment. As he grew older his real life blossomed full of hard, dramatic achievement. His competitors tried and failed many times to destroy him while his flatterers needlessly persisted in trying to invent a new Whitworth; they wanted to change his self-educated, self-made character into a more decorous, but thoroughly bogus image, essentially because they believed that men of Whitworth's standing and character should be the privately schooled sons of either the military or the affluent. Whitworth was neither. From the age of twelve Joseph Whitworth learned to plough a lone furrow. He was always an adept creator in the making. Certainly he was a survivor but never did he behave as some sorrowful self-pitying soul. On the contrary he asserted himself throughout his life, eventually attaining the world leadership of his own industry – a pre-eminence he sustained for over twenty years.

Not unnaturally bashfulness was seldom, if ever, part of Joe's character. Nevertheless he must have blushed many times whenever he read the fictitious magazine accounts of his upbringing; or years later, as a preliminary to his many lectures, he would have sat in silence through the introductory pleasantries always offered by welcoming chairmen. Invariably, they repeated the spurious stories based on a make-believe boyhood which have now passed into the biographical scripts as a true record. Yet he himself remained silent. Somewhat dishonestly he chose never to put the record straight: why?[1]

Naturally some writers have critically interpreted this assumed indifference on Joe's part to be plain deception: in their opinion such dishonesty was typical of a man who was in their opinion a design plagiarist; it was yet another of the many labels the critics pinned to his cross. Other writers thought it suggested an inherent pig-headedness, which, they say, he never lost. And while there can never be more than a wafer-thin line between determination – of which he had plenty – and pig-headedness, those who knew both the young and the older Whitworth would agree that in both periods, yes, he was often brusque even with friends but seldom, if ever, was he obstinate to the extent of being stupid. The only thing Whitworth's autobiographical silence did confirm, it seems, was that he probably never kept a secret record of his personal life. Perhaps he wasn't interested: an assumption which, if true, pretty well nails the myth that a private diary plus his personal papers were maliciously destroyed after his death by those to whom they were entrusted.[2] It would have been illogical and thus out of character for him to have remained silent throughout his life only to have the truth revealed after he died. Not being a literary man – but being of the same mould as most engineers – he probably never saw the relevance of recording mundane personal matters. If those around him wanted to spread fancy stories then so be it. Biographers and the like should be left to draw their own conclusions: the hard way.

From what we now know about the Whitworths it no doubt suited Joseph's purpose to let it all pass: to allow the sympathetic bits about himself to mature as honest gospel. He may have realized, even at a very young age, that to be granted a college education – albeit a bogus one – was a prestigious and helpful thing to do. Perversely of course he may even have been acting out some private, slightly more vindictive posture. What is true – and it needs to be said – is that little, if any, of this published biographical fiction was actually of his own making: rather it was an image hankered after by those who honestly believed all engineering genius – or genius of any kind for that matter – must start with a comfortably off childhood followed by a college education. In fact, Joseph Whitworth as a boy had very little of anything, particularly comfort. But unlike the majority of his contemporaries he escaped childhood disease and took full advantage of a father who could actually read and write. Furthermore, until he was eleven or twelve years of age – when probably his family life came to a tragic end – he enjoyed a mother who warmed and cherished both himself and his younger brother, and who cuddled and loved his baby sister.

Joseph's father, Charles Whitworth, when just twenty-one years of age, married Sarah Hulse, a Cheshire girl two years older than himself. The marriage was solemnized at the Stockport Parish Church, on 14 March 1803. Their first child, Joseph, was born five days before Christmas that same year, most probably in a two-roomed dwelling at the top of some stone steps leading from a place they called Fletchers Yard. Twenty-five years later (1828) the dirt roadway which originally fronted this yard was finally cobble-stoned by the Stockport town authority and named John Street.[3]

The nearest house which rear-ended the Whitworth's stone back-to-back later became No. 13 John Street: the upmarket but highly improbable house frequently named by past researchers not just (in their opinion) as Whitworth's birthplace but as a more reputable address in keeping with their belief that Charles Whitworth was a highly successful schoolmaster. When the few available facts failed to fit this assumption most researchers merely regretted the absence of worthwhile information, usually ending their abortive searches with the query: is it relevant? The answer surely must be yes, it is relevant! If Joseph Whitworth's upbringing influenced his adult personality – and it is taken as read that it did – then it would seem all the more important that we understand as much as we can about his birthplace.

But why Fletchers Yard and not No. 13 John Street? To attempt an answer the strongest evidence pinpoints not just Hillgate, Stockport, as his birthplace, but a particular conglomeration of dwellings, mixed in both age and style, which lay to the west of Hillgate and opposite Watson Square. Of the available accommodation in 1803 most of it lay around this rectangular open space, which for decades had been called Fletchers Yard; so named because of a somewhat dubious character who there peddled any old iron and middle-class cast-offs. Visible from the yard entrance, up some stone steps and across a landing above the store, was the most likely dwelling occupied by the Whitworths when they first married. Back-to-back with this, facing outwards, was a four-bedroomed brick house, built around 1800, namely No. 13 John Street.

However, once the Whitworths' income and social status are taken into account the choice of a John Street house cannot be substantiated. As we know, Charles Whitworth was primarily a reedmaker; only in a secondary sense was he ever a lay preacher.[4] The house in question, No. 13, was essentially the kind of place which would have been rented by a young mill manager or his deputy. Certainly neither a factory worker or a lay preacher, particularly one who depended upon a part share of the Sunday school collections, could ever have afforded almost new four-bedroomed accommodation. When the Whitworths first married and were looking for a suitable place, this particular house was probably less than three years old. It would have been most unlikely for its owners to have agreed to let just one or two rooms, especially to an impecunious young couple.

Not surprisingly, it was only when Joseph Whitworth was heading for an international reputation that the question of his educational background and birthplace aroused interest. Suddenly such queries appealed to a wider magazine readership, compelling one or two British trade papers to trail after a German magazine which considered the birthplace of an engineer important. But once Whitworth himself failed to respond, interest was dropped, in much the same way as another magazine journalist complained that the issue was 'unnecessarily tedious'. But far from it; although the actual distance between Fletchers Yard and No. 13 John Street was only a matter of fifty feet or so, the two places in reality represented two profoundly differing cultures. It was this particular aspect which had interested the German press. They were right to ask about Whitworth's cultural background because it related to much of what he did in later life. It is important, therefore, both to distinguish and in this instance to reject – on the basis of what family evidence there is – the upmarket alternatives (i.e. 13 John Street or 49 Duke Street) suggested as his place of birth – especially if credence is to be given the idea that Joseph Whitworth's resilient personality was first moulded by the crude and aggressive conditions he experienced at Fletchers Yard. Educationalists and psychoanalysts have picked over bones like these for years and still found plenty of meat to keep themselves interested. In fact, in their language, Joseph's origins represent a culinary feast.

Two other human characteristics for which biographers have a penchant are intolerance and egotism. They are the two most powerful symptoms regularly claimed by analysts to have originated from the same kind of background as that of Fletchers Yard. Indeed, leading engineering journalists of the day tailored their examination of Whitworth's character to suit a third quality: arrogance. They repeated this portrayal so often that the three words, intolerance, egotism and arrogance stuck as a perceived wisdom. Interestingly, even the more erudite of analytical writers have never linked Whitworth's alleged egotism or his so-called intolerance with either a physically deprived childhood or a rags-to-riches scenario. Their more regularly argued thesis which some magazines have deployed very persuasively – but never in regard to Whitworth – was that when an intellectually gifted man or woman had escaped from an impoverished background and done so by his or her own efforts, then both intolerance and egotism were spawned very easily. Of course, one could think of many examples to prove this tenet, but it was not so in the case of Whitworth.

By the same token, the same could be said of courage and fortitude, both attributes of which he had plenty. In fact, all the recognized boyhood ingredients from which the experts would say his adult temperament was compounded could easily have been recognized when he was quite young. The characteristics which fuelled his lifelong dedication to using machinery as a way of improving national living standards remained consistent throughout. One added dimension was brought about by his family's perpetual dread of temporary accommodation; an affliction Joseph suffered until he was turned thirty years of age. Nothing could be more demanding of a family, nor compelling in its search for stability in later life than having a constant memory of a nomadic and insecure childhood. In Joe's case, moving home was a constant strain; he and his younger brother John literally grew up on the move. Indeed, Joseph was barely fifteen months old when his father Charles was accepted by the Orchard Street Congregational Chapel as a Sunday school class leader.[5] And who knows, his father must have pondered, could it perhaps lead in the future to an offer of accommodation by one of the chapel elders who had by then built a row of small terraced cottages between the Wall Butts and Lamb Street, Stockport? But to eke out his family's existence, paradoxically, because Charles no longer could stomach a dawn mill start, he was obliged to travel even more miles in search of part-paid Sunday school teaching. And although it occasionally meant tramping a great distance in all weathers he no doubt found the Sunday School a more helpful way of locating the better-off parents prepared to pay one shilling and sixpence per week for him to teach their children to read and write.

It must have crossed Charles Whitworth's mind many times that full-time preaching could perhaps one day provide for him an escape route from the mill. But he didn't know how to start nor where the money would come from. All millworkers – like most pitmen – would endlessly day-dream of the joyful day when they would perhaps depart the consumptive lint-laden bedlam inside the mill or the hard blackness down the pit. Sadly for most it remained just a cruel fantasy – 'till death do us part' they joked – except that most workers knew that the 'till death do us part' bit was true: most men did in fact die while still at work. To some extent, as a reedmaker, Charles Whitworth would have avoided the worst of cotton's notoriously bad conditions mainly because reed and sleymakers worked separately away from the looms. But for everyone alike, both young and old, the most compelling incentive for scholarship had always been the ability it offered men to break free. However, for Charles there were other deeper reasons: first and foremost he was a committed Christian believer, an extremely able and intelligent man, well-read and a dissenter but above all, he was conscious of what was about to happen in places like Stockport once the new millowners brought in their new steam-driven industry. He wanted none of it.

The congregational church record implies that Joe's father was never a high flyer. It would have been pleasing to describe him as leaving the mill with 'fire in his belly' as though pre-ordained: preaching the Christian gospel with passion. The truth was far less fanciful. Of course, like most young evangelists – Charles was not yet twenty-five – he no doubt pictured himself ready to spellbind Stockport with his oratory. If only he could. Truthfully he never became other than a very reliable missionary and bible teacher. Perhaps it was just as well he didn't take too seriously the grandiose ideas often given to young evangelists. Otherwise he may have been tempted to give up long before he even started his chapel apprenticeship as a very mundane Sunday class leader. His great forte was a robust willingness to work hard – a characteristic he depended upon more and more once he ventured out into the surrounding communities in search of young Bible students.

The man most responsible for Charles Whitworth's Christian mission was a fifty-nine year old pastor, the Revd William Evans. He had arrived in Stockport to take over the Hanover Square and Orchard Street Congregational chapels in September 1803, just six months after Charles and Sarah were married. Bill Evans was one of the most charismatic preachers ever to enhance the Stockport Congregational circuit. From the beginning he set out to find young men who could read and write and possibly encourage them to teach others. Charles Whitworth was waiting to be found: he needed no other encouragement. He was irresistibly attracted to Bill Evans like metal to a magnet. Evans was inspirational: he taught Charles many things but most important of all he taught him how to survive without a mill wage – and by implication in the most autocratic fashion, he lectured Charles's wife and little family too on why they also were going to exist without a mill wage.

Of all the fanciful tales which used to fabricate Joseph's boyhood the most popular usually began with the deceptive claim that his father was a mature schoolmaster from the age of twenty-one; that he kept a high-class boarding school and that Joseph his son was one of his pupils until the boy left for Vint's Academy at the age of twelve. It was no doubt an enviable picture to paint but hardly true. Written on Charles Whitworth's marriage licence was the real truth: a disappointingly cold douche for the romantics, but there it was, described as nothing other than a reedmaker (i.e. a loom framemaker), an occupation which as we now know meant hard and dirty work seldom likely to pay even a weaver's money. The point is: far from living like private school proprietors, the Whitworths lived like most other working couples in the same situation, poorly paid and having to make their small amount of money go even further once their second son, John, was born during the closing months of 1805. Again, it was the Revd William Evans who was instrumental in raising Charles's ambitions to include the idea of himself training to become a minister within the next few years.

TRAUMATIC BOYHOOD AND MILL RIOTS

Around this time, that is about 1805 onwards, Stockport began to change quite dramatically. Ordinarily it was a small plebeian township, situated six or seven miles south-east of Manchester. It had long served as a natural coaching stage on the Manchester–London run. Sweating horses welcomed a breather climbing up Hillgate Brow after crossing the Mersey. Still bantam in size, the town was an important wool and cotton centre, about ten or twelve thousand people scattered in neighbourhood communities mainly in lower Stockport around the Rivers Tame and Mersey but gradually spreading upwards towards villages like Romily and Hazel Grove. These were all modest communities straddling the Etherow Valley, a lush crag and tail gulley either side of which the town's smaller mills built their waterwheels to be powered by water gulched from farmed moorland higher up the valley. The town's more progressive mill owners, however, were turning towards steam engines to pump water back up the bank and to drive their machinery far more profitably once it was moved away from the river. House builders started to convert the green sites surrounding each new mill, thus joining together in one continuous development a much enlarged Cheshire town.

Over a period of about twenty-five years the town witnessed the most phenomenal growth in England. Some three or four thousand dwellings, mostly clinging to the hillside in tiers, appeared in no time at all. Stockport in fact grew six times in size reaching 70,000 by 1852 – the very year the town suffered its most serious riots between Catholics and Protestants. The town's growth had been too fast, and although the cotton mushroom had not started while the Whitworths were living there the dreadful deterioration of the place was already beginning to show even in their time.

The putrefying effluent – including that from the new felt and leatherwork industry top o' Hillgate – tended to percolate downwards via the open street gullies making less agreeable the once pleasant old town centre. The slops in the gutters, the open cesspits and the earth closets; the bleachers, the dyers and the sheepskin people all contributed to the sickening pollution of the two rivers: the Mersey and the Tame. The teeming population bulge, so obvious in Stockport, had swiftly become the most dreaded bane of practically all the northern mill towns once cotton started to become steam driven. But progress it was. Steam power just couldn't wait for mill owners and their like to find a new morality.

Perhaps it was a sense of guilt which prompted northern employers to build chapels out of their own pocket whenever an active congregation could be organized. But that they did, especially in mill towns like Stockport and the surrounding areas. Possibly other reasons came into it: their belief perhaps that a new morality and code of behaviour preached from the pulpit would deter factory burning and frame-breaking and persuade strikers back to work.

As early as January 1812, small Luddite attacks had already spread south of the River Mersey and by March of that year frame-breaking had been made a *capital* offence. The single concession granted by the then Home Secretary, Richard Ryder MP, prevented employers who doubled as magistrates from passing the death sentence on their own employees. Not forgetting of course that once a loom-frame was smashed, Joe's father, Charles, as a reedmaker, was immediately called upon to repair it. If he agreed, his life was threatened by the weavers. If he refused, his job was taken away by his employer. Whenever young Joe heard a commotion in the street his terror-stricken eyes never left the door.

Arson had already been suspected as the cause of two mill fires in Manchester and mill owners immediately cast doubt on the restraining influence of the Church. Even though the courts could now use the death penalty its deterrence was not immediate. During the year 1812 eight 'machine vandals' were taken from Manchester to Newcastle and executed, including one poor woman also accused of stealing potatoes. Some two years later about the time of Stockport's own food riots, the trauma must have seared even the dullest of wits. Young lads like Joseph Whitworth were sufficiently mature even at ten or eleven years to be apprehensive of evil; to imbibe and fear terror. As we shall soon glean, he was certainly old enough to comprehend the serious risk to life of open street sewers: no doubt the original source of his lifelong abhorrence of such things.

There were other fears too, no doubt discussed between parents in the way they naturally would have been in the Whitworth family. The widespread fear at the time that militant Catholicism was about to engulf the town dominated conversation. Local mill owners had until then genuinely supported the Methodist and Congregational churches and their political radicalism. From the beginning they had made one essential demand from which they never veered: that both Catholics and Jews should be permitted by law to become Members of Parliament. Local employers had long hoped Stockport's laudable record in the forefront of Catholic emancipation would bring tranquillity but it mattered little. It could be that when Catholic weavers fought against Protestant weavers they just failed to recognize their true enemy. Confusion ran in all directions. Was it that Catholic immigrants were taking their jobs or was it that the new power-driven weaving looms threatened their wages?

Just how much of these early years young Joseph Whitworth would remember is difficult to gauge: his experience of Stockport in any case wasn't very long; he had left the town for good before he was twelve years of age. But the six years 1809–15, which meant for Joseph his sixth to his twelfth year, were very impressionable years. The trauma was such that most small boys of seven or eight were then already streetwise and if Charles Dickens's study of Manchester's cotton children is well-founded then ten-year-olds like young Joe self-survived by their own audacious mimicry of street hawkers. Undoubtedly he would have remembered the violence inside the mill, not particularly the issues involved but certainly the daunting effects it had on his parents at home. Joe didn't go to school as such but his father would have set lessons for both him and his younger brother John. No evidence has remained that father sermonized the boys or that they resented in any way the doctrine he laid down. The most chilling thing for all the family throughout the period must have been the personal hatred, the whispering campaigns and the brutal betrayal of one man against another.

Whitworth's most fervent life interests represented a total repellence of the fears his mother suffered constantly. First, the threat to her family of disease from open sewers: who knows, her son's ambitions perhaps being thus motivated to later design his mechanical sweepers and new drainage systems. Secondly, the constant threat of violence for those like her husband who repaired looms: her son didn't seek revenge but later on gave inspired leadership by designing faster and better looms. Then there was the threat from new industry to urban peace: her son responded by building more powerful machinery – all in all, he learned from his mother's despair the desperate necessity there was for technical education and engineering science. Not so very remarkable perhaps in such torrid circumstances but indicative of his sensitivities that he could recognize the way ahead from a very early age. He always knew there could be no going back.

Though Joe's father had virtually left the mill by 1810 he was still well known locally as a reedmaker – or as a reed and framemaker depending on the type of loom that the reed or frame was to fit. And if some Luddites that week had smashed up local looms, any known framemakers seen associating with men either repairing or making new frames would quickly be taken out and beaten up. The reality meant that all reed or sleymakers and their families lived in constant fear in case a local gang should fancy their blood or put out their windows.

Although some thirty years time-span separated these troubles it is nonetheless interesting that when the less damaging Plug riots reached Stockport in 1842 (Charles Whitworth was then living in Leeds and had almost finished preaching, while his son Joseph had made great strides and had designed without regard to his personal safety the most advanced labour-saving looms to date) the Free Churches also had learned from the past and were suggesting a more enlightened view. Instead of smashing up machinery they advised cotton workers to pull the plugs from steam boilers thus – they argued – after a strike was over workers could get back to work sooner, and their wages would therefore bring food sooner to their families. Contrary to general belief the Plug riots were a rational advance on the violent destruction of machinery and the Free Churches could rightly rejoice that they once had an influential part in showing men a better way.

The Chapel newsletter confirmed that Charles Whitworth had left Orchard Street Chapel around 1806 and had turned up at Moorfield, Denton. We also know that his second son, John, was baptized at Gee Cross Unitarian Chapel – a village near Hyde, Cheshire – a few months after he was born in 1806. The longer journeys Charles now intended made sense. Moorfield, Gee Cross and Stockport roughly formed a triangle, five miles each way. Charles always claimed to walk prodigious distances so he and Sarah may have kept on their tenancy in Stockport. It could be that now and again he borrowed a pony and trap to visit the more distant villages. The chapel house at Gee Cross was then almost a century old with most of the regular congregation coming in from places as distant as Marple. It was territory Charles Whitworth knew well and in much the same way as he got to know the Revd Bill Evans so he came upon yet another equally powerful personality, the Revd James Brooks, Unitarian pastor at Gee Cross. They had met for the first time just before Charles had taken his son John to be baptized. James Brooks was a totally dedicated teacher. Only when young people could read and write, he believed, would the morality and habitual bad behaviour of society improve. He and Charles Whitworth wholly agreed. *In later life so did Joe.*

As an adult, Joe Whitworth came to recognize there could be no freedom of choice in society if illiteracy prevented an understanding of the options: that is to say both those on offer and those still to be won. It was the universal assimilation of ideas like these which made them central to the emancipation of society as preached by the Revd Brooks.

Two anecdotes from the scene of Joseph's boyhood set the background with remarkable clarity. The first: John Hurst's (1880) eyewitness account of Middle Hillgate and Watson Square, which, he claimed, had remained unchanged since the Whitworths had lived there. He recalled two shops on the brow, barely eighty yards from Joe's birthplace: Seaton the greengrocer and Price the butcher. Price killed his animals in the shop; a sheet was hung up to hide the slaughterer from the customers, 'meat 'twixt pasture and plate 'tis not a treat to see' it was said. Some little distance away a somewhat larger slaughterhouse supplied the Watson Square market trade with hide and sheepskins.[6]

Whitworth remembered these places with loathing although he had an affectionate memory of a certain personality, a memory which remained with him all his life. This man was Ephraim Hallam. He lived next door to his own mill fronting Hillgate and opposite to where Christy, the felt hat manufacturer, had now moved. In his office Ephraim kept a stock of pharmacy drugs for sale to his workers. He also extracted teeth and dressed the injuries of any employee meeting with an accident. At Christmas time and on special occasions he distributed tickets to his employees, which, on presentation to Price the butcher, ensured that wives and children were supplied with meat. Other employers did similar things but their philanthropy was often misunderstood and sometimes resented. Cotton mills were built to make profit from cloth, a pre-condition thoroughly understood by weavers; naturally they expected to be paid money, not meat for wages.[7] When the time came, Joseph's own wage creed also remained firmly opposed to payment in kind ever after. In 1870 though, he equipped his own factory with a health centre, some drugs and a dentist, just as Ephraim Hallam had done sixty years before him.

FAMILY GRIEF AND FOSTERED SEPARATION

Going back to his boyhood: as Christmas 1812 approached, Joseph made the most of his ninth birthday. His mother was expecting her third child around March 1813. When the birth came it was not easy. Indeed, soon after Sarah Whitworth had given birth to a daughter – who her father also christened Sarah – serious complications set in: lying-in fever being suspected. Though Charles had done what he could to provide the best conditions, their hygiene perhaps wasn't good enough to prevent an infection. The child, though sickly, survived, but Charles's dear wife never really left her bed before she died early the following year, 1814, at the age of thirty-four. The two boys grieved their mother's passing deeply. For six months both Joseph and his younger brother were silenced by their utter despair. Their father Charles was also at a loss to know what to do. His once close friend, the Revd Bill Evans, had died three years before. Now a widower, Charles no longer had anyone to whom he could turn. Left with a twelve-month-old daughter and two sons, one aged nine and the other eleven, he pondered hard as to how best he could resolve his situation. In the end he took a most remarkable decision to disperse his family; he made each go their own way alone, pointing them in four different directions: each facing a life entirely different from the others. When it came to Joseph's turn to say goodbye to his father it was probably the last time the two were to see each other.

Joseph's mother Sarah (née Hulse) had brothers but no sisters. The Hulse seniors were all male. Early nineteenth-century tradition usually implied that a surviving sister would take care of any bereaved siblings but in Charles's predicament no such arrangement was possible. In the event Sarah's one-year-old child was taken to an orphanage.[8] Of what happened after that during her teenage years we know little. We do know, however, that her sadly impoverished and ailing life came to a premature end on 5 March 1833 at the age of twenty and that Charles, her father, three days later had her buried at the base of his pulpit inside the Congregational Chapel at Shelley, near Huddersfield.[9] Whether he did this in a fit of remorse or whether his daughter was then sharing his accommodation at Shelley and would thus qualify for burial by the Chapel, we do not know. She could have joined him a year or two earlier to work in the manse helping her father. The situation however may have been complicated by the presence of another, younger daughter Ellen, the result of an entirely separate liaison Charles had pursued eleven years before. In regard to his first daughter Sarah, the orphanage at Bristol where she probably lived for the first ten years of her life almost certainly would have placed her into domestic service as a maid immediately she was old enough to handle the kitchen chores. In that sense she was a natural and would have wanted desperately to go back and help her father. Significantly, however, there is no Chapel record of Sarah's burial service, only a local newspaper and the tombstone itself. Almost certainly Joseph was not present (but because of his international fame in later life someone in retrospect would almost certainly have reminisced about his presence at the funeral service had he been there), nor is there any mention of any other relation of Charles either being present or even being associated with the Chapel at Shelley.

The problem of finding two foster families to whom the boys could be farmed out must have been difficult for their father. Obviously, being so young the boys themselves would have had little say in the matter. Of John, the youngest, only the minimum of references still remain barely suggesting an outline of his subsequent journey through life. It is now known, for instance, that John went to live in Queensland, Australia, and married there in 1830; that he had two children, the eldest of whom was Frances, born in 1832. Evidently, she was named after his brother's wife, Fanny Whitworth, suggesting that the two brothers remained in touch with one another. Frances, John's daughter, got married in Australia, to a man named Richard Uniake. They travelled widely and were living at Rue de la Madeleine, Rouen, France, when Frances died on 28 October 1908, at the age of seventy-six. Richard, her husband, died at St John's Wood, London, in 1909. Two pertinent questions arise: did Charles Whitworth know that the family with whom he had fostered his son John, intended to emigrate to Australia? Or was it that the boy so hated his fostered life that he himself emigrated as soon as he could afford the passage? Whichever way it was, the day Charles left his son John with another family he said goodbye to his second boy – again for ever.

Much the same had happened to Joseph, the eldest son. He was fostered out at the same time as John, 1814–15, but of the more popular biographical stories which have since circulated worldwide, particularly those describing his teenage years, the most quoted paragraphs usually repeat the claim:

> Joseph was educated until the age of twelve years by his father, the proprietor of a Stockport private boarding school. He was then sent to Mr Vint's academy at Idle, near Bradford, where he remained for about two years. Afterwards he was 'placed' with an uncle, a millowner at Ambergate, near Derby, to learn the business.[10]

Seemingly, the intention behind these highly glamorized yet dishonest accounts was to create the impression that Joe's youth was not only pleasant but of a middle-class and comfortable standing. The fact that such stories were printed long after the event, in the late forties, early fifties, when it was fashionable – aye, almost essential – to 'gild the lily' before engineers would be taken seriously was a considerable tribute to Joe's accomplishments. For him to have warranted a deliberate mythology all his own to the extent that he needed a rich mill owner for an uncle; that while he himself was educationally gifted he also needed the myth of a private education: all this was surely the involuntary defence of an élitist society. It could also have been no more serious than the romantic necrology of those who believed that certain educated middle-class people were born to be leaders.[11]

The truth is, Joseph Whitworth was the product of a pretty hard school. He was lucky to have had a father who could read and think for himself.[12] For the rest, especially in the early years, Joe very much depended upon his own 'streetwise' intuition. Certainly the myth of having a rich uncle again smacks incredulously considering the tough decisions he was forced to take as a young person. So desperate was he to make something of his life, he would have clung to anything solid, let alone privilege or money had there been any. In fact, he so hated the real life his father had let him in for that he ran away to Manchester at the earliest opportunity. Probably he made the break during the year following Peterloo, around July 1820, with Joe not yet seventeen. How he then must have wished his luck had provided a rich uncle. During the five years or so he lived with foster parents he must have long brooded and planned for the day he would go it alone. But why Manchester? He was almost too young at the time to know that Manchester would offer what he most wanted.

Derbyshire is the most frequently named county indicating where he had lived since the death of his mother. But as he himself once happily recalled, as a boy he had read about engineering and Manchester and all the mechanics he could possibly find. His knowledge of machinery was already well above average: he recognized the leading machine makers by name and if he got to Manchester he would know where to look for them. Further evidence of this could be that his foster parent was probably a millwright; in which case young Joseph almost certainly would have accompanied the older man at first light each morning to work in the mill smithy. Life for the lad would never have been pleasant, indeed it must have often been frightening; but his experience suggests he knew what he was doing when he fled from his foster parents to seek a job in engineering. Even as a boy his ambition signified clear ideas: at least he was now on his way to his beloved engineering eldorado.

MANCHESTER APPRENTICESHIP

On arrival in Manchester Joe's first problem was to find suitable digs. He wasn't quite sure how much he would need to earn to keep himself but in anticipation of being short he probably added a year or so to his real age of sixteen and a half. The first employer he approached for a job was W.J. Crighton and Company. Astonishing or not, they immediately offered him a start. The foreman who interviewed him must have been quite impressed. At the time Crightons were making mill steam engine pumps for Boulton and Watt and here was a young lad asking for a job who had actually read a great deal about them. He had also read about machine tools and the limited progress made. Though still crude, Crightons would have had the best machinery available and although Joe stayed with this firm only fourteen months he probably gained much experience being allowed to work each machine in turn.

From Crightons he moved a short distance across Manchester to Messrs Marsden and Walker in Water Street, a firm well known for its textile machinery. Again he stayed about the same length of time, which suggests he himself valued his own skills more highly than did his employer. The lad wanted more money and no doubt protested that he was already doing the work of a time-served tradesman. Joe would not be twenty-one till Christmas 1824 – he had almost twelve months still to go – but Marsdens would not be aware he was under the age he had given; nonetheless for whatever reason they refused to pay Joe the full wage and so he left. This time he moved towards St Stephens Square, the heartland of Manchester's cotton empire. For the sake of earning more money he had left actual machine making and gone for a job as a skilled millwright. He finally got the job of his choice working for Houldsworth and Company, a firm which possessed an internationally renowned cotton mill in Lever Street. They paid him the full rate. 'It was the happiest day of my life', he recalled years later, 'to be recognized as a journeyman and to be paid as such'. In fact, from the moment he had arrived in Manchester, July 1820, till he left for London on his twenty-first birthday, December 1824, the whole period had been truly remarkable. Not only as a lad did he secure employment with Manchester's most prestigious engineers but he gained the kind of experience for which he had set out. All this speaks volumes about his character; not least the single-minded determination he was proved to possess even as a youngster. Moreover, he got his full money two years before most others. He was entitled to be happy.[13]

Whether or not celebrities of any profession have the right to pick and choose those parts of their lives which they themselves deem public remains a controversial issue. In regard to both Charles Whitworth and his son Joseph there were many veiled non-accountable periods mainly because they themselves chose privacy; periods which included some rather important events. These excluded periods have not only proved to be scholastic irritations for historians but have actually prevented the Whitworths themselves being rightfully acclaimed. Biography should only be deeply intrusive for reasons of serious learning, never for reasons of idle titillation, and though the most interesting pages missing from the Congregational Church journals may only have referred to Charles Whitworth's ex-marital indiscretions, the real concern here is a lack of explanation for those of his decisions which so hurt his son Joseph. Of course the missing knowledge is regrettable but at least from the Church's point of view its loss appears innocent.

Reference has already been made to Joe's own biographical dishonesty which he himself found to be 'helpfully convenient', but what still remains inexplicable is the consistent way Joe turned aside the questions put to him by various magazines concerning his Stockport and Manchester beginnings. For example, a close friend of Joseph in later years, James Kershaw MP, who sat for Stockport from 1847 until his death in 1864, when performing the opening of a local Sunday school pointed his finger in the direction of Fletchers Yard and recalled ' . . . the childhood of Joseph Whitworth top o' Hillgate'. The point was locally reported and the magazine *The World* followed it up but Joseph, when asked, appears not to have heard the question. His evasion on this occasion was almost as interesting and just as corroborating as if he had actually supplemented James Kershaw's reference to his birthplace with an added point of his own.[14]

One additional unresolved question remains: if there ever was an element of rags to riches about Joe's life why didn't he turn the analogy to his own advantage? For twenty-five years he made technical education and its state funding his most dedicated crusade but possibly his own boyhood experience made the analogy altogether taboo, mainly, one assumes, because publicity of his youthful years would have embarrassed him beyond his tolerance. Central to these memories would have been the death of his mother and the splitting up of the family shortly afterwards. Oblivious of the pain he was to cause, Joe's father had secured a college education for himself while leaving his son to educate himself. Although Joe occasionally hinted with some pride that he largely overcame his disadvantage by reading a great deal, he never elaborated further. A possible reason for his sensitivity was the fact that his father had very selfishly not only secured a chapel bursary but had also found for himself a place in a residential college as an assumed single man. In Joe's opinion his father had shown little or no thought for his two sons or his daughter. It rankled with him as deeply as did the envy Joe later felt for his father's free access to a marvellous library. If only a smattering of this bitterness ever mingled with the intense hatred provoked by his years with foster parents then the combination must have caused him severe emotional stress.

Joe heartily detested living with the strange family his father had decreed. Not surprisingly the great affection he had for his mother blossomed quite expressively. It could well be that his lifelong reluctance to talk about his own boyhood was part of a shield he lovingly wrapped around memories of his mother. And quite probably these memories, as against the ongoing ostracism he dealt his father, were two sides of the same coin, quietly kept to himself. Discernibly, the gap between Joseph and his father grew very much wider as Joseph's own life matured. Emotionally, he entered his adolescence as an 'orphan' and no doubt he himself would have described practically every other aspect of his teenage years as equally deprived. These early debasements could well have been his first inducement to read his inspirational preceptors, Francis Bacon and to a lesser extent, Jeremy Bentham, the main sources of his lifelong philosophy.

His Father Becomes a Congregational Minister

Joe's father had long wanted to become a minister of the Congregational Church but lacked the scholastic background. The opportunity for him to remedy this shortcoming came only after his wife died and after he had fostered out his young family. Perfunctory it may have been but Charles, now rid of his family obligations, was ready to enlist the help of the chapel elders. Originally prompted by the Revd Bill Evans and others, Charles, at the age of thirty-five, was allocated a small bursary and a place at the Congregational college, the Idle Academy, near Bradford. The tutor there was a brilliant classics scholar, the Revd William Vint. At the time Charles Whitworth entered the college, September 1815, there were ten students in residence, shortly to be increased to fifteen. All were single men, including Charles, ostensibly now shorn of his family commitments and 'on a par' (albeit the eldest) with all the other students.

Vint's Academy depended for its income upon one or two generous subscribers living in the West Riding. The original premises had been rebuilt in 1810 and considerably enlarged six years later. One of the students, Tom Taylor, described the accommodation: 'Our apartments', he wrote, 'consist of a large room where we dine and read. There are two bedrooms in which eighteen of us are stowed every night, Sundays and Saturdays excepted, when these epitomies of the stuffing system are left to sweeten. The Revd Vint gave instruction in theology, Latin and Hebrew, ethics and public rhetoric. To supply pulpits, near and far, Vint's students travelled on foot many hundreds of miles satisfying a dominant interest in preaching and pastoral work.' It was not really the kind of tuition young Joseph would have appreciated, yet it was precisely this curriculum which was so regularly attributed to Joseph rather than to the bona fide Vint student, his father.[15]

Gratefully, the elder Whitworth finally satisfied his tutors and became the Revd Charles Whitworth in June 1819. Just prior to that the County Union had requested that he be allowed to undertake pastoral work in Woolton, a large village about six miles south-east of Liverpool. It was agreed in February 1819 (three months earlier) that the Revd Charles Whitworth should become the minister at Woolton. Within his first year's work he had opened a new schoolroom capable of seating one hundred and twenty persons. As a preacher he successfully attracted a sizeable congregation and within six months every Sunday evening more parishioners came to the hall than could obtain admission. In addition, every Friday evening he preached the gospel over at Garston, a small village about two miles away, the work growing to such an extent that he was granted a full-time assistant to help 'work the countryside'.

Charles Whitworth had not yet served two years at Woolton before the church committee queried whether he should continue as their minister. The committee was already divided on theological grounds; presumably then as now, a division had grown up between the rigid Calvinists and those like Charles Whitworth who wanted to support the younger libertines; but the committee – quite dramatically – now faced an entirely new situation: the Revd Charles Whitworth had disconcertingly entered a new liaison. He and his companion were living together; she pregnant, carrying his child. Prior to all this an earlier County Union report had warned that 'unpleasant circumstances had caused the interest to drop at Woolton'. The child was born in 1823 by which time Charles had given notice he would resign his pastorate. Fortunately he was not 'defrocked'; the County Union in fact (no doubt in recognition of his pioneering success at Woolton) raised no objection to his taking on work elsewhere as a visiting preacher till he had found a new pastorate.[16]

The identity of Charles's partner is not known. The Revd B. Nightingale, writing in 1893, once referred to Whitworth 'and his wife' at Woolton but no other evidence exists as to whether they ever married or, indeed, whether they ever had more children. Their known daughter was born in 1823 and christened Ellen; she married, aged twenty-five, a druggist, John McGowan. They were living in Halifax, Yorkshire, and married there in 1848. John McGowan was the son of a surgeon and when he and Ellen moved to Northfield Villas, Leeds, Ellen offered a home to her father. Long retired, Charles Whitworth died there January 1870 at the age of eighty-two. Ellen herself, then widowed, sold up and moved to Rowan House, Christchurch, near Bournemouth, where she died in 1906. Judging by the information available, it seems unlikely that Joseph Whitworth ever contributed financial help either to his step-sister Ellen's comfort or to his father's upkeep until, that is, the time came for him to make a will. Northfield Villas was of course very much a middle-class home, in addition to which Ellen was married to a druggist, a professional man. It was only towards the end of her life – long after Joseph had died – that her lifestyle became less comfortable.[17]

Retracing our steps to around the time of Ellen's birth, the Revd Charles Whitworth managed to eke out a small living between leaving Woolton and 1826 when he was appointed minister in charge of the church at Shelley, near Huddersfield. Again he worked hard, but still he was unable to hold the congregation and was compelled to resign his living in 1834, twelve months after Sarah, a daughter from his first marriage as we already know, died at the early age of twenty years. A long time afterwards, many elderly people at Shelley remembered Charles well. They described him as a kind, active little man. During the chapel services he would pitch the tunes himself, and in his energetic way call out 'Now boys, Sing!' He was considered a true evangelist, exuberant and dedicated.[18] It was a pity really that his son Joseph didn't inherit just a little of his father's evangelical exuberance – the IMechE, when the time came, would have loved it.

JOSEPH'S WHIRLWIND COURTSHIP ENDS IN MARRIAGE

Joe reached the age of twenty-one at Christmas 1824: clearly he had decided well beforehand to leave Manchester and to seek work in London. He had been in receipt of his full tradesman's money for some time and was probably able to save a little. It could not have been very much and he faced a tough journey. Rather than travel by coach (to ride outside it would have cost him eight shillings and sixpence) he most likely decided to work his way towards London travelling by canal, sleeping wherever he was offered a bed. He left Manchester via Cheshire making his way towards Nottingham. And the reason why this particular route became known was its all-important outcome. He got married 'en route'.

During his canal meandering from Manchester, hitching lifts aboard canal boats, Joe chanced upon his bride-to-be, most likely a twenty-four-year-old bargemaster's daughter from Tarvin, Cheshire.[19] Their whirlwind courtship was brief and impulsive: love at first sight, it seemed. They eloped by making their way towards Nottingham, first stopping at a place called Ilkeston to seek out a priest and the Parish Church. There, by licence, on 25 February 1825, Fanny Ankers, bargee's daughter, married Joseph Whitworth, son of an independent minister. Unlike Joe, Frances was unable to read or write and confirmed her marriage by making an 'X'. They didn't remain together 'till death do'th part', but they did endure many somewhat bumpy years together and she at least ended her days comfortably off, back at home near her sisters in Cheshire.[20]

Much of the detail setting out Joseph's journey to London can only be imaginative conjecture. Though the principal points used here are verifiable, the alternative versions developed by earlier essayists lack essential support and can perhaps be safely discounted. For instance, it has always been an interesting interpretation of events to have Joe's bride, Frances Ankers, in domestic service at Ambergate and to have Joseph employed by his supposedly 'rich uncle' at the same place. Ambergate is only twelve or thirteen miles from Ilkeston and an elopement from there would have been a most attractive strategy to have the couple pursue. Unfortunately, the whole ploy is too discursive and cannot be taken seriously – too many inconsistencies. It is far more reliable to stand by an Ankers family around Tarvin, nearly all of whom were canal folk, than court the few farming people of the same name scattered throughout the district. Fanny was a bargee's daughter all right – a fact which proffered an early strength, a sense of fun perhaps adding gaiety to their relationship, but also no doubt answerable for its ultimate weakness. Most likely, because her bargee style perched so uncomfortably alongside Joe's success, it eventually became their swan song. Nevertheless, their marriage adventure endured nearly thirty years – latterly not always under the same roof – but the story of their melancholy union has yet to unfurl.

WHITWORTH'S LONDON EXPERIENCE STARTS AT MAUDSLAY'S

Whitworth commenced work with Maudslay in May 1825. He started work there, not as Brunel did nor as Nasmyth was later to do, but as an ordinary bench fitter and turner working at the trade. The foreman who met him at the gate in what is now Westminster Bridge Road was quite impressed – he could hardly have been otherwise – listening to Joe's Manchester experience: he asked him to start immediately. At the time Maudslay employed about 120 men, more than a third of them working either as moulders or as blacksmiths. During the three and a half years Joe was employed by Maudslay none of the men who were later destined to become household names worked in the factory at the same time as Joe. Men like Bryan Donkin, Richard Roberts, Joseph Clement and Sam Seaward had all left Maudslays before Whitworth had arrived, while I.K. Brunel, James Nasmyth and William Muir did not start with Maudslay until after Joe's departure. Prior to his death in 1831 Maudslay's reputation in the leadership of mechanical engineering was such that all young engineering talent craved to work there, hence the remarkable roll-call passing through the gates. Whitworth was the one exception; unlike the others he worked on the 'bench' as a tradesman during the whole of his time with Maudslay. Once when he was interviewed by a leading magazine as to why he went to London at the age of twenty-two and sought to work at places like Maudslay's, he replied quite simply 'that he wanted to attain perfection': a marvellous sentiment, if a somewhat trite ambition.

Whitworth remained in London for nearly eight years being employed first by Maudslay and then by Holtzapffel, followed by Wright & Sons and finally Joseph Clement. The sequence was exactly right for his purpose. And without being too sycophantic the record seems to suggest that it was Whitworth himself who had decided the sequence in which he intended to gain his engineering experience. It could have been mere luck, of course, which took him first to Maudslays and finally to Clements but the proximate significance of his two intervening employers suggests otherwise. By getting his priorities correct he was able to operate certain machines during their *initial construction* which enabled him to judge for himself their origin and allowed him to see the various factors which led to their subsequent development. This invaluable experience was, no doubt, stored at the back of his mind and perhaps aided by odd bits of paper in the time-honoured engineering fashion. Nonetheless, it is still strange that this deliberate sequence has never been considered to be special, considering that here was the man destined to finalize what L.T.C. Rolt described as 'the most momentous revolution in human history'. But Joseph Whitworth, being the man he was, indulged himself amidst 'a positive ferment of new ideas, the fulfilment of which called urgently for new methods'. Sadly, he documented very little. Presumably he relied on old-fashioned memory.

In answer to Rolt and others who had earlier suggested that Whitworth's impulsiveness was the reason why he didn't take a supervisory job in London, the very positive way he went from one employer to another in the predetermined order of his own choice surely meant that his behavioural pattern was much more compulsive than ever it was impulsive. One doubt does arise however: was it possible for Joe at the young age of twenty-two to be so far-seeing and decisive? Early last century the answer must have been yes! Henry Maudslay for example was a mere eighteen and working at Woolwich Arsenal as a blacksmith when friends of Joseph Bramah were told of his outstanding abilities. Bramah himself, on hearing that an eighteen-year-old lad could solve the tooling impasse suffered by his new locks and plumbing gadgets, immediately offered Maudslay a job. The eighteen-year-old accepted and stayed with Bramah for over seven years during which time he helped make engineering history by first making and then improving the somewhat crude (lathe) slide-rest patented by Bramah in 1794. Three years later, Maudslay asked for more money; Bramah refused. He thought a beggarly thirty shillings per week enough. Maudslay left and set up his own workshop: Bramah's act was thoroughly mean and commercially shortsighted, a decision he was made to regret for the rest of his life.

The comparison with Joseph Whitworth is interesting. Maudslay was twenty-five years of age when he opened his first tiny workshop at 64 Wells Street (off Regent Street) but he was forty when his famous Lambeth factory became full swing. By comparison Whitworth opened his Manchester factory when he was thirty. Both of them benefited from the original work of their engineering predecessors, and both launched their own new inventive ideas at about the same age, thus laying new trails for others to follow. In that sense both men were equal leaders, each participating during their own quite different engineering generations in the 'most momentous revolution', as it was aptly phrased.

In regard to Maudslay's first move up the ladder in 1802, he went only a very short distance from Wells Street to 75 Margaret Street. There he stayed eight years until 1810 before moving on to his main Lambeth works that same year; just twelve years after leaving Bramah. Earlier the Lambeth site had been used as an indoor riding school – it was principally a wooden structure – half of which Maudslay pulled down and replaced with a foundry and blacksmiths shop. When Joe Whitworth started work there in 1825 Maudslay had by then built a new fitting shop together with a primitive drawing office. He had already erected a number of big machines for his own use which he had specifically designed to accommodate his largest cylinders and crankshafts, intended for his early marine steam engines. The steam paddle-ship Enterprise for instance, which was to make the first steam passage to India, was being engined as Joe started work. In all probability the first machine work Joe did for Maudslay was either on the Enterprise engines or for one of the steam vessels whose engines were at that time also being commissioned at Lambeth by the British Navy. The biggest engines to be made by Maudslay were in fact built for HMS *Dee*. Joe however must have been very disappointed; he left the Lambeth works as Maudslay started up his biggest borer; machining what were then considered huge crankshafts – later to arouse lively interest in the locality as they were trundled down the street towards Maudslay's wharf in Belvedere Road for loading on to Thames barges and on down to the Chatham Dockyard.

Soon after Maudslay got started at Lambeth the machine tool work he was then doing began to take on awe-inspiring importance. It was probably no more advanced than the work of two other engineers – both Frenchmen – Vaucanson and Senot. But because all of it was being done behind locked doors no one knew for sure. Then, as now, spies would be despatched immediately rumours of something new filtered through but by and large not even Clement – responsible as he was for much of Maudslay's earlier machine designs and screw work – knew exactly how far his old employer had progressed. Why was it then (Jessie Ramsden, the eighteenth-century instrument maker, had already pioneered some primitive mechanisms) that the three leading machine tool makers of the period 1790–1820, Jacques Vaucanson, François Senot and Henry Maudslay (in principle) all came up with almost identical lathe designs within a few years of each other? Secrecy alone, one assumes, would have prevented any one of them knowing what the other two were doing, or indeed what the others had already achieved. Although the work was revolutionary, the truth is probably not difficult to surmise. The principles involved had been known since Leonardo da Vinci and were followed by the great pioneering work of Christopher Polhem in Sweden: what men like Vaucanson and Maudslay succeeded in doing was to translate the techniques of manual screw-cutting into machine technology. As to be expected, it didn't take long for other machine techniques to follow but the real explanation lay with the machine designer copying exactly the human function.

When James Nasmyth describes the slide-rest as an 'iron-hand' that's exactly what it was. Its revolutionary purpose enabled a metal-cutting tool to be held in a rigid position and moved in a very controlled way along a flat machine bed primarily by hand turning a lead-screw. And because the machine actions – genuinely and independently invented by all three men more or less within the same period – had slavishly copied the earlier manual action the resulting concepts were bound to be somewhat alike. But of the three, Maudslay particularly not only advanced his screw-cutting techniques far beyond the others but also processed his original work in so many other directions that it allowed him to compound his ideas, thus gaining a clear lead. Vaucanson had by then died but Maudslay's work was so innovative as to make him the father of modern cylindrical machining. Of course there were others. James Fox and Joseph Clement for example were also innovative leaders within their own right and of the same period; but more of them later.

Much of this machine parentage relates to the first phase of modern world technology. Joseph Whitworth went to London in 1825 and as we now know he stayed for seven-and-a-half years specifically to see and to learn everything he could. The mythology suggests that he went to London as a college graduate – in much the same way that pupil civil engineers were articled to masters – but in Joe's case it was quite different. He worked on the bench and had to deliver that which he was paid to deliver as a manual worker. As it turned out however he used this much rougher experience to his own advantage, no doubt being left by each foreman to follow through the development of each basic component he was asked to make. Whitworth considered the work a privilege. He was, after all, working on the most revolutionary machine ideas anywhere in the world. Twenty years later he established himself as the international leader – the father of the second revolutionary phase – transforming existing technology into a new, still more advanced phase.

Such was Maudslay's marine reputation however that his engines tended to overshadow his machine tools and other development work. His one really personal interest was always screw-cutting – his great ambition being to unify the pitch of a lead-screw throughout its entire length – which he believed to be, as indeed it was, the real key to almost all precision machinery prior to 1825. Some five years earlier he had cut a lead-screw 5 ft long by 2 in diameter giving it fifty threads per inch. It was an ingenious achievement; still not perfect by any means, but it not only generated reasonably accurate lead-screws for Maudslay himself but when the screw was later sold to the Greenwich Laboratory it was there used to calibrate their astro-instruments. It was considered a landmark in both engineering and instrument making and HM Treasury awarded Maudslay £1,000 in recognition of his feat. Joseph Whitworth himself could not have avoided both using and making special threads of a similar kind and in doing so fired his own imagination, thus storing away ideas for the future.

A good example of this learning process was Maudslay's own invention of a notching device which enabled him to accurately punch rivet holes for ships' tanks thus eliminating laborious marking-out and drilling. Years later both Fairbairn and Whitworth perfected similar machines when they each designed a heavy-duty punch to which Joe added a nibbler – a genuine invention of his own – particularly as his machines were power driven from a line shaft. Much of this non-engine work at Maudslays went unnoticed, which prompted A.S. Benson to write in the *Engineering* magazine of January 1901: 'Maybe the fame of Maudslays as marine engineers tended to obscure their great reputation in the earlier part of the century as pioneer toolmakers of England – possibly of the world'.

Apart from his seeing for the first time really flat surfaces and new measurement techniques, the most profound impact the Maudslay years had on Whitworth was probably Maudslay's lathe designs; in particular Maudslay's own development of a synchronized lead-screw and slide-rest. This latter named invention was generally agreed as the greatest single advance at the time; it was instrumental in transforming the primitive techniques of the years pre-1820 into the first phase of modern machine tool technology. This particular genre started when Maudslay was working for Joseph Bramah, but there is good reason to suspect that it was young Maudslay who actually devised and made the very simple arrangement which the two of them famously called their slide-tool. As we have seen, Bramah the employer patented the invention in his own name in 1794 making no mention of Maudslay. This particular fact needs to be repeated in this way to illustrate Whitworth's own experience: starting work for Maudslay, as he did, eight years after his employer had opened his business at Lambeth and helping him construct some of the most mechanically advanced lathe and boring machines anywhere in the world, surely meant that Joe, even as a very young man, was never far from the forefront of the industry. Certainly the machinery he worked upon was never the world's best looking – most of the Maudsley machines had a Heath Robinson appearance – but from Joe's point of view he was already constructing in his own mind the next stage of their development. Maudslay, however, preferred to work behind closed doors rather than rely on patents for the protection of his ideas. Whitworth therefore never really experienced the same meanness practised by Bramah when the celebrated inventor excluded Maudslay from all recognition of their joint work.

During the year 1828 – Whitworth's last at Maudslays – the great engine man designed and constructed (in Whitworth's presence) a lathe with a faceplate 9 ft in diameter operating over a pit some 20 ft deep. This lathe had a massive bed and was used to machine flywheel rims. It was also capable of boring out steam cylinders up to 10 ft in diameter. With the exception of a small treadle-operated lathe (similar to the one he kept locked away in his own private workshop) Maudslay did not manufacture machine tools for sale. As Rolt and others have written: 'Not to have done so is a puzzling feature. The superiority of his tools at the time was so great that we should have expected to find him manufacturing them for others as did Matthew Murray and James Fox of Derby . . . but no such record exists'. Machine development however was not entirely exclusive to Maudslay; equally important work was very quietly taking place elsewhere in Europe.

About the same time as Bramah patented his 'slide-tool' (1775), the special-purpose lathe built by the French textile engineer, Jacques de Vaucanson (to make rollers for his weaving looms), also made world history. Fortunately, this particular lathe has been saved and is now in the Conservatoire Nationale des Arts et Métiers, Paris. It was the world's first ever all-metal lathe with prismatic guideways. Vaucanson had perceptively set 1½ in square wrought-iron bars at 45° to form 'Vee' slides. And although the machine still had to be hand-cranked it was nevertheless an ingenious invention. The Frenchman had mounted on its 'Vee' slides a saddle and toolpost which traversed the full length of the machine pushed along by a continuously 'in-mesh' lead-screw. As a piece of machinery it was years ahead of its time; most experts now agree it to be the first in the world, certainly the first ever screw-traverse machine.

This Vaucanson machine, proudly displayed, very noticeably includes one or two components so well machined as to raise doubts about the precise design of the original parts. But there really is no doubt about the machine's overall mechanical authenticity – each piece logically fits as it was originally intended – and there are full marks too for its remarkably advanced workmanship (not forgetting that most of the machine parts were then hand-crafted) but the whole concept is so brilliantly purposeful that the machine itself, if considered as a total piece, proves both its own origin and its original purpose. Possibly, additional misgivings were aroused by the fact that the machine has a screw-operated cross-slide and a square-threaded lead-screw, two features so far ahead not just of Vaucanson's own pre–1775 textile machinery but also of most pre–1825 French textile machinery as to *underline* the original doubt.

When the lathe was first exhibited industrial historians linked with it another, but later, French lathe. Twenty years after Vaucanson (1795) another Frenchman, François Senot, made further progress with his own beautifully constructed all-metal screw-cutting lathe, this time complete with interchangeable gears. Again, however, as with the earlier lathe, there were one or two curious traits which seemed to strengthen similar doubts to those expressed about the Vaucanson 1775 lathe. That machine, as already mentioned, embraced prismatic guideways; a remarkable advancement both in its concept and in the quality of its making. Why then did the younger Senot ignore the obvious benefits he would have gained by adapting the older man's prismatic slides? By 1800 he would have been aware of the more advanced work claimed for his fellow Parisian rather than revert to the less helpful flat slide-ways on which he himself had simply screwed parallel guides? Unbelievably, Maudslay did the same thing also, in 1800: perhaps the actual making of 'Vee' slides was far too laborious a job at that time; or maybe Maudslay like Senot considered the benefits not worth the effort. But as difficult as hand-crafting precision parts must have been, it didn't prevent either of the two Frenchmen incorporating for the first time some exceedingly fine original mechanisms; the most outstanding perhaps being François Senot's back-gearing and steadies. Despite their brilliant achievements, however, the two Frenchmen could not prevent the leadership of the machine tool movement remaining with Britain. The major initiatives first taken by Maudslay, then by Whitworth represented the new machine technology: a new era, the ascendancy of which rightly remained this side of the English Channel forty years or more.

Curiously enough all three engineers, Vaucanson, Senot and Maudsley had another quirk in common. They each preferred their lathe headstocks to the right of the operator, a somewhat inexplicable design decision wholly inconsistent with natural comfort for those born right-handed. (Some continental writers have implied that Maudslay was thus influenced by Vaucanson and Senot: that he must have known of their work). From around the year 1828 (not before) headstocks were moved to the other end of the lathe; for both ergonomic and engineering reasons to the left of the operator; a factor which then established recognizable methods for dating these interdependent changes. A third equally significant pointer then cropped up. If the headstock was made to the left of the operator, the workpiece must revolve anti-clockwise to enable the cutting tool to be seen and fed from the front: the question whether to use a left or right-handed lead-screw must then have come into the reckoning. Historically it was not until 1836 and the coming of Whitworth's back-gears mounted on a banjo arm that the new anti-clockwise fixed rotation and common lead-screw gearing became the accepted practice.

Whitworth left Maudslays in November 1828 and secured a job with Holtzapffel and Company of 64 Charing Cross. The firm had a lathe and planer manufactory at 127 Long Acre and it was here that Whitworth spent the whole twelve months either working a machine or on the bench. He appears never to have worked on the drawing board although some writers have suggested he worked alongside Holtzapffel himself. The theory is quite feasible. The factory was situated just around the corner from the main office but it was at the factory where Charles Holtzapffel himself spent most of his time. The Charing Cross area was new for Whitworth as it lay on the other side of the Thames from Maudslays. Holtzapffels was essentially a jobbing shop working to the customer's own specification, but according to some early writers they occasionally worked to machine drawings prepared by Joseph Clement. At the time Whitworth was there Holtzapffel's own lathes were mounted on mahogany legs but the new headstocks and slide-rests which they built for sale were designed by an up-and-coming draughtsman, Frederick Ronalds. The firm's very high standing in 1830 as one of Britain's leading expert lathe and lead-screw manufacturers was earned on the basis of their 1½-in diameter lead-screws, reputedly of any length. Whitworth must have been in his element making them. Not only that, it was at Holtzapffels he probably first met Henry Wright, son of a well-known London millwright who, like Joe, was intensely interested in lathe design and machine tools generally. He and Whitworth were of a similar kind and got on well together.

During this period most leading toolmen in London were known to each other and would regularly call in to see Charles Holtzapffel. It could hardly have been otherwise; it was the custom for each manufacturer to acquire his competitors' products for 'research purposes' and no doubt Charles was able to supply their needs. One such regular visitor was Henry Wright's father; he owned a foundry and machine tool business back across the river, in Whitworth's old Lambeth territory, halfway between Maudslay's factory and Joseph Clements. The name of the firm was L.W. Wright and Company of 91 London Road, Southwark, a mere three hundred or so yards from Maudslays.

L.W. Wright had two sons, both about the same age as Whitworth, and being a traditionalist of the old school he probably had them serve an apprenticeship with both Maudslay and Clement followed by a period at Holtzapffels. It was here that one of his sons, Henry, worked alongside both Holtzapffel himself and Whitworth (Henry had previously worked as a draughtsman while at Clements) but became obsessed with the perfecting of long lead-screws. He and Whitworth obviously shared these same interests. When Henry Wright went back to work with his father at their premises in London Road he didn't forget his admiration for Whitworth's knowledge and skills. It was probably he who suggested to his father that they employ Whitworth to help establish a new toolroom and with it a reputation for the manufacture of good quality lathes. Whitworth accepted his invitation and went to work for Henry south of the river.

Joe was six months short of his twenty-seventh birthday when he left Wrights to make his final move in London. Going only a short distance he started work for Joseph Clement at Prospect Place, Newington Butts, in May 1830. By this time Whitworth's reputation would have been known to Clement and just as Henry Wright had done earlier, Clement may even have invited Joe to come and work for him – an opportunity the Manchester man would have grasped in view of Clement's reputation. It was said at the time that within his workshop he possessed the finest machine tools in Britain. They were designed almost wholly by himself and built in the privacy of his own workshop – by general agreement his machines being much in advance of any other maker including Holtzapffel and Maudslay. How contemporaries like Robertson Buchanan knew what Clement was doing, or how good he was, remains a mystery because Clement was extremely secretive about everything he did – except of course about his famous 1827 constant-speed facing lathe which was well publicized by the Royal Society. There can be little doubt that it was this particular machine more than any other which attracted Whitworth to work for Clement. Some years later Whitworth himself was credited with the invention of such technology and although Whitworth's design was much more sophisticated by comparison there can be little doubt that the original seeds germinated in Prospect Place. During the first few months of his employment there Joe must have thoroughly enjoyed an enriching experience surrounded as he was by such sparkling innovation. A pity he himself never recorded his personal impression of Clement's workshop; his account would have filled a crucial gap and would have been an excellent historic record.

At one time Maudslay employed Joseph Clement as his chief draughtsman and the story has it that he was the person most responsible, not only for Maudslay's best machinery but also for the improvements made to his employer's first side-lever table engines. The Clement-Maudslay engines were eventually fitted into the first cross-channel paddle steamers on the Dover–Boulogne service which secured for Maudslay much fame. Another landmark clearly established – Whitworth would have been immensely interested in the work – was Clement's verified effort to improve the quality of the old type threading taps and dies similar to those which Clement had originally designed for Maudslay. According to Holtzapffel, Clement (not Maudslay) was the inventive brain responsible for the modern stock and die, not a lot different from those still in use today.[21]

AN ASSESSMENT OF WHITWORTH'S LONDON YEARS

Whitworth's greatest disappointment must have been the decision by Joseph Clement to end the work he had undertaken for Charles Babbage. For the previous two years Clement's factory had worked non-stop on the Cambridge professor's 'Difference Engine'.[22] Babbage had been abroad till January 1829 and it was only on his return to England that he again applied to the Chancellor of the Exchequer – via the Royal Society – for an additional grant to enable his work to continue. But the Cabinet were not convinced. Both the Chancellor and the Prime Minister (the Duke of Wellington) visited the works twice before partially agreeing to Babbage's request. The situation was not encouraging though, as little engineering progress had been made.

The slowness was directly due to the Lucasian professor of mathematics' habit of 'thinking on his feet' (he repeatedly changed his mind) and Clement's insistence that the work must be paid for as it progressed meant constant argument as to who paid for the scrapped pieces. The two men regularly disagreed and the Government instructed Babbage to remove his papers and any components so far completed to a fireproof building in Manchester Square in Central London. The year was then mid-1831; Whitworth's second year at Prospect Place. Babbage's 'Difference Engine' – some denigrators have called it a grocer's shop cash register

– was a matter of considerable controversy, but for Whitworth it must have been a very satisfying experience making some of the most intricate parts Clement had designed for Babbage. Sadly for Joe, the Government prematurely brought the work to an end by finally cutting off their financial support.

The Babbage affair dominated life at Clements for a number of years. Special purpose machines had been constructed to undertake the unusual nature of the machining. Babbage too was an unusual character: son of a wealthy banker, professor of mathematics; he twice unsuccessfully contested the London Parliamentary constituency of Finsbury, in 1832 and 1834. He did so as a Liberal candidate but his outstanding contribution which later very much influenced Joseph Whitworth was his book published in 1830, *Reflections on the Decline of Science in England*; a theme which directly led to the formation of the British Association: a forum Whitworth himself used on a number of occasions, while Babbage's general critique of the Oxbridge anti-science, anti-engineering stance no doubt helped push Joe towards his future support for an Owens College Engineering Department.

While working at Clements Whitworth appreciated that he was getting the equivalent of a technical education. The practical experience he gained was tremendous. Nor was Joe alone in the lavishness of his praise; another engineer – later to be employed by Holtzapffel and also by Whitworth himself – shared the same view. His name was William Muir, a talented Scotsman Whitworth came to know very well, their relationship tending to swing from close amiability to one of outright petulance. Muir was an obsessive note-taker filling dozens of sketchbooks with simple outline sketches of the great variety of machine tools and detailed mechanisms he came across during his many travels. Muir was three years younger than Joe and commenced work at Maudslays in April 1831. Shortly after starting, Maudslay's son appointed Muir as works foreman at the age of twenty-five, two months after Henry Maudslay senior had died. The illustrated record which Muir then compiled became an indispensable encyclopaedia without which much historic knowledge of engineering would have been missing.

From Whitworth's point of view Muir's sketchbooks cleared up a great deal of confusion.[23] The old workshop secrecy which still tends to obscure original dates was helpfully clarified by Muir's extraordinary notetaking. Whitworth, for instance, was once posthumously accused of copying Clement's shell (or sleeve) bearings for his own lathes. It was not true. The sketches made at the time by Muir and Sellers plus those by other contemporaries, prove that Whitworth's bearings started out from an entirely different concept than Clement's and finished up much in advance of Clement's earlier work. Clement did in fact use hardened steel (parallel) sleeve bearings backed by hardened thrust plates but they didn't run in oil baths. All that had to wait until Whitworth himself introduced fully lubricated adjustable *tapered* shells and thrust washers about the year 1837 or 1838. Whitworth also grappled with the problem of grease pads which at that time tended to dry too quickly. Clement's, after Whitworth had gone, themselves introduced some improvements but not until 1840 or so, the year both he and Maudslay's son started to *purchase* Whitworth's Manchester machine tools for use in their own London workshops. They did so because of their pure technical excellence.

For many reasons the year 1832 was an historically significant year. Joseph and Fanny Whitworth were themselves ready to leave London and return to Manchester but first they had to carefully think over the general situation. Politically, it was the first great year of parliamentary reform. For the cotton industry, its new methods were beginning to blossom and a new trade boom was within sight. For engineering, better machine tools, more efficient steam engines and the promotion of the new railways combined to promise not yet the end of the old system but significantly, the beginning of modern times. The same applied to the Whitworth's themselves; they saw an end to the horrifying past, the arson, the machine breaking and the riots – some of which still went on in London. But these were not the reasons why Joe wanted to leave the city – Manchester in fact continued to endure much of the same aggravation. It was Whitworth's own glimpse of the future which, for him, was the main attraction pulling him back north. Manchester was rapidly becoming the centre of all that was new in engineering and Joe wanted to be part of it. Cotton and railways sounded to him like the coming millennium.

The political atmosphere throughout parliamentary London was tense; it was an essential part of any business judgement Whitworth had to make as to whether he should then leave for Manchester. The House of Lords had defeated the Reform Bill. William IV had asked the Prime Minister, still the Duke of Wellington, to form another government, but he failed; not enough experienced ministers would chance their careers serving the anti-franchise duke. The king next asked Earl Grey. Yes, he would try, but Grey insisted on the king agreeing to make enough new peers to form a majority and to do so from those who were committed in advance to the Reform Bill going through. Manchester, the Whitworths' imminent destination, was then quiet having become a beneficiary (being allocated two MPs instead of one) once the Reform Bill went through at the second attempt.

Admittedly then, Whitworth's stint in London lasted seven and a half years. By and large it had been exactly as he had wanted it; an experience of working for the four leading machine tool makers and doing so in the order he wanted. One thing he had not done – he later regretted it – he never sacrificed bench work for a spell in a drawing office. Each of the four firms where he had worked had what passed as very primitive design offices but, in reality, they were no more than combined pattern and drawing shops. The fact that he never enjoyed the glorified status of a draughtsman answered those critics who pictured him as some kind of workshop dilettante: he was nothing of the kind; he deliberately did nothing other than benchwork for the whole of his London period.

Perhaps one other reason Joe didn't work on the drawing board at Maudslays was an incident during his second year there, 1826, when the drawing office collapsed into the engine bay below, killing two men and injuring some others. Sadly, it was later revealed, Brunel senior had warned his friend Maudslay that the flimsy structure he had erected would in fact collapse. Fortunately for him, the coroner decided it was an accident, so Maudslay escaped the consequences. Another aspect this tragic event pinpointed was the sheer weight of patterns and castings which draughtsmen tended to use; drawing full size on the floor in a very practical way then adding the adjoining patterns or mock-ups for the pattern maker to copy.

Reference has previously been made to the fact that Whitworth, unlike his friend William Muir, never methodically recorded in either note form or sketches his private evaluation of the engineering work he did. What little evidence there is points to his reliance on an extraordinarily fine memory. Of course it was marvellous that Joe was able to memorize so much, but disappointing for those of his devotees who would have found his notes a treasure to sift. Not that he was unique. Many famous engineers have claimed, incredibly, that little if any of their preparatory work was ever committed to paper but almost wholly carried in their head and it may be that Whitworth was of this order. The work he accomplished during his first years at Chorlton Street, Manchester, more than suggested that he knew exactly how he intended to set about his early machine construction long before he left London. Certainly his ideas on metrology were already thought through as were his new lathe and planer mechanisms. Maybe Whitworth did possess a remarkable mind; equally retentive as some leading mathematicians have claimed in that they too could memorize theoretical formulae at chapter length. If Joe was of this same ilk it would explain a great deal, not only how he was able to pursue simultaneously three or four entirely different experimental constructions but also how he kept track of his own ideological thinking – and to have done it, seemingly, without the aid of either sketchbook or paper.

Intellectual enlightenment is not something which happens in an abrupt manner: by its very meaning it must be an evolutionary process. Whitworth himself was a fairly late starter; but he had a luminary mind – he had exceptionally advanced ideas for his time. But how soon in his life did this intellectual enlightenment become apparent? Naturally, such a question poses implausible perplexities but as a twenty-nine-year-old engineer Whitworth made it known that he was fully conscious of most science and engineering achievements at the time he left London.

He also made a point about his powers of engineering and political prophesy when he predicted the leading role mechanical engineering would play in bringing about quite revolutionary improvements in society. Indeed, he would have had to be both lumpen and imperceptive not to have been excited by the potential of Maudslay's engineering, for instance, or Clement's machine tools. The fact that later he developed a proven designer's facility for visualization of necessity meant that he could also imaginatively envisage life in Britain fifty years on. No doubt he compared the miserable down-and-out poverty of everyday living in the 1830s with the brilliant potential he was convinced steam power and machine tools would make possible by 1880. That in itself would have stimulated sufficient ambition.

Whitworth was so persuaded he could see the social potential of mass production that he couldn't wait to leave London and start working for himself in Manchester. He appreciated the privilege living in London had bestowed on him. He had worked and helped create some of the world's latest machinery but alongside his practical engineering he had read appropriate theory and listened to the best brains elucidate the laws of dialectics. He read the kind of philosophy which urged upon the reader his or her own physical participation in the shaping of events.

London had many learned societies to encourage the likes of Whitworth. He sought their advice and the use of their libraries. He had no fixed route ahead of him. As he arrived in London he could read, yes, but without the help of a university tutor he didn't yet know how to *use* books or the library. London did that for him. For much of the time he burned the midnight oil reading the industrial philosopher Francis Bacon, particularly *The Advancement of Learning* and *New Atlantis.* These books gave him a philosophical perspective and method. Bacon was so convinced that a lack of engineering technology would stultify society that he pleaded in 1620 that either Eton or Westminster School should be converted into a technical college – a view to which Whitworth two hundred and fifty years later would have given a standing ovation, as also he would have applauded Bacon's view that scientific experiment should be funded by the government.

Whitworth's later 'inductive methodology' assuredly seems Bacon inspired. Incredibly, even today Bacon's methodology reads like the theory and practice of invention: some modern manual perhaps on laboratory procedure. In his first seventeenth-century major thesis Bacon rejected a metaphysics approach. He angled his work towards the development of a genuinely scientific method. He taught that true philosophy must be based on the actual observation of nature. He made an outstanding contribution to the empirical method; teaching that all science is based on experience and consists in subjecting the data furnished by the senses to a rational method of investigation, involving induction (i.e. logic) analysis, comparison, observation and experiment. Of course, today's geneticist or nuclear physicist would want to modify parts of such simplified thinking but for Whitworth it provided a basis and a perspective.

During the mid-Victorian period there were many Baconians in Parliament. There was a Bacon Society in fact. In later years Whitworth himself would have enjoyed their conversation. He is reputed never to have been one for abstract speculations but more important, his Baconism taught him there were no short cuts in experimental engineering; a premise he thoroughly respected. The more general Baconian thesis however, suggested that the course of history is determined not just by material conditions but is explicitly steered by the great leading personalities of the day being in the right place at the right time; thus in Bacon's view material existence plus pre-elected coincidence combine to make history – a lesson Whitworth himself was later to ruefully learn by his own personal experience.

This philosophical introduction for Joe was no abstract speculation. Whitworth's first machine designs implied he was convinced that no mechanism should ever be considered in isolation; that no collection of axles, plates and gears should ever be considered as just an arbitrary collection of objects, independent and isolated one from another. He thus gave the four most naturally linked phenomena – growth and development, decay and disintegration – an entirely new meaning in terms of mechanics and machine tool design. This clear but simple example explains what should be understood as his own Baconian approach to machine design. One further point about the theory of related progression: Whitworth realized from the beginning that the structural strength of his machine designs was far in advance of the tool metallurgy available. The metal bulk he added to his machine frames to absorb vibration was far in excess of 1840 tool steels. The maximum cut possible was barely a quarter of the machine capacity he designed. But he clearly understood each aspect had to move forward in unison – speeds and feeds in unison with machine strength – and, interestingly, he deliberately created his machines with excess capacity feeling sure that tool metallurgy would soon catch up: a related progression in fact.

Joseph Whitworth freely acknowledged that he personally had derived a great deal from his London experience. Though not yet an accomplished engineer he was nonetheless now ready to return north. He and his wife Fanny lived for the future, justifiably they hoped for better times. In 1832 they packed their bags and booked two 'outsiders' seats Manchester bound, atop the Lancashire express mail coach.

Once back in Manchester and among friends, the frequent Baconian interjections with which journalists and writers spliced their Whitworth interviews somehow indicated that it was still Joe himself who enjoyed quoting the great philosopher. The lectures he attended in London had clearly left their mark. By way of illustration let us for a moment skip some years and quote *The Engineer* magazine, 6 June 1856. The result is a fascinating glimpse of a more mature Whitworth cultivated by his Baconian scholarship.

In this instance the journalist was interviewing Joe during a visit to the Chorlton Street works. He was probably paraphrasing his subject (this is a truncated version) when he wrote:

> The world of theoretical science, as yet, is but a very partial and one-sided view of the world reality . . . but the Baconian method of induction and experiment has made our new system (of mechanics) square with the outer world of reality. . . . Such men as Stephenson, Bidder, Brunel, Fairbairn, Whitworth and Nasmyth are not in general very profound mathematicians, or even very deeply read in the theory of mechanics; but they are all men of deep research and profound knowledge in the science of reality.

The magazine then turned to what reads very much like a direct interpretation of Whitworth's own 1856 views. The profile continued:

> A man of this mould is Mr Whitworth; he saw that abstractions, whether

> mathematical or mechanical, could be of little service to the science of reality: that, if it be true that mechanics is but the mathematics of motion, then real mechanics must be founded on real mathematics. It had so long been regarded as an established truism that mathematical points, lines, surfaces and solids, could only exist as abstractions, and could have no existence in reality, that it required no ordinary courage to call it in question. This however, Mr Whitworth not only did, but he undertook to produce them (in reality).[24]

Despite its melodramatic prose *The Engineer* renders a useful analysis posing the theory-v.-practice polemic in the way it did. Thus, in a Baconian sense, Whitworth's opinion is rightly allowed to represent the synthesis of the argument. Though he yet faced a further decade before he finally accepted the necessity for scientific (theoretical) knowledge at least he was beginning to see the need for what the mid-Victorians called 'abstract learning'.

William Fairbairn particularly loved the phrase 'science always relies for its source of verification upon practice, thus making practice the most profound criterion of truth'. In September 1861 Lord Wrottesley, the scientist, eulogized Fairbairn when he welcomed him as President of the British Association. Fairbairn responded, indicating that he too had moved on philosophically.

> If the British Association had affected nothing more than the removal of the anomalous separation of theory and practice it would have gained imperishable renown.
>
> The present epoch is one of the most important in the history of the world. At no former period did science contribute so much to the uses of life and the wants of society; and in doing this, it has been only fulfilling that mission which Bacon, *the great father of modern science,* appointed for it when he wrote (in 1620) that '*the legitimate goal of the sciences is the endowment of human life with new inventions and riches*'.

In 1862 – thirty years after Whitworth had left London – Sir J. Emerson Tennent LLD, FRS, a stalwart upholder of Whitworth's work at a time when both government ministers and competitors combined to attack the quality of the Manchester man's military engineering, wrote a passionate defence:

> Mr Whitworth does not belong to the ordinary type of inventors, quick, versatile and ingenious, acting from impulse or apparent inspiration; his productions, on the contrary, are the results of slow and deliberate thought, bringing former observation to bear upon tentative experiment and accepting nothing as established till it had undergone proof. Proceeding with a logical severity to rest further operations only on ascertained facts, his process is so strictly inductive, that he might justly be designated the Bacon of mechanics.[25]

CHAPTER TWO

How He Set Up Shop

The twenty-nine-year-old Whitworth instinctively felt that he had been away from Manchester a long time – it was less than eight years in fact. Now it was summer 1832 and he and his wife Frances – or Fanny as he now called her – were back from London impatient to pitch Joe's skills against established Manchester engineers who were then just starting to taste the very beginning of the cotton boom.

Neither Joseph nor Fanny had visited Manchester during their time away – they had no reason to do so – neither of them any longer had close relatives still living in the area. Not only that; the ramshackle journey from London by the fastest and least rickety coach-and-four took at least twenty-two hours, that is if all went well. And usually it didn't; most passengers stayed overnight somewhere in the Midlands if they had that sort of money. Yes, the Whitworths had probably saved a little, not more than a few pounds, in the hope that Joe could one day get himself started pretty quickly. But over the past few years every penny saved had been longingly set aside for the day he moved into his own little workshop: things like travel had to wait. The big day for which they had worked, however, had now arrived and Joe was full of invention, ambitions, and bursting with personal confidence: he wanted to get started as soon as he could.

Like dozens of other industrial fledglings Whitworth recognized that the rapidly growing Manchester area was fast becoming the engineering capital of the world. The belching smoke stacks bore witness to its muck-and-brass creed. Noticeably the place had changed a great deal since he last worked at Marsden and Walker in Water Street, or before that, at Crighton's the machine builders.[1] But the biggest and most noticeable change for him of course was the rise in the local population. The place was now so overcrowded, the back streets teeming with people. In the past seven years the number of people in the town had increased by half as much again and was still growing at the speed of some western gold rush. The horrifying truth meant that the poky stone-floored back-to-back houses which were already bulging had to take in even more families who were still swarming in from the surrounding countryside and from places as far away as Ireland. Naturally their essential traditions died hard – the animals came too – even the cellars had become packed to a reeking suffocation.

Not that Joe and Fanny had any intention of living in that fashion. Tight as their money was they were hoping to avoid sharing an earth closet or a 'midden privy' with, on average, another fifty or more households. They considered themselves entitled to a little more dignity than that but realized that even the most decent lodgings suffered the same appalling pressures as all the rest. But rather than make too much of their present plight they could hardly forget that things generally had not been too good for them in London either, especially around the Waterloo area where they had lived prior to moving to Manchester.

Moving back north was not some fantasy, it was essentially about establishing themselves in their own business; a vocational mission. Joe the engineer wanted desperately to forge for himself his own company and to build machines to his own design. But for Fanny his wife, her very last flicker of romance was no doubt far too weak to survive. Moving back to the stench and decay of the Irk and the Irwell must have seemed to her like moving backwards into wretchedness. Indeed, when Joe had left Marsdens – which then backed on to the River Irwell – he remembered the air at that time wasn't too bad. That was 1825. Now the river was caked over with the multi-coloured effluent of the new dye works, the iron foundries and the new cotton mills which – together with the untreated human outflow – just about enabled the bravest sparrows to ride on top and gently float downstream, unbelievably towards the wild flowers and butterflies of rural Salford.

But even Sir Oswald Mosley's Manchester couldn't stomach depravity on this scale. Commensurate with the enlightened ambitions of the new engineers, a young doctor – a Dr J.P. Kay – published the first of his 1832 Reports which catalogued the moral and physical conditions of working people in Manchester. His report was so devastating that it even stunned the few in Parliament who cared.[2] It provoked an awareness in support of better sanitary arrangements far more effectively than all the Chartist tub-thumping. It also concentrated the mind of another great Stockport man, Edwin Chadwick who, like Kay, linked disease with filth and bad conditions.[3] But unlike a great many of the other social pontificators of the day these two men intended serious business. Chadwick for instance, only accepted membership of the 1833 Royal Commission which had been set up to investigate the conditions of factory children so that he could actively pursue his now famous vendetta against child abuse and industrial disease. And if it is any indication of the way Joe Whitworth's own social conscience was working out, it really wasn't so surprising that years later both Whitworth and Edwin Chadwick came together to become firm political allies.

Not to rush our story, however, Manchester was never a Klondyke. While its wages were generally higher than those paid in the surrounding districts the real reason why its textile industry continued to attract whole families was the illusion that it represented an escape from rural serfdom and the heartbreaking cruelty Tolpuddle deemed agricultural slavery. Sometimes perhaps, according to Kay, they wished they had stayed in the fields. Perhaps their children would have been healthier – who knows? But now an altogether different dimension started to emerge which attracted young men in particular to the rapidly growing engineering industry. There was a chance, they thought, of learning a skilled engineering trade. The more resourceful of them had even heard of the new highly skilled pattern-making trade and the idea that it offered them the chance of starting their own small jobbing shop: and for the really gifted the idea of draughtsmanship was a way to the top.

Mechanical engineering in the shape of machine tools was then at the centre of the new age and because of steam power and textiles Manchester was fast taking the lead. Nor was it surprising that the few really innovative engineers of the day, blessed as they were with outstanding mechanical genius, were seeking their fortune in the same way as their less intellectually endowed brethren. They too were prepared to put up with the most dreadful conditions in search of fame and perhaps a fortune, equally anxious to pioneer, if they could, some part of the new technology: to pit their engineering wit against the best. Manchester it would seem also had its own engineering Whittingtons.

Cast against such an aggressive background, how good was Whitworth? Was he as strong and as talented as his admirers claimed? Did the vulnerability of his youth plus the lack of a supportive family affect his early drive as a machine tool maker? Palpably, answers to all these questions can only be properly assessed if he is compared on an equal basis to his contemporaries. Fortuitously, circumstances offering such relevant comparisons did exist.

Arriving in Manchester – within a year or so of each other – and roughly for the same reasons, were three other rather special engineers. And as if by some divine right, all four were destined to achieve world class engineering reputations. Their names were John G. Bodmer, Charles F. Beyer, James Nasmyth and, of course, our man himself, Joseph Whitworth. And yes, if first impressions mean anything at all, then Whitworth's limited education (and the fact that he had arrived in Manchester still wearing his manual worker's overalls) did set him apart from the others. From the beginning it was obvious his rise to the top was always going to be the steepest climb. Of the quartet however, the absolute fortuity making possible these particular comparisons makes them historically significant.

The Quartet – Whitworth Compared with Bodmer, Beyer and Nasmyth

The eldest of the four was John G. Bodmer. Born in Zurich in 1776 he had previously worked as a millwright and had gone on to set up his own factory in the Black Forest making textile machinery. By 1806 he was producing 'interchangeable' parts for rifles in much the same way as Eli Whitney at New Haven in America. When Bodmer arrived in Manchester (his third visit to England incidentally) some four months after Whitworth had arrived, he was already an experienced engineer and because he also spoke English and German fluently he naturally fell in with the local German community. They were an extremely influential group but whether or not they actually helped him secure a job with Sharp Roberts and Company is not known. He went there expecting to become their works superintendent, or at least chief draughtsman, but as things turned out he became neither and promptly left the firm to set up on his own. He did so in partnership with a Hugh Birley, an intriguing Manchester man of some wealth. The fact that Birley had a questionable past (more about this aspect later) didn't seem to worry Bodmer, although the younger German radicals in the town were extremely critical of Birley. It is an interesting point because although Bodmer had tried to put down roots in England on two previous occasions this time he made straight for Manchester and, following his disappointment with Sharp Roberts he immediately proved that he knew what he was doing by teaming up with John Kennedy in addition to the questionable Hugh Birley; the two biggest (but by no means the most agreeable) mill owners in the country.

Surprisingly the triumvirate went very well. Birley, like Kennedy, owned a number of spinning and weaving sheds around the Cambridge Street area of Manchester along the south bank of the River Irwell, in fact just across from the notorious Little Ireland district; and he offered Bodmer – for use as an engineering factory – the biggest weaving shed in the area. Birley immediately pumped enough money into the venture to allow Bodmer free rein. Bodmer didn't let him down. Within five years of starting he had designed and developed from scratch some very fine machine tools and was offering them for sale to the wider trades; he also made and sold some of the most advanced textile machinery then available.[4] By 1839 he had patented the world's first circular planer – or vertical borer as it would be called today – considered by experts to be a truly remarkable innovation. It was Bodmer's design genius using Birley's money which had given the world such a marvellous machine. It gave the steam engine constructors, and therefore the engineering industry as a whole, considerable assistance mainly because it was multi-operational and for the first time cylinder flanges square to the bore could be machined while the casting was in an upright position. But the machine had one glaring weakness. It was without a vertical power feed – a major design fault which remained uncorrected for at least three or four years.

For our purpose here, however – that of making a comparison between Bodmer and Whitworth – it needs to be said that a major omission from a machine of this importance (i.e. not having a mechanism for taper boring) must say something significant about its inventor. In mid-Victorian times, more so than today, it was crucial for a machine inventor to be an exceptionally good visualizer. And although it has sometimes been suggested that Bodmer never actually sold any of these flawed machines there still exist sufficient drawings from which a judgement can be made. Careful examination of his original machine, especially the cast shapes of its structural pieces, clearly suggests that he intended adding a vertical power feed once he could see the thing working. Unfortunately it never works out like that and seldom is it possible to add a central feature to a machine after it is built, thus a designer who has the wonderful ability to fully visualize a machine before a casting is poured was worth his weight in gold. And though drawings prepared for the Patents Office are seldom a proper way of judging a machine (on occasions some patents are deliberately misleading), in this instance, examination of the vertical borers Bodmer made some years later do reveal that he substantially redesigned the cross-beam and its vertical slides to give his machine a power feed and tapering facility. The point is that the marketing of his first machines was probably delayed some four or five years due to his lack of visualization. Whitworth, on the other hand, was *par excellence* in this field. His design record as a visualizer stands supreme. There is no doubt that in his prime, Whitworth could always see the end result with absolute clarity. It was this special ability with gave him such a sizeable advantage over his leading rivals.

Bodmer's Cambridge Street business continued very successfully for twenty-four years but it was his early period which proved to the world his scintillating inventiveness. He came up with some tremendous ideas although, even in his case, the gestation period between first thoughts and the final product was inevitably a long one. Protracted design gravidity is not new. It has frightened financial backers throughout time. Long before anything tangible satisfied their investment even a recognized genius of Bodmer's standing had to be well funded; a predicament Whitworth himself faced early in 1833.[5]

During this same year a quite remarkable event occurred in Manchester which was to trigger an entirely fresh boost for local engineering employers and encourage them to go for larger premises. William Glasgow's Caledonian Foundry wheeled out its first 2–2–0 locomotive (which they named 'Manchester') while further down the road Sharp Roberts did the same, but in a rather less presumptuous way, naming their own locomotive 'Experiment'. Which locomotive came first is a moot point. The Caledonian people claimed that the 'Manchester' was built in August 1831 but Sharp Roberts countered by insisting that both locomotives were completed in July 1833. In the event the issue mattered little: both firms discontinued production of locomotives until late 1837 when they both started up again. Fairbairns and Nasmyths started up two years after that, making a total of six Manchester companies attempting for the first time to manufacture railway engines. It was the beginning of a new era for the town, especially for John Bodmer and Joseph Whitworth. For them, it succulently revealed an unoccupied kingdom and a vacant throne.

Not surprisingly the initial difficulties of locomotive manufacture were immense and worldwide. Northern engineers talked of little else. Whitworth, for instance, considered the basic geometry of steam traction to be at fault and patented an alternative 'motion' in 1837. And though his ideas on steam were somewhat blemished to say the least, his specially adapted machine tools – like Bodmer's, as yet unveiled – proved in the end to be extremely relevant in overcoming the difficulties. The chronicle of events was in itself a revelation. The twenty-seven-year-old Robert

Stephenson in 1830 had persuaded his father George to break from his 'Rocket' design and build what was tantamount to a modern-looking 0–4–0 locomotive: that is to say, he positioned the cylinders directly beneath the smokebox inside a metal-clad frame. He did so to make for steadier running, to reduce condensation and to save fuel but the more sophisticated components required much more advanced engineering techniques than were commonly available.

Much of Stephenson's 'link motion' engine design remained for some years in advance of his own factory's ability to make the parts accurately. Earlier he had relied very much on his works foreman, a James Kennedy, an exceptionally gifted mechanic with a flair for loco design. So much so, that when Edward Bury enlarged his Liverpool engine plant he persuaded James Kennedy to leave Stephenson and join him as a partner. The move had the effect of dividing the design strategies of all six new locomotive factories in Manchester. In fact William Fairbairn himself commenced building Bury designed locos and was assisted by Kennedy: an 1839 arrangement of such emphatic vigour as to sway Manchester's other rising loco engineer, Charles F. Beyer, over at Sharp Roberts, also to use Bury's designs. The split had one other indirect consequence; it pressurized both Bodmer and Whitworth – probably provoked would be a better term – towards their best ever special purpose machine adaptations. It was the making of the Manchester machine tool industry; the fact that Sharp Roberts and Fairbairn became Bury orientated (their locos had 5 ft linked driving wheels – the biggest so far) while Nasmyth and the others resumed their personal friendship with the Stephensons, sharing the work of the Newcastle man's Forth Street drawing office.

Before leaving this matter it is worth recalling a point which dramatized the obvious lead Bodmer and Whitworth had amassed prior to 1840. The first British bogie locomotives built by Tayleur and Co. in 1834 (non-Whitworth tooling) were exported to the United States at a factory gate price of £1,700 each. In 1840, Norris 4–2–0 locos (using some Whitworth machines) landed at Liverpool from America priced at £1,500. Not only was their delivery on time but they were better machined and they climbed better. Superior machine-shop standards were the prime reason. Another example concerned Messrs G. & J. Rennie, a reputable London engineering company. They built five engines at their Holland Street works but they were so poorly engineered that within twelve months they had to be taken to Fairbairns (part Whitworth machine shop) and rebuilt, inadequate machine tools again being the culprit. The point was that Whitworth's acclaimed accuracy and skill consciousness was at last permeating Manchester engineering. It was this which gave them the lead, an improvement not noticeable elsewhere until the late 1840s.[6]

Still in the year 1840, over at Sharp Roberts, the youngest member of our engineering quartet, Charles F. Beyer, was made the firm's senior draughtsman in charge of loco design. He had been the last to arrive in Manchester in 1834 at the age of twenty-one. Son of a poor weaver from Plauen in Saxony, he had won the benefit of a scholarship to Dresden Polytechnic. When he first came to

Manchester he carried with him letters of introduction to one or two leading members of the German people already established in the town. He was soon in touch with a merchant family named Behren. Unlike their earlier experience in trying to help John Bodmer they were on this occasion successful in assisting Beyer get a job in the drawing office at Sharp Roberts. Predictably, because of Beyer's outstanding talent, in less than nine years he had become their chief engineer. And by 1853 – having been refused in marriage by one of Sharp's daughters (more likely he was refused a partnership in the firm) – he decided to leave the company and set up his own business. This he did in partnership with a locomotive man named Peacock – thus the internationally famous locomotive builders, Beyer Peacock, came into existence.

Charles Beyer was universally recognized as a great mechanical engineer; his prowess as an engine designer became legendary throughout the world.[7] An early colleague was John Ramsbottom, a draughtsman almost the same age as Charles Beyer who, during their drawing office days at Sharp Roberts, first became a protégé of Beyer and then his assistant, going on to become locomotive superintendent for the whole LNWR network based at Crewe. Arguably for a time they became the country's leading locomotive engineers. During their best period they innovated some of the most important railway developments. Significant indeed that both of them should become devotees of Whitworth. They accepted his leadership in most matters concerned with machine tools and engineering production, their own work portraying Whitworth's objectivity. Years later Charles Beyer and Whitworth came together very closely to play a decisive part in the foundation of a science and engineering faculty at Owens College; it was their personal combined generosity that made it all possible. And while John Ramsbottom never enjoyed the grand, personal wealth of his two colleagues he too shared their enthusiasm and contributed both effort and money. All the more poignant that Manchester should never have bothered to sing their praises from the roof-tops. All three engineers exerted immense influence yet their identities now border on anonymity.

One other past enigma of equal shame helped to humiliate mechanical engineers. During these early days engineering was essentially empiricist as against the scientists' more learned approach. Disregarding their élitist urbanity most Victorian engineers liked to play the part of hard practical men; 'we are not against foreigners as such, you understand,' but nonetheless they believed they had good reason to be firm chauvinists.

Charles Beyer, in later life particularly, had good reason to feel shunned by this prejudice. Being both German and Jewish – a brilliant engineers' engineer, no less – it was probably this kind of hidden trade bigotry which triggered his own sensitivity to these matters. Other German engineers working in the town also sensed a degree of hostility especially, they said, from within Manchester's learned societies; yet none of this resentment ever applied to the many Heidelberg chemists tutored by R.W. Bunsen entering Owens College as tutors. Indeed, Owens scientists enjoyed a special reverence, until then reserved only for the likes of the late Dr Dalton and James P. Joule; but this intended slur against engineers was sufficient to impassion within Beyer a profound resolve to do for his own profession what the thinking person's 'canonizing perception' had done for the scientists.

Post-1850 the Manchester-Heidelberg influence started to grow appreciably, ultimately having sagacious consequences, not just for organic chemistry but for scientific research generally. It was this local milieu which rubbed off on men like Beyer and Whitworth; both appreciative but indirect beneficiaries of this ambient spirit of learning and research. As time went on, the wider Manchester engineering community also became enriched by the now powerful succession of Bunsen-Liebig graduates attracted to Owens. It could hardly be otherwise. Best described as a 'learning orientation' it perceptibly sharpened Manchester's pioneering edge, persuading its engineers to do something different rather than just rely on their empirical 'hard-headed' approach. Whitworth's own self-taught reading of Francis Bacon had already enhanced his theoretical approach. Coaxed perhaps by the likes of Beyer, animated by the chemists, what he and the others achieved was inherently the product of a unique German-cum-academe situation.

Whitworth never allowed his manual worker background to prejudice his attitude towards the need for science education, nor did he allow it to inhibit his early design work at Chorlton Street. Indeed, in comparison with the spectacular success achieved by Charles Beyer's own company, Beyer Peacock, Whitworth not only matched it financially but also led Beyer with the superior quality of his engineering: any notion that he might have trailed behind due to some kind of inferior intellect should be discarded. Clearly Joe inherited his father's twin attributes: a dogged stamina and a resolute willpower to see him through. Naturally any judgement as to how well Whitworth stood the test must depend on many considerations other than engineering; first as a self-employed person and then later as a young manufacturer he had to compete with the best in a very competitive Victorian free-trade orientated town. Indeed there could be no more exacting test for Joe than to stand him alongside James Nasmyth, the third element of our quartet of comparables.

Born in 1808, James Nasmyth was almost five years younger than Whitworth and very much the product of middle-class, well-educated Edinburgh parents. He really was a potential engineering giant from whom much was expected right from the start. As a professional artist his father was the doyen of the Scottish Academy and later exhibited at the Royal Academy in London. And much of this talented panache rubbed off on young James. Certainly he was more of a finished product than Whitworth could ever be: even as an engineer, it is recorded that Nasmyth was commissioned by the Scottish Society of Arts at the very young age of nineteen to design and build a steam carriage capable of carrying half a dozen passengers. Indeed he must have had an engineering precociousness second only to the boy Leonardo. On the other hand, Whitworth, at nineteen, was working as a bench-fitter – not yet on full money – at Marsden and Walker.

The differences between the two could not have been more pronounced; thus a systematic comparison between them contrives a most interesting and objective exercise. Not only that; because both Nasmyth and Whitworth had worked in London – at Maudslay's no less, though not at the same time – they no doubt were by sight familiar with the same small circle of top engineers. Notwithstanding the fact that they were about to compete against each other for jobbing work handed out by the same mill owners, it would be inconceivable they didn't know each other from their first days in Manchester. And though their paths were to meet a thousand times during the next twenty years they seldom, if ever, spoke to one another. Moreover each made a studied point of not referring to the other by name in what must have become a very strange and, at times, spiteful relationship. But let these personal aspects rest until the events themselves explain the reasons. What is not known is whether either of them ever bought the other's machinery as would be the customary practice between leading machine builders of the day.

It would have been helpful for our purpose in comparing their work to have been able to recognize the original sources from which each had gained his inspiration. Sadly their mutually practised pique, alluded to earlier, ensured that neither man ever mentioned a spanner touched by the other. One other curio which cropped up soon after Nasmyth started building Stephenson-inspired locos; he became an anti-craft, anti-education-for-the-masses adherent. It followed exactly the view taken by both Robert Stephenson MP and Brunel. Curious indeed![8]

SEARCHING FOR SUITABLE PREMISES

Just prior to Christmas 1832 Whitworth was the first of the two to look for suitably small workshop premises. He went back to the district he knew best, the central area of Manchester, north of Piccadilly. He had little or no money and wanted a small place already equipped with one or two simple pieces of machinery for hire. Eventually he found such a place in Port Street and with great pride screwed his name-board above the door, 'Joseph Whitworth, Toolmaker, from London', in much the same way as a violin-maker or a dressmaker. It was a humble start but at least he had made a start and he was satisfied.

Soon after Christmas 1833 James Nasmyth did the same: he also went off in search of suitable premises. He was then just twenty-five years of age and Whitworth twenty-nine. On the whole Nasmyth's ideas were a little more ambitious than Joe's and he finally settled for a more elaborate place in Dale Street: a double-fronted workshop occupying the first floor perched above a glass-cutter. He was just around the corner from the place Whitworth had chosen but Nasmyth's Dale Street workshop was better equipped and described as emporium in style. He soon developed the place as a thriving business and within a year of starting Nasmyth was employing seven or eight men, whereas Whitworth probably never employed more than one or possibly two while he was at Port Street. Unlike

Nasmyth, however, Joe never got to grips with his small repair and jobbing shop and soon moved on. Certainly the reason he moved was never a shortage of general mill work. As Nasmyth himself wrote: 'I was able to take advantage of the new steam-age boom and within two-and-a-half years I had outgrown the premises'.

This latter point was rather a novel description of what actually happened. His business not only outgrew the premises but literally outweighed the strength of the floor. He had piled that much heavy machinery and solid metal on the floor that it was inevitable that one day it would crash through into the place below – and that it did – bringing to an abrupt end both his tenancy and any goodwill between himself and the glass-cutter. Nasmyth himself called it 'a propitious accident'. Years later he recalled in his autobiography that the glassman was in such a terrible state when it happened that he rushed out to call the landlord. The landlord came and saw the smashed tumblers and decanters. He also saw the gaping hole in the ceiling and a steam engine poking through. Without more ado he told Nasmyth to take his machinery elsewhere, thus terminating a very profitable business which not only made a lot of money but had also established for Nasmyth an engineering reputation.

Nasmyth doesn't declare a precise date when he first started to plan his new factory at Patricroft but it would almost certainly have been around Spring 1835. The factory opened in August 1836 and while he claimed that 'going through the floor in Dale Street' was a 'propitious accident' the truth more likely was that he had actually planned a new and much bigger factory a year or so before moving in. Nasmyth was like that: two of his strongest attributes were organization and planning.

Comparing all this with Whitworth's initial experience it is worth recalling the kind of friends Nasmyth had nurtured early on at Dale Street. The list is a tremendous insight, not only in regard to how the two engineers got started but also how their quite different interests and personalities grew further apart over the years. The first of the friends Nasmyth had was a young merchant nine years older than himself. He was in textiles and his name was Edward Tootal. Yes, it was the same Edward Tootal who years later was best man on the occasion of Whitworth's second marriage, so he's a name to remember. Before he knew Whitworth he did Nasmyth a very good turn by introducing him to a Daniel Grant – one of two brothers who ran a finance house in Cannon Street – and they immediately offered Nasmyth £500 at 3 per cent, no security, to get him started; with plenty more to follow. Daniel, who had a glass eye, was quite well known in Manchester although he and his brother became even better known – albeit posthumously – once Charles Dickens had personified them as the Cheeryble brothers in *Nicholas Nickleby*. Another friend was John Kennedy, like the Grant brothers a great benefactor of the town. A further supporter was Hugh Birley, already mentioned: the same two men in fact who funded John Bodmer.[9]

The rich diversity of friends Nasmyth attracted was boundless. In part, it reflected his own family background in Edinburgh. Typical of the circle in which he was raised was the business partnership he entered into around 1840. Holbrook Gaskell, his partner to be, was related to the Revd William Gaskell of Cross Street Chapel fame, husband of Elizabeth Gaskell the writer, so it didn't take too long before he was sucked into Manchester's lettered fringe. In fact, Nasmyth and his wife were soon to become regular guests at the Gaskells' home in Plymouth Grove; James being much sought after by the Gaskells' daughters as their favourite uncle and tutor, for astronomy and geology were their mutual primary leisure interests.

Mention of all these names is important in that they throw light on the way both James Nasmyth and Whitworth afterwards crossed sides and drifted off into their respective factions, illustrating perhaps that from the beginning their political and religious differences were big enough to create some personal animosity. As the two grew older, Nasmyth in fact moved away to the right from the political centre while Whitworth adopted a more radical stance, progressively moving leftwards. After the 1852 engineers' lock-out, however – in which Mrs Gaskell took a profound interest – Nasmyth saw little of the writer's family and more or less withdrew from Manchester's scientific society. Whitworth, on the other hand, as each birthday passed, grew to enjoy not only political friends from the radical left of centre, but also academics and writers. Certainly Nasmyth was more calvinist than a natural dissenter. Joe by nature was less orthodox and instinctively sympathized much more with manual workers and their idiosyncracies. It tended to soften his approach as an employer. They were both very private persons but of the two Whitworth was the more radical and in time became quite a determined campaigner for those causes in which he passionately believed. Nasmyth was never that: as an example, each became very friendly with the then leading Manchester engineer William Fairbairn – one of the biggest and most influential engineers in the country at that time – and although Nasmyth was a regular visitor to Fairbairn's home, Medlock Bank, he never really warmed to the older man's campaigning.

When Fairbairn wanted to start a quarterly magazine called *The Workshop* (with the intention of trying to raise the status of engineers), Nasmyth was at first enthusiastic but soon faded as the preparatory work began. Most of their joint efforts were in fact short-lived for the simple reason that Nasmyth never saw himself as a champion of anything, let alone a serious campaigner for causes. Whitworth, on the other hand, was quite different. Almost a Jekyll and Hyde character on occasions, he was essentially a private man yet when his cause beckoned he threw off his self-consciousness and became a campaigning self-publicist. On this occasion, however, it was Fairbairn himself who was attracted by Joe's campaigning spirit and it brought them together to form a most formidable duet whenever the need arose.

While ostensibly the events were in no way related, it is fascinating nonetheless to recall that once Nasmyth had taken early retirement at forty-eight years of age in 1856, and left Manchester for Penshurst in Kent, William Fairbairn and Whitworth started to regularly attend many engineering meetings together.

Whether Nasmyth's absence induced them to do so is perhaps to credit the coincidence with too many undertones, nonetheless their cleavage over the years was quite remarkable. Under these post-Nasmyth arrangements Fairbairn and Whitworth frequently travelled the length of the country as companions, ironing out any technical differences, intent on unifying their approach and both determined to promote their joint campaigning in the most effective way. Such diverse matters as precise measurement, decimalization, steam boiler safety and many other issues became part of their joint presentation. In fact, so often were they reported in the trade press performing this combined rôle, that privately, no doubt, leading opponents would waggishly refer to them as 'prop and cock'. Not that either of them would ever have taken offence had they overheard these remarks, because that was in fact the very nature of their joint activity. Whenever Joe presented a paper, say, to the Civil Engineers, Fairbairn was always first on his feet to endorse Whitworth's thesis. It was an invaluable service and much appreciated by Joe, coming as it did from industry's much-revered leader.

Reverting back to James Nasmyth's early friends, that is to say, those close acquaintances he enjoyed during his Dale Street days – the mid-thirties – it is probably true that he was equally at home with all of them, Hugh Birley just as much as Edward Tootal and John Kennedy. In regard to the last-named, Nasmyth wrote in his autobiography, 'My kind friend, John Kennedy, continued to take the greatest interest in my welfare, more than that, he recommended me to his friends' – meaning of course the big employers and the bankers. Years earlier, Kennedy had also supported William Fairbairn in exactly the same way. Kennedy's firm, Messrs McConnel and Kennedy, had erected a new yarn mill and engaged Fairbairn to engineer the whole plant; shafting, steam engines, the lot. With the help of Kennedy's own money and Benjamin Heywood's Bank the contract made Fairbairn's reputation. He never looked back. Now it was the turn of Nasmyth. The fact that he had both Hugh Birley (a High Churchman) and Kennedy (a Unitarian) befriending him simultaneously says quite a lot for the placidity of Nasmyth's character, because Manchester's internecine Church politics in those days were extremely turbulent.

It must have been quite jittery for Nasmyth to have two such polarized and eruptive personalities as Birley and Kennedy regularly calling, knowing that he still wanted to borrow more capital and that if he had tried to sit astride either the political or the religious fence it would not only have been uncomfortable but offensive to both his financial backers. Nevertheless Nasmyth's successful record proves he took such matters in his stride. The other friend of Nasmyth previously mentioned, Edward Tootal, was an up-and-coming radical-thinking young merchant; he certainly wouldn't have taken kindly to the views of Hugh Birley, nor any of Nasmyth's right-wing friends. In fact Manchester was fast becoming a dominant talking point up and down the country, in that its more forward-looking businessmen were constantly trying to play down the town's rampant class alienation, However *The Times* said in 1835 (of Manchester's workers) . . . 'their wretchedness seems to madden them against the rich, who they dangerously imagine engross the fruits of their labour without having any sympathy for their wants'. Some time later Canon Parkinson of Manchester declared: 'There is no town in the world where the distance between the rich and the poor is so great, or the barrier between them so difficult to be crossed'.

The historic reasons which prompted these profound divisions, not only between rich and poor but also between the various strands of Manchester's commercial leadership, were truly horrendous. Peterloo, the 1819 massacre, had continued to torment the town. Intense anger was deliberately kept alive presumably by the Chartists and Liberal radicals. It suited their book. They accomplished a way of linking Captain Hugh Birley and Sir Oswald Mosley with those who opposed the idea of an elected town council and parliamentary reform; the Liberals thought the Tories were 'all tarred with the same brush' and were happy to see them thoroughly discredited *en bloc.* Indeed it was 1822 before a lawyer named David Ridgeway – a radically minded Quaker – finally got Hugh Birley and others hauled before the Assize Court at Lancaster and charged with brutal assault at Peterloo. Needless to say Birley was acquitted but Ridgeway the lawyer was sentenced to twelve months' imprisonment for criminal libel. As time went on both Peterloo itself and the subsequent trial gained more and more political significance. The reasons were clear. Looking back to Peterloo itself, when 60,000 citizens had assembled – mostly dressed in their well-darned summer frocks and their wistful little extras, which they had to make do for Sunday best – they had gathered peacefully to listen (that is if they could get close enough to hear) Henry Hunt demand parliamentary representation for Manchester. But concealed in the notorious Star Inn nearby was the same Captain Hugh Birley and his volunteer fellow officers of the Manchester Yeomanry, steadily getting drunk, awaiting orders from the magistrates to break up the meeting. The *Manchester Guardian* reported: 'The orders came; the yeomanry – now more or less intoxicated – rode down the people as they were massed together and then sabred them left and right'.

The years rolled by; it was soon fifteen years on, 1834, the Reform Act 1832 was through and Manchester had its first two MPs. The young Richard Cobden, however, was not yet elected to Parliament but was courageously campaigning for a democratically elected Manchester town council. Bravely he continued to work against the dictatorial powers exercised by Sir Oswald Mosley. 'I will put an end to feudalism in Manchester', promised Cobden; but it was another ten years before Mosley was made to sell his manorial rights. The poet Shelley, outraged by Peterloo, had written in 1820 his magnificent 'Mask of Anarchy':

> Shake your chains to earth like dew
> Ye are many, they are few

It was still regularly recited from every Nonconformist platform; it was sung to the tune of a well-known hymn by crowds everywhere; for two decades it stirred passions just as it had nagged the likes of William Gladstone and the new Oxford Movement almost into conceding the right of dissent. But Oxford, like Cambridge, held out. Even Gladstone, as radical as he became, wasn't yet ready to be pushed too far by the likes of either Cobden or Shelley.

From Joseph Whitworth's point of view, although he personally had so far experienced only a short period of actual residence in Manchester – mostly as a youth while still an apprentice – he nevertheless had sufficient political gumption to know what was happening. He didn't need a clairvoyant to tell him, now that he was back, that he too was getting closer to the leading personalities of the town and therefore he himself would soon be judged by the company he kept. Not that he had any personal doubt as to who his real friends were. Joe had long realized that his choice of friends would generate implications far beyond the usual social niceties. If they appeared too heretical, he realized, he would be turned down should he attempt to borrow money from the bank – unless that is, the bank happened to be sympathetic towards the Unitarians, or perhaps the Liberals. No doubt these were important considerations; but Joe had the guts and independence to ignore them. Until now he had made good lifelong friends, most of them fortunately 'well heeled'. All were dissenters but they were supportive and loyal to him, and he to them.

Like Nasmyth before him, Joe also seemed to gravitate towards men like Edward Tootal and John Wallis (a young Manchester radical) plus the younger end of the Peel family: nephews, that is, of Tamworth's Robert Peel, the Prime Minister, but in this case, it so happens, of more importance to Whitworth: they were also the sons of another part of the Peel family, Jonathan Peel, a well-known Manchester iron-founder. But first: Edward Tootal. His close friendship with Joe was a little different in that it blossomed early, then faded somewhat during their forties and fifties. On reaching their sixties, however, the friendship resumed its original close warmth.[10]

Edward Tootal was a remarkable character. A Yorkshireman by birth, he was four years older than Joe. During their earlier years he profoundly influenced Joe in many ways. He encouraged, more likely inspired – in fact he probably persuaded Joe to stick at it for at least ten or fifteen years to design and build what eventually became the magnificent range of machine tools he exhibited at the 1851 Great Exhibition. By the same token Joe clearly influenced Tootal. He impressed his friend sufficiently to imbue him with an instinctive feel for all things engineering, even to the extent that Edward Tootal became a determined railway enthusiast. Textiles were his original business but ever since Robert Stephenson attended an engineers' gathering at which Tootal was present the cottonman became absolutely convinced that a continuous railway line between Manchester and London was an irrefutable priority. And because of the persistent way in which he tackled these immense problems one can clearly see why so much of Whitworth was Tootal in origin.

Tootal's father was a wealthy corn merchant in Wakefield and gave each of his ten sons a good start. Edward particularly made good use of the money his father left to him. Soon after he arrived in Manchester around 1820 he set about making his own fortune, in the main derived from his merchant business in silks and fancy dress materials. He laid a secure foundation from which his own nephew, Henry Tootal Broadhurst went on to build the world-famous company of that name. Young Henry in turn devoted much of his life to promoting the furtherance of Whitworth's technical education ideas once his uncle, Edward Tootal, died in 1873.

Politically, Edward Tootal was a Peelite. He sometimes wavered between Tory and Whig but always remained a very good radical. And if there was ever one single person who pushed Whitworth closer towards his Peelite-liberal views, it was probably Edward Tootal. In fact, some twelve months after Tootal formed his Atkinson-Tootal partnership (the forerunner of Tootal, Broadhurst Lee Company Limited) Edward became intensely interested in railways, rightly believing as it did that railways and steam power would transform society.

Originally in partnership with Lord Wolverton, he was later left alone to successfully bring about the railway amalgamations which created the London and North Western Railway system. In his opinion the line had to cut through Tamworth to make the London run a commercial success. Tootal was suggesting quite a different route from that originally envisaged, but he was convinced about Tamworth. In consequence he almost single-handedly promoted the Trent Valley line. He spent days on end lobbying the House of Commons; pushing, cajoling MPs to get through all the legislation. But once the trains were running and its commercial success proved, he not only earned the immense gratitude of the L&NW Railway Co. shareholders (who later presented him with 1,800 guineas' worth of silver plate) he also won the very close and lasting friendship of Sir Robert Peel through whose constituency the railway then passed.

From the very close links Joe's friends enjoyed with Peel it is disappointing there is so little written about Peel's interests outside politics. Otherwise it would have made a much needed insight into the engineering politics of the 1840s; railways and clean water were the Prime Minister's pet subjects. As it was, Edward Tootal was obviously an influential insider. Not unnaturally for both Whitworth and Tootal – both were on fairly intimate terms with the wider Peel family – Sir Robert was their political masthead. When Joe himself eventually got around to setting out his own political views they were as to be expected, thoroughly Peelite; that is to say, free trade, financial reform and so on. His one antipathy concerned the Cobdenites' refusal to intervene in non-trade matters – a ridiculous extension, he considered, when applied to things like engineering standards and common welfare.

It was this principled difference which distanced Joe on many occasions from his other friends, particularly Cobden and Bright. It also sustained for him some of the most satisfying and challenging relationships he ever enjoyed –

those of liberal-radicals Edwin Chadwick, George Wallis and the architect Edward Walters. This fascinating but split grouping which was so frequently convulsed by the drama of political events never drifted completely apart. Chadwick and Walters were both free traders but like Whitworth, wanted state intervention in many matters from child protection to town planning. Cobden and Bright – libertarians incarnate, vehement anti-state interventionists – wanted none of it but their friendship never wavered. They were all, in terms of the big issues, genuine allies. The story's telling, however, must patiently await the sequence of events. Suffice it to say for the moment that Joe's own story perpetually bubbled, was always controversial but never dull.

Practically all these political relationships however were more than a decade on from the business rough-house Joe survived from the day he first moved into Port Street in 1833. Although he was no advocate of easy credit he could now happily name sufficient prestigious friends if he required banking references. Not only credit but actual jobbing work; that too had political and religious undertones and one had to have 'friends' to get contract work. And although Whitworth's Manchester was thus splintered in so many directions, its quarrelsome cliques often pursuing extremely spiky vendettas no evidence exists to suggest Joe 'trimmed his sails' nor 'ran after' influential people to make things easier. He was neither a sycophant nor a toady.

But despite the support he received Whitworth didn't remain at his dingy Port Street workshop more than five or six months. Almost from the first moment he started there he felt dissatisfied that his somewhat meagre resources were being squandered wastefully. It was obvious too, judging by the amount of 'midnight oil' he was burning that he was desperate to get to his patenting agents his roughed-out machine drawings. Not only that, he needed more 'bench' space and better security to work on his experimental mechanisms and keep them safe. Moreover, up till then he had been compelled to take on mill repair work – which he didn't like doing – but by sticking to the very high standards he had set for himself he was quietly establishing a good reputation. Word soon spread, particularly as there was a dearth of good millwrights in the area. Both new and old jobbing work was plentiful and Joe felt confident about the future.

From the first day he started at Port Street he worked as long as he had daylight. The few oil lamps and candles which he had, enabled him to tidy up after dark and prepare for the following day. The most important thing he wanted to do however, was to get out 'factory hunting'; touring the various places he considered possible sites for his new workshop. It would have to be a small place at first; he needed access to an existing steam engine of course; it would have to have an empty mill in good condition next door so he could expand when ready. Such was his audacious faith – he wanted the site to have a major canal alongside and for the main workshop to have plenty of roof light till he could afford the new gas lighting which Manchester was proposing. The list was endless but finally he found exactly what he was looking for: the

Chorlton Street site. Whitworth couldn't wait to get started and by May 1833 he had taken down his name board from Port Street and proudly screwed it above his new double gates at 44 Chorlton Street. At last, he sensed, he was on his way.

In later years it became known that Whitworth didn't like credit – either for himself or to assist others buy Whitworth machinery. Throughout his life apparently he never relaxed a self-imposed rule which forbade machines leaving his premises unless payment had been made in full. But this curious hard-headed quirk must have been a double standard. The exceedingly fast rate at which his own business expanded must surely verify that most if not all his early plant and machinery was funded by loans either from a bank or a partner. A quick glance at Whitworth's own account book for the first three months (May–July 1833) at Chorlton Street shows his total wages bill as £2. 10*s.* per week. This rose to over £21 in October and by April 1834 it had reached nearly £50 per week, sufficient to pay well over 20 workmen plus a clerk. By this time, to have employed more than a dozen millwright fitters plus machinists he must have had at least two lathes and two planers, no doubt built by himself from castings, gears and shafts which he probably bought locally. By all accounts it was pretty crude, especially if one studies the descriptions written at the time by contemporaries of Whitworth about similar materials and their hammer and chisel methods. Nevertheless, the speed by which engineers generally were progressing – not just Whitworth – it all must have been immensely impressive and their ingenuity was incredible.

On the income side Whitworth's accounts illustrate the wide variety of work he undertook. One very interesting reference mentions regular payments from a Dr Howe 'For work etc. on Pin Machine' suggesting perhaps some sort of early fly-press and pin-dies: probably designed by John Bradbury, the calico printer. Another significant order he received was in respect of a machine for fluting rollers connected with cotton spinning. In the main however his work was a mixture of simple orders for things like a wine press, a beam compass, plus, of course, his regular speciality: stocks and dies and screwing taps of all sizes.

Interestingly, accepting that Whitworth's father Charles taught his son to write, both Joe's order books and his accounts – like his letter writing – were written in a beautifully smooth copperplate style. Legible in every sense, both the early and late examples show that Whitworth's basic style remained consistent throughout his life, even when the necessity for speed gave his hand a firm maturity. Handwriting analysists no doubt would say that his personality must also have remained consistent and that it simply matured with experience: the theory being that Joe's excellent penmanship shows an absence of psycho-abnormalities. And if that were to be the graphologists' conclusion it would confirm the subsequent reading of events: Whitworth did behave in a mature fashion throughout his life and seldom, if ever, did he give way to histrionics. One additional thing, however, must surely be said. Joe's letters and accounts right from the beginning were a tribute to his father, a 'mere' Sunday school teacher; the way he insisted not only that his son – but also the young people he tutored – set about their handwriting and working habits.

During the first few months at the new Chorlton Street factory the machinery available to Whitworth was very limited indeed. William Fairbairn had already experienced a similar situation fifteen years earlier when he was trying desperately hard to complete his mill contracts. In his autobiographical notes he recalled, 'even Manchester did not boast of many lathes or tools. In our case we erected a lathe, and with the assistance of James Murphy, a muscular Irishman, we contrived to turn and finish the whole of our work in a very creditable manner'. In other words, Fairbairn depended wholly upon Murphy's 'handraulics' for power until about 1830 or so and to a large extent the same limitations must also have applied to Whitworth both at Port Street and, until he had organized a steam powered line-shaft, at Chorlton Street. In fact some machine-tool catalogues until about 1870 still showed treadle lathes and the occasional hand-turned shaper. This was an indication possibly that Whitworth himself spent time trying to improve the efficiency of his own 'foot-treadle' machines to help the self-employed or may be he had a sympathetic awareness that others were trying to emulate people like himself, and start up on their own. Certainly his own major submission to the Patents Office in 1835 included a design for a small treadle-cum-hand-cranked planing machine.

Whitworth's apprenticeship and early frugal existence was something about which he often expressed a perverted satisfaction. Included within his first accounts were items like 'House Expenses' – £6 per month rising to £8 per month – proof if proof were needed, that he and his wife during their early marriage lived totally devoid of pleasures: a kind of vow to some deity of suffering? Many years later John Bright MP recorded in his diary that Joe had told him – again with some pride, Bright thought – that Whitworth, when a youth, had spent only five shillings and tuppence per week on food; an achievement of some fortitude considering that bread cost eight or ninepence per loaf. Bright also recorded at the time that Joe had said to him, 'I was a very good lad, never a better', before he went on to emphasize his constant anxiety to study everything he could get his hands on connected with mechanics and machine making. It was a point noted not only by Bright but also by other friends, particularly those associates of Joe who were later connected in some way with academe. Not that this boasting about self-education was exclusive to Whitworth. It wasn't. Others in the leadership of the engineering industry did the same to the extent that an anti-university phobia became both deep-rooted and permanent.

Whitworth's Chorlton Street site was about one and a half acres. At the north end it had a small disused weaving shed with a steam engine already in place; at the other end there was a fairly new but small warehouse. It was in fact an idyllic arrangement. The site was bounded on two sides by the Rochdale Canal – or at least in 1833 an additional extension to the canal was then being excavated, thus promising Whitworth access to canal transport on two sides almost from the beginning. From Joe's point of view it had all the basics and he was confident he could afford the place but for anyone less assertive the gamble would have been a dreadful nightmare. Here he was, committed to the whole site, mortgaged up to the hilt – gambling his whole future in fact – but Whitworth didn't lack courage. He was back contradicting his one blind spot; borrowing money. If he was to take advantage of all the work coming his way he needed extra plant and new machinery plus having to pay a sizeable rent, hence his need to borrow. No precise record exists of the actual rent he contracted but properties in the town centre similar to Chorlton Street suggest that he paid about £250 per year rent. It was a lot of money, compared to his wage bill which didn't reach that figure for at least three or four years. By comparison, in 1836 James Nasmyth moved to Patricroft, five miles away, a site perched on the edge of an estate belonging to Lord Egerton. It cost Nasmyth £36 per acre for a 999-year lease. He was granted six acres on which to build his Bridgewater Foundry which meant, spread over 1,000 years, it was virtually a gift. Lord Egerton, a very active participant in Victorian science, was anxious to encourage Nasmyth and for him to make his Patricroft initiative a success. His six acres giveaway was a perfect blessing, plus a very fine cottage which Nasmyth and his wife were to enjoy for the next twenty years. Whitworth's position was somewhat different – nonetheless engineering survival for both was to be a massive test of their personal talents.

Though the Chorlton Street site itself required considerable building work over the years starting with new line-shafting and wall-strengthening (to support wall-jibs) the whole undertaking was remarkably composed; buildings and plant always abreast of his machine tool progress. Whitworth's 1837 book valuation of plant and equipment plus work done on the buildings, suggests loans of at least £1,000 or so per year until about 1839. As to the identity of his money-lender it would take little imagination to picture Edward Tootal marching him off (screaming no doubt) to the newly opened District Bank of Manchester (the oldest joint-stock bank in Britain) to get Joe started with 'proper' credit. The District Bank claimed from its inauguration to include cottonmen and engineers among its earliest customers and Edward Tootal, who by then was fast moving away from his Cannon Street days (remember, he introduced Nasmyth to the Grant brothers) and was now but a year or so away from his own famous Manchester partnership – Atkinson Tootal and Company.

For Whitworth, the question how best to develop his new works was a matter of considerable conjecture. His knowledge of the engineering industry was superior to most: the fact that he had worked in both London and Manchester gave him knowledge of the two most advanced engineering centres at that time. A further advantage the thirty-one-year-old Whitworth held was his familiarity with cotton spinning and if it suited his immediate needs, it would be the sort of alternative work he would pursue. Not that the sheer complexities of mechanized spinning had ever interested him more than his machine tools. It hadn't. But clearly he had given a great deal of thought to the matter long before he returned to Manchester, suggesting that at some stage he suspected he might require a second string to his bow.

As things turned out the possibilities he feared most were manifestly wrong. His prime worry that his machine tools would take a long time to get going and that he would need to diversify his fledgling business, proved upside-down. He also misjudged cotton spinning as being starved of innovative ideas. Truthfully, it was the Lancashire mill owners who were not yet ready to contemplate the leap forward Whitworth's machinery was offering. Logically he had concluded that the spinning mule was ready for improvement and spent time thinking through some very good ideas. What he never really understood was that improvement for the sake of improvement was not part of the mill owners' language. For them improvement had to mean less men to do the same work thus more profit; plus something to compensate for the risk of arson and the personal death threats which inevitably arrived at the same time as the new machinery. Intuitively Joe had feared that building machine tools, even small bench type machines, would leave him without money for the long generative periods his new machines would take, hence the serious thought he put into a new spinning mule. As it was, he was able to sell his first machine tools within eighteen months of starting, while every mill owner he had approached refused even to think of new technology. Their spinning mills when Joe called upon them with his new fangled models were all making profit, so let someone else grope their way forward with such novelties. It was this gross failure to understand mill owners which puzzled Joe for many months. Nevertheless he still went ahead and patented his new spinning machinery: he even submitted two further mule patents the following year, 1836.

TEXTILE MACHINERY AND KNITTING MACHINES

Ten years prior to Whitworth's own patents another Manchester engineer, Richard Roberts of Messrs Sharp Roberts and Company, had taken out a patent in 1825 to convert Samuel Crompton's mule into a self-acting spinning machine. It was an advanced design for its time but even so it was 1880 before the concept was universally accepted.

Whitworth's presumption was to advance Roberts's self-acting mule two generations; to mechanize the thing in line with current engineering practice. But as history records (like Roberts's ideas before him), it was again the turn of the century before anything akin to Whitworth's 1836 ideas were adopted by yarn spinners in Lancashire. Needless to say, not one self-acting jenny, the drawings of which were so assiduously hawked around the district by Whitworth, was ever ordered. It was a salutary lesson Joe never forgot. Though it was common knowledge at the time that the big mill owners like Kennedy and McConnel were desperately anxious to curb the relatively high pay earned by their skilled mule spinners they didn't see Roberts's or Whitworth's ideas contributing towards that end. Around 1840 or so, a mule spinster (as he was then called) together with his assistants, handled well over 2,000 spindles apiece and made comparatively good money as a result. But none of the patents put before John Kennedy actually cut out the spinster.

Total automation of the spinning mule as such was never really a possibility until the final decade of the nineteenth century. Engineers still had many years work ahead of them before anything so sophisticated became available. Naturally there was a great deal of exaggerated talk about automation spread by operatives. Surprisingly, it was also given credence by the mill owners themselves; presumably they feared that some competitors may secretly invest and catch them unawares. 'Yes', they quietly mocked, 'we will automate when the time comes'.

In reality, mill owners steered clear of anything new, mainly because they considered it better to stick with the devil they knew. Secondly, the fear of violence and risk of arson were very real considerations. Nor were engineers exempt. News of Richard Roberts's self-acting mule had somehow leaked out and Sharp Roberts factory immediately became the centre of violent action. On 30 March 1825 it was destroyed by Luddite arson.[11] But to his everlasting credit Richard Roberts ignored even the most personal of threats and continued to improve his machinery before publicly announcing a final version of his mule in May 1829. Arson, rioting and much looting inevitably followed and Roberts himself finally succumbed to the appalling stress of it all and for a time suffered a serious breakdown. Lancashire engineers throughout this period paid a dreadful price, but thank goodness for the sake of today they courageously endured these mindless threats and carried on.

Six years later Joseph Whitworth was certainly aware of the danger, but it didn't prevent him taking up the cudgels on behalf of good engineering. His approach however was somewhat different from that of his predecessors in that he believed his machinery would free the nation from its sterile penury. He also had an abhorrence of all things for which early textile machinery was famed: bits of dangling wire; weights swinging on string . . . Heath Robinson ad lib. He wanted to tidy up the whole business along the lines of sound engineering practice. By now he was learning very quickly. No longer an innocent when it came to the criteria by which mill owners judged innovative ideas; money first and money last with very little else in between. That was their creed.

Of course he was still convinced that the three patents which he had previously submitted to the Patents Office would have improved conditions and speeded up production immeasurably but they would have fallen far short of removing the operatives' jobs. Nonetheless his machines would still have made money for the mill owners. For one thing he had completely redesigned the winding mechanism (the very heart of the spinning jenny) thus increasing the number of bobbins an operative could safely manage and, for the first time ever, he had mounted the mule carriage on metal rails and propelled it backwards and forwards with the aid of pawl-wheels engaging a power-driven worm-shaft. His rollers and tumblers feeding the yarn worked like clockwork. The whole thing was mechanically phased, precise and smoothly co-ordinated. But it was still not enough to attract the mill owner. The real issue then – which has remained so ever since – was the full automation of cotton spinning.

But consider for a moment the problems which faced both Richard Roberts and Whitworth. First the yarn was pulled through and carded by special rollers; then fed through revolving tumblers, entwined by twisters and guided towards spindled bobbins, each one of which had to be slowly raised and lowered to ensure the equal winding of yarn on each bobbin. The complexities were immense, especially when the bobbins required mounting on a reciprocating carriage with each movement locked in precise harmony. No wonder the essential deft touch required from the attendant spinner gave the operatives a sense of secure employment and slightly improved their piecework money.

Like so many other industrial situations in mid-Victorian years the attitude on all sides was contradictory. Again consider for example the frequent annoyance and stoppages caused by breakages in the yarn. Whitworth's ideas would have gone a long way towards overcoming these problems but neither operative nor mill owner wanted different machinery. As it was, millworkers were accustomed to taking their young children into the mill and training them to crawl between the machines, pick up the broken ends of yarn and join them together. It was filthy, disease-ridden work; the children like their parents would finish their long stint choking with dust and covered like snow in dirty grey fluff from the yarn. And in fairness it must be agreed that had they been given the chance the likes of Whitworth (for reasons of good engineering) would have had the children out of the mills long before Dr Kay or Lord Shaftesbury. Whether or not engineers were ever motivated by the possible emancipation of their fellow beings, or whether they were driven by self-interest is a difficult question. One thing is clear. It was absolute short-sightedness on the part of the mill owners to turn aside the half-way mechanization offered to them in 1825 and again in 1836, first by Richard Roberts and later by Whitworth. To some extent it was irresponsible mimicry by the employers of the operatives' Luddism. Had the employers agreed to re-tool their mills around the 1830s and 1840s, almost certainly the 85 per cent automation which entered British mills after the First World War would have been working decades earlier. The cotton operatives would have been far better off and the last whiff of anti-machine Luddism would have been safely buried.

Whitworth's failure to sell his ideas to the likes of the Sykeses, the Phillipses and the Kennedys must have taught him some memorable lessons. Although he was firmly rebuffed on his first venture into selling textile machinery it never jaundiced his attitude permanently. Like many good engineers before him Whitworth soon realized that mill owners and employers generally considered social improvements insufficient reason for investment in new machinery. Any new machinery, he learned, had to earn its keep by increased production and a better made product. It was significant thereafter that Whitworth always prefaced anything he had to say about machinery with a homily or two about reduced labour costs based on increased output. Historically, it could seriously be reasoned that Whitworth's experience in this way subconsciously made him Britain's first production engineer.

As luck would have it, Joe's skirmish with the cotton business triggered some extra allied interests. Soon after he moved into the Chorlton Street factory a man named John Wilde called to see him hoping to persuade Whitworth to assist him in designing and building knitting machines. The subject had been much discussed that year among engineers especially in the Nottingham area. Speculative merchants agreed there was a phenomenal prize awaiting the first person to design a successful knitting system, wool or otherwise, and Joe's inventive mind intuitively would have toyed with Wilde's proposals. But yet again, irrespective of the attractiveness of the challenge, it would have seemed to him a diversion from his central ambition: that of building machine tools. Not that he turned his fellow inventor away. On the contrary, any discouragement John Wild may have sensed was short lived. Whitworth not only became keenly interested in the idea but midway through 1834 he agreed to work jointly with Wild for the purpose of doing some experimental work. He also agreed to their jointly submitting a patent for a small table-top knitting machine.[12]

The primary function of this miniature machine was not some new cottage industry but rather was it to demonstrate knitting techniques suitable for flat-bed industrial machines. In this regard the wording attached to the Whitworth-Wild patent is misleading and in reality it merely seeks protection for the needle assembly and its yarn feeder. The fact that Whitworth set aside a special room at his new factory and called it the 'Knitting Room' signalled his great dream that one day he himself would challenge the Nottinghamshire monopoly and perhaps make an industrial knitting machine. Unfortunately he never did, but he kept his hope alive for fifteen years or more. He employed throughout the years at least two toolmakers full time, working on various experimental mechanisms but the secret breakthrough never came. In fact his flirtation with knitting must have cost him a lot of money and much effort, yet he was forever denied even a momentary reference in the annals of industrial knitting.

The great stumbling block preventing progress was always the needle assembly. It defeated Whitworth just as surely as it had all other pioneers before him until Matthew Townsend came along in 1847. His brilliant latch needle opened up many new avenues in both coarse knitting and in the making of fishing nets. Townsend's needle was altogether more sophisticated than anything before it and changed completely the outlook throughout the industry.

Characteristically, Whitworth stubbornly continued to work on his own improvements but failure to overcome these problems finally persuaded him to get rid of his 'Knitting Room' in 1850, just ahead of the Great Exhibition. During the room's existence he had suffered a number of inexplicable set-backs – due partly, one suspects, to frustration and having to divide his attention elsewhere – but rather than prematurely anticipate the row between himself and his partner, William Muir, in 1842 he let the one final irony be revealed; that which countenanced Joe's last gasp as a knitting novice.

John Bright MP, on 7 March 1864 – by then a close confidant of Whitworth – was visited by an American engineer, a Mr Dalton.[13] He came to Bright's flat in St James, Westminster, armed with a full set of drawings detailing a flat-bed knitting machine. He wanted it made in Britain and offered Bright full right of manufacture for £4,000. Bright was extremely impressed. He immediately contacted Joe and invited him round to view the drawings. Whether Joe took them away for further study (having paid £4,000) is not known but by the time they came to a decision they were both shocked to learn that a British inventor named William Cotton had beaten them to the Patents Office.

Astonishingly, the American design which Whitworth then held was almost identical to the Cotton patent handed in a month before. Any ambitions the two may have cherished of manufacturing the machine in Britain were destroyed overnight. Both men suspected villainy – double-dealing perhaps – on Cotton's part. Tantalizingly, the machines were designed to shape heels and toes and for the first time could fully shape whole knitted garments. Of course it could have been pure coincidence which brought together these two similar designs at the same time; hence it evoked for Joe the most ironic memories. Over the years he recalled many such incidents but this time it irritated him: Bright's American visitor was the nearest Whitworth ever got to making a successful knitting machine.

CHAPTER THREE

Early Machine Tool Genius

Most engineers find it baffling that Whitworth should be remembered for his screw theads but never his machine tools. In fact very few people know anything of Whitworth's early years at Chorlton Street, yet for half a century or more his award-winning machine tools were a priority for all leading manufacturers. There are other equally puzzling bygones. His metrology and the Whitworth inch for instance were both unveiled during the same period – yet when set against the Whitworth 'thread', both are now wholly forgotten.

Whitworth himself went on for two whole decades not just in the leadership of the industry but by his open creativity he lifted machine tool design to the level of a new era. He did so, not by inventing some great machine colossus but by enriching existing machine tools with his own universally acclaimed mechanisms. The result was at once historic and brilliant. In consequence, for two decades (1840–60s) he led the world.

Without their blushing in the slightest, historians of technology are fully justified eulogizing his ideas. Whitworth's power cross-feed for example, and his instant-drive clasp-nut are pure inventive genius. Small mechanisms maybe; but in both instances his work literally freed design blockages which had frustrated the advancement of lathe design since the early 1820s. Internationally, machine tool engineers didn't hesitate to take note. They were quick to recognize and copy his outstanding work and within a period of five or six years following the Great Exhibition a number of imitative variations appeared on the world market.[1]

Whitworth's first solo invention – his first patent in fact, dated 27 February 1834 – a machine for turning and screw-cutting studs and hexagon headed bolts – did two important things. First, it established Joe as an original thinker and confirmed that he possessed that somewhat rare and most precious of gifts: an inventive and resourceful mind's eye. And secondly because his machine on this occasion did nothing other than thread bolt shanks and studs it thereby introduced into the workshop something quite new: the special purpose (semi-automatic) machine tool. Prior to Whitworth's machine, nuts and bolts were largely threaded by hand – for anything better they were quite often screw cut between centres on a lathe – consequently they were prohibitively expensive frequently forcing engineers and millwrights to use the crudest alternatives. Understandably, engineering progress so far had been seriously hindered by this one handicap, hence the coming of

Whitworth's machine not only got his Chorlton Street works off to a good start financially but it also liberated the industry.

His patented bolt machine carried with it a whole series of entirely new innovations including a three-jaw self-centring chuck designed to grip in one single turn hexagonal bolt-heads. It also had an auto-set duplex tooling box which first cleaned up the bolt shank followed by a die-box which, in two passes, could finish screw cut the bolt. It was a clever piece of design whereby an auto-trip and reverse motion (synchronized with self-adjusting dies) ensured that once the workpiece had been locked into the chuck the remaining operations were completed by the machine alone. No further handling by the operator was required – not only that: a set of change wheels made size and thread variations possible. The machine was a success and Whitworth fully deserves the credit for the inventive way he raised bolt-making from hand-screwing to powered production.[2]

Should there have been a competition for the engineer who made the most inventions, Whitworth would have been correct in claiming, along with his many others, the three-jaw self-centring chuck. As this particular idea got into production he devised a way of tightening the chuck jaws with a single screw by rotating a back plate containing three tangentially curved slots. The jaws were stub-keyed into the slots and moved inwards as the plate turned. Unfortunately it never looked like a lathe chuck; consequently it was left to a James Dundas in 1842 to pick up the accolade for the invention of the chuck. One little bit of evidence in favour of Whitworth's claim, however, was the fact that bolt-heads in the north largely became hexagonal (as against their remaining square in London) purely to facilitate three-jaw chucks. Ideally it would have been fascinating to learn from examination of this 1834 machine just how good Whitworth's men were at making his tangential cam-plates and things of that sort without the help of modern vertical milling machines. The only historic understanding we now have is that it taxed Joe's draughtsmen another two generations before they were able to replace manual chipping and filling by the installation of suitable milling machines – an unusual paradox for Whitworth – for he routinely built in-house his own special machines, afterwards making with them his more polished machines for selling to others.

Early in the new year, 1836, Whitworth's bolt-making machine was in production and Lancashire engineers were anxious to place their orders. The income enabled him to concentrate his more ambitious ideas for a new universal centre lathe and for a new, more adept planing machine. During the previous year he strained at the leash, willing every day forward, anxious to consolidate his position yet increase his workforce. Sometimes he worked by oil lamp – forgot to go home – driven on by a torrent of ideas all competing for his attention. For his wife Fanny, life must have been an emotional roller-coaster, not knowing when or what Joe was doing, never knowing what was next. Pioneers, be they chemists or engineers, shared with actors and composers the absolute ecstasy of success, but they also shared the plunging depths of despair when failure halted their work.

And so it was for Whitworth. By and large this stretch was outstandingly successful, the best sustained for long periods. Fanny however – denied the ecstatic peaks, her adrenalin seldom aided by praise – was left to cope alone, perhaps ever searching to find her own way of sharing her husband's success.

In order to build his first centre lathe, Joe had long realized his most urgent requirement must be a decent planer, capable of machining flat surfaces equal to his own top standards. In his opinion, the planing machines already available in either Manchester or London were not good enough. He had no alternative but to build his own, starting with a somewhat unusual design suitable for either hand or treadle operation: it was the same small unorthodox planing machine in fact which he later patented.[3]

During the period that Whitworth himself was employed by Joseph Clement in London – the two years immediately preceding his return to Manchester in late 1832 – he gained a great deal of practical experience using hand-operated machines. Clement himself had experimented with a whole series of constructions designed for machining both cylindrical shapes and flat surfaces. Clement's small planer had a tool clapper-box on each side of the cross-beam facing each way to give the machine a cutting stroke in both directions: each tool able to swing upwards and out of trouble at the end of each stroke. Remarkably the table ran on flanged wheels – about two feet in diameter – and was super-smooth in operation. Almost certainly Whitworth himself worked this machine on occasions – as he no doubt also operated and studied Clement's other renowned power planers – thus he became familiar with the great man's approach to machine design. In fact some historic reconstruction of both Clement's and Maudslay's machinery clearly reveals that of the two the original design responsibility seems in the main to have been Clement's rather than Maudslay's. Recognition of this hypothesis adds credence to the view that the dominant progeniture of Whitworth's own design work is essentially Clement rather than Maudslay.

If one recalls Whitworth's own patented hand or treadle planers a number of conclusions can be drawn. Contrary to the criticism frequently voiced by technical writers – that Whitworth merely copied – he didn't: he continually strove to sophisticate existing constructions, replacing old technology with innovative systems. For reasons already explained, Whitworth was to Clement and Maudslay, say, what Rutherford the scientist was to his intellectual begetter Dr Dalton. It is a good analogy. Whitworth was tremendously impressed by the smoothness of Clement's machines yet he did something quite different, and did it Rutherford fashion: he turned the Clement machine on its head. He realized that the best way to take a light cut across the flanged face of a heavy steam chest was to clamp the heavy casting to a floor bedplate and reciprocate the tool itself backwards and forwards rather than having to power-drive or hand-turn a heavily loaded table. Especially in the case of a manually operated machine it was important to keep the heaviest weight stationary. This simple (but as it turned out extremely complex) conclusion was typical of the man.

Whitworth thus created the moving gantry planer, his first experimental machine operated by a cranked handle aided by a flywheel. To his second small machine he added a treadle. Unlike the Clement table which worked backwards and forwards on wheels, Whitworth mounted the gantry itself on flanged wheels (much smaller diameter of course) running them between two parallel rails, one above the other. His other major departure was the tool-holder itself.

While smaller manually operated machines long remained essential for the industry the Whitworth company itself became far too involved in big power-driven machinery for it to retain a leading interest in treadle design. By 1836 he had commenced a four-year project to provide his own workshop with a mammoth planing machine capable of machining keyways 40 ft in length.[4] Nonetheless, the experience gained from his smaller machines was never lost. To make the treadles work more easily, for instance, he discovered the necessity to balance centrifugally all moving parts – particularly crank assemblies – a lesson from which he benefited enormously. He was the first engineer to do so although railway historians wrongly credit a railway engineer with discovering the need for perfect balance almost a decade later. Understandably rail traction and early locomotive link systems visibly demonstrated the mechanical necessity for eccentrics and cranks to be perfectly balanced but machine tools from their crudest beginnings so exaggerated the slightest eccentricity that Whitworth was quick to identify the problem early on as a major impediment.

Excitement started to mount as Whitworth commenced building his first big 12 ft planer. The huge castings were brought in through his Chorlton Street gates pulled by four, sometimes six, powerful chain-horses. His iron founder, Jonathan Peel, was equally interested, overlooking the fact that his famous foundry had been supplying Manchester machine makers for many years. One thing Whitworth had learned from Richard Roberts was the importance of good pattern makers. The handsome appearance of any machine depended upon its proportions; similarly the quality of the work it had to do depended upon providing plenty of solid metal in all the strategic places: the gussets, the lugs, the platforms: all had to be right first time. The pattern maker was supreme arbiter. But in this case it was Whitworth's own constant, and perhaps at times his irritating vigilance which so fascinated men like Jonathan Peel. The work was brutal and hard. Moreover it had to be precision finished with the lightness of a clockmaker's touch. Anything short of the very best just wouldn't do, for it was this obsessional insistence by Whitworth that his machines be engineered to the highest standards which earned for him a world-wide reputation.

For reasons already understood, Whitworth laid down a basic rule for all toolroom practice: the necessity for a flat surface. And once it was accepted, the planing machine in 1836 became a must. As a power driven machine – roughly with the same shape and function it has today – it first made its appearance about 1820. James Fox of Derby probably tied with Joseph Clement as the first pioneer builder of the early Victorian machines while Matthew Murray, Richard Roberts and the French clockmaker Nicholas Forq must come into the reckoning because of their late eighteenth-century innovative work. But the two outstanding designs which influenced Whitworth most were the Fox and Clement machines.

Interestingly, these planers were the world's first all-metal machines, although Whitworth – fifteen years later and quite uncharacteristically – took half a step backwards during one of his weaker moments and introduced a cotton rope-motion for his 'Jim Crow' reversible. It was a misplaced novelty. Sensibly he later discarded the method although one such machine was shown at the 1851 Great Exhibition. He continued to build them only if they were specifically ordered, as surprisingly they were, for instance, by the railway workshops at Crewe and at Doncaster.

According to his 1837 inventory the first big machine Joe bought in from another maker was probably an 18 ft planer made by James Fox of Derby. Indeed he could never have started the progenitive process of building his own machines from scratch without it, unless, that is, he reversed his policy and resorted to endless months of hammer and chisel drudgery.

He also bought in a couple of drilling machines plus a whole pile of gearwheels and shafts and various machine parts from which he was able to cobble together the initial machine capacity he wanted. Poor Whitworth must have cringed every time he entered the workshop and saw his improvised concoctions but they delivered what he wanted. He was never a muddler; even less could he tolerate makeshift arrangements.

By December 1837 he had accumulated plant and equipment to the value of £6,720 (well over a million pounds at today's prices).[5] His stocktaking list comprised twenty-five lathes, six planing machines, three vertical drilling machines plus a whole assortment of bench equipment and hand tools. It had been a prolific three years during which he engaged architects and builders to commence what really became a continuous programme of building and extensions and renewal of plant.

The first big power-driven planing machines built by Whitworth all had central wormshaft drives rather than rack and pinion systems although the latter method, started by Fox and Clement, became the more generally accepted system of converting rotary power to a linear-reciprocating movement, especially for planing machines. But Whitworth would have none of it. His fundamentally different approach involved the use of a wormshaft and pawl-wheels (see fig. 1), a design Joe consistently claimed to be superior to all others. The trade, however, remained sceptical. They preferred the simplicity of a rack and pinion drive. It was cheaper they said, and easier to build. To them, Whitworth's system was an unnecessary refinement, a criticism which Joe repelled on the basis that the new engineering industry wanted better machines capable of producing better finishes. The rack and pinion drive inevitably produced a rough 'rippled' surface, a problem the wormshaft overcame. Writing in the *Practical Mechanics Journal* many years later, Robert Mallet FRS

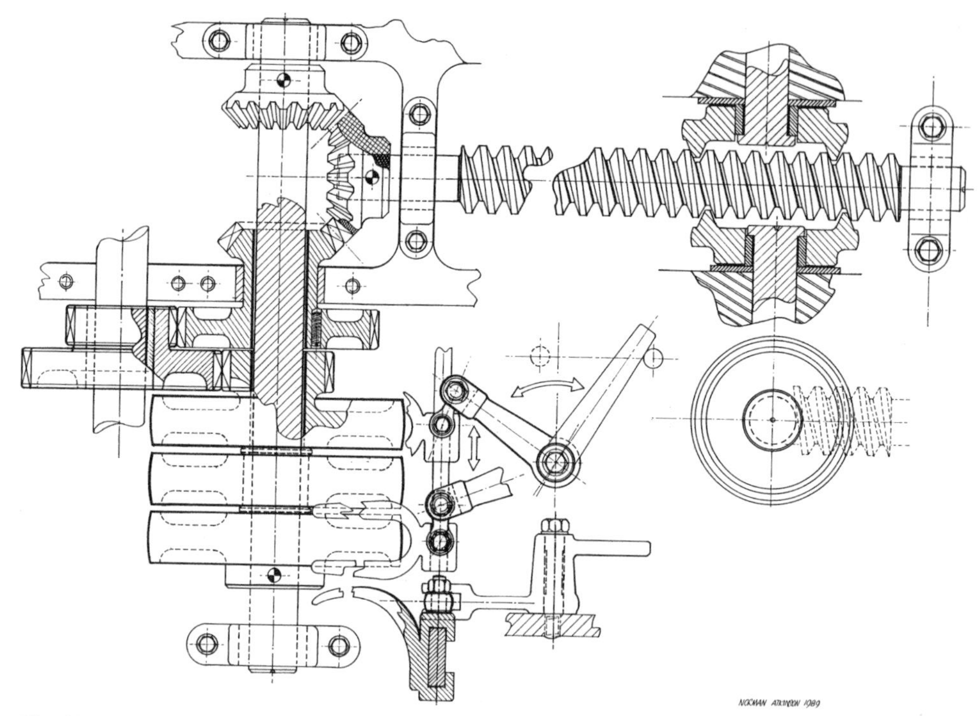

Fig. 1 Whitworth planing machine 1835–40. A general arrangement of his 'quick-return' heavy duty wormshaft drive with dished pawl-wheels. It is a twin teleshaft system with bevel wheel cluster, 3-pulley single belt drive with quick-return gearing. The belt shift is activated by stops attached to the table.

referred to the effortless ease and beauty of Whitworth's great planing machines travelling to and fro along inverted 'V' bedways. 'The traverse is still performed by Whitworth's peculiar combination of the double threaded screw and a pair of revolving teeth taking into it' he wrote. 'The half-learned say, what an old dodge, why on earth doth he stick to it? But Whitworth is right, the grand requisite of a planing machine is that the table should stop dead; stop instantly without elasticity, tremor, or recoil, as if arrested by the hand of Atropos himself. This cannot be done by the original chain, nor by the rack and pinion, nor in a word, by any method as yet proposed so effectually as the swiftly whirling double-threaded screw'.[6] What more can be said?

J.G. Moon, who afterwards became manager of James Watt and Company, was apprenticed to Maudslay Sons and Field around the late 1860s and during a lecture to the Junior Institution of Engineers said: 'Most of the planing machines [at Maudslays] were made and supplied by Joseph Whitworth and Co., and the toolboxes were of the "Jim Crow" type. The forerunner of this [idea] used to interest me', declared Mr Moon, referring to a very old machine kept in the fitters' loft at Maudslays and variously called a shaping machine or a 'steam arm' machine. 'It was driven by means of a disc', he said 'about 3 ft diameter with a slot down the disc for varying the stroke'. The toolbox was fixed at the end of a reciprocating arm; the intriguing bit being a toothed link mechanism attached to the top of the toolbox which reversed the tool at the end of each stroke thus making it cut in both directions. Mr Moon concluded his point by saying, 'I understand that it was from this machine that Whitworth developed his "Jim Crow" toolbox'.[7] Ah well!

Manchester Politics and the Scramble Club

All work and no play was – and still is – a pretty miserable formula. Whitworth's intense workload was increasing daily. And as the daylight working hours lengthened so his leisure pursuits disappeared. Never one to allow his mind to wander very far from his work, he nonetheless recognized the penalty for his obsessional behaviour. As a prickly monastic he was fast becoming an ogre, and he knew it. Regardless of the bad effect it was having on his work, he found his wife's inconsolable struggle trying to cope on her own also disconcerting. He and Fanny had been married twelve years without children and looked set to continue that way. Her sisters lived near Chester – some 28 miles away – so little more than an occasional visit was possible. While they had lived in London their weekends at least were their own, especially when they could get up on Hampstead Heath or out walking the parks, but nowadays Joe's total devotion had shifted from Fanny to his machines. Back in Manchester it was noticeable that he was desperate to get back to the factory rather than make an effort to revive with his wife their skimpy but happy walking occasions in London. His future beckoned a very different life from that of the past, Joe's male chauvinism steering him towards the town and club-nights out with the boys.

When he and Fanny first returned to Manchester, the little workshop he rented at the back of Piccadilly – Port Street to be exact – had first attracted him because he knew the property. Now he had moved away from the area he again drifted back there because he knew its characters and he was looking for a more satisfying companionship. One hundred yards from his Port Street workshop was Cannon Street, home of various textile firms and money houses. The Cotton Exchange was also in the vicinity and it was a lunchtime practice for the more adventurous merchants to gather at the Unicorn Inn, Church Street, for a fourpenny pie and a glass of ale. Twenty-three years earlier, on 9 January 1813 to be precise, someone had suggested that the whole lot of them should meet more formally. Straightaway the landlord at the Unicorn, a Mr Froggatt, offered a room upstairs. This was quickly agreed and at their first Tuesday dinner, Jonathan Peel, the iron founder, then a young man, was proposed for the Chair whereupon he suggested they should adopt the title 'Scramble Club' in recognition of their daily scramble to get back to their work. The Scramble Club it became.[8]

What persuaded Whitworth to become an active Scrambler is not clear, but that he did around Christmas time 1837. And assuming it was necessary for a new member to be introduced by an existing member it is safe perhaps to guess that either Jonathan Peel (with whom Joe would now rank as a valued customer and friend) or possibly James Kershaw, a radically minded cotton spinner who had expressed interest in Joe's earlier spinning jenny, would have been his nominating host and companion. James Kershaw, it will be remembered, went on to become MP for Stockport and as such long remained supportive of Joe's many incursions against established convention. Whichever of his friends it was who had formally introduced Joe to his first dinner it was fairly certain that once he sat down one or two of those present would have recognized him from his apprenticeship days in the area. The sons of both his earlier employers for example, William Marsden and Henry Walker, were both members as also was a local surgeon plus one or two lawyers. It was very much a middle-class-cum-professional gathering to whom someone like Whitworth, a bright thirty-one-year-old up-and-coming engineer now employing close on sixty men, would be an engaging curio. They would have been even more curious, of course, had they at that time had the slightest premonitory hint of the royal shoulder-rubbing-cum-international path he was to tread over the years. More's the pity, that one journalist founder member having set down the origins of the club and written something about its personalities, later discovered that most of his work had been destroyed by fire. Had it survived it would have further verified a piece of fascinating Manchester history: a truly absorbing story.

The Scramble Club was never quite so casual nor so innocent as it appeared. It enjoyed a rascalish Liberal Party undercurrent, often being the source of some political mischief or other. About the time Whitworth joined the club, members had decided they would prefer to take claret rather than beer with dinner. Unfortunately it was unavailable from old Froggatt at the Unicorn – he didn't have a wine licence – so they decided on removing the club to the Blackfriars Inn, a commercial hotel just off Deansgate, near the Cotton Exchange. By strange coincidence it just happened to be the traditional watering hole of some Liberal Party activists. A Mr Challoner was the landlord. Like Froggatt at the Unicorn, he offered to the club his dining room every Tuesday at 2 o'clock and as soon as the 'after-dinner' port was served he would place before the Chairman the table salt box with the total cost of the meal chalked inside the lid. Only once did the Chairman suffer apoplexy. That was on the occasion of the thirtieth anniversary dinner, 9 January 1843, when inside the lid Mr Challoner had written £18 which included £7 10*s* for the dinner and dessert. It worked out at twelve shillings a head – almost double Royal Ascot prices – and by any standards in those days it was a very expensive meal indeed but the shock never stopped the traditional club toast – 'To the Salt Box Lid'.[9]

Everyone in the club obeyed the rules; fines for not drinking, fines for getting married, wives having children, moving house: plus no doubt all the usual silly confessions associated throughout time with male gatherings. The Scramblers' more significant jesting, however, was the tell-tale character of the semi-jocular bets they ventured across the table – who next would get into the Cabinet; Palmerston's next gaffe; by-elections; anything – usually for half a dozen bottles of claret – practically all were political wagers. Joe's first year as a member, 1838, was an intensely political year and it is not surprising that more wine in the form of bets crossed the Scramblers' table that year than would have normally crossed a wine merchant's counter. No one, other than a handful of Tories, for instance, thought William E. Gladstone would have been defeated in Manchester as a Liberal candidate. Yet he was (and Scramble Club bets were laid) yet the town had to wait until 1841 (more bets were laid) before it firmly elected its first true radical-Liberal MP, Thomas Milner Gibson, a Manchester merchant and a Scrambler.

Manchester politics of the late 1830s was full of clandestine manoeuvring and was extremely agitational. The atmosphere was aggressive, ignited by the brazen failure of one or two dishonest councillors to cover their naked despotism. Whether it sparked in Whitworth a reformist urge for himself to participate is difficult to pin down. He did in fact step up his attendance at various meetings and interceded in one or two debates but anyone the least bit conscious about moral issues could hardly have remained aloof from the intense political heat at the time. One assumes any middle-class clamour would have included Whitworth. The whole situation was thoroughly undemocratic; the hapless and the disaffected no doubt felt just as outraged as middle-class radicals – but very few of the victims had votes. The slow fading away of anti-machine tool agitation however was Whitworth's one consolation. He was grateful for that.

William IV died in June 1837 making way for Queen Victoria. Parliament in those days had by law to be dissolved following a monarch's death, and this particular parliament did so in July. Viscount Melbourne was the Whig Prime Minister and contrary to her uncle's anti-Liberal prejudices the young Queen Victoria asked him to continue. He did so for four years until his defeat at the polls on the question of the secret ballot – a 'concession' which had to wait until 1872 before it was granted. It was this latter point which so aroused the anger of Manchester Liberals in 1837 that the very vociferousness of their long campaign set them apart from the rest of the country.

Their leading parliamentary advocate was Richard Potter, the MP for Wigan, universally known as 'Radical Dick', a man of great courage but who due to illness decided not to contest the 1837 election. Instead, he returned to his business in Manchester; a firm called Potters of Cannon Street, and together with his brother Thomas Potter (the first ever Mayor of Manchester) successfully moved their business to a new warehouse in George Street, a firm which was shortly to become famous in the annals of Manchester politics.

Within the warehouse itself the Potters set aside a large room which, for the next twenty years or so, became nationally known as the 'Plotting Room'. Not only did it accommodate debates which helped formulate some of the most important Liberal Party policies of the last century but its political influence became legendary as one after another of the 'Plotting Room' wranglers were adopted as Liberal Party candidates and subsequently elected to parliament. And although Richard Potter had himself retired from parliament, his enthusiasm and his ideas visibly went forward with renewed vigour, particularly those taken up and voiced by Richard Cobden – a fresh, youthful and extremely articulate Potterite.

Richard Potter senior was quite proud of his early membership of the Scramble Club; understandably he was delighted when the Blackfriars Inn – the Scramblers' new venue – was chosen and he visited the place whenever he could. Given his presence, together with other leading political personalities, it is not surprising that many of Manchester's up and coming Liberal dignitaries wanted to attend, making it difficult to decipher from the attendance list who was who. Their political associations however were quite clear. All were radicals, whether Whig or Tory, and although Whitworth remained for a time an instinctive Peelite the radicalism of his new companions was beginning to rub off. In later years much of what he said and did lay so easily alongside the ideas of Richard Potter that the late 1830s and early '40s could be established as Joe's politically formative years.[10]

The two leading Potters were founders of the *Manchester Guardian* and the *Manchester Examiner* – two newspapers Whitworth later associated in his own mind with the *New York Daily Tribune* and passionately defended all three as prerequisites of democracy and learning. But there were so many things during this period which influenced Whitworth's ability to think politically; events which in the main occurred during the five years preceding 1842. Manchester at that time was veritably the womb from which the radical wing of the Liberal Party grew: indeed the evidence suggests it was the same incubating source which partly spawned the Independent Labour Party almost fifty years later. A contributor towards this theme was Richard Potter's son, another Richard; back in Manchester from Cambridge in 1841 when he too became active in Liberal radical politics. He eventually had nine daughters. All were politically motivated but two of them in particular made a Labour niche for themselves. Theresa (Lady Parmoor) married C.A. Cripps while her sister Beatrice married Sidney Webb; both men being included in the first Labour Government. Both women became famous in their own right. The Potter stable was a place of profound political influence and though it cannot be claimed that Whitworth himself was a product of Manchester Liberal politics his later political ideas were unmistakenly more Potterite than Peelite.

One further point: Manchester radicalism was essentially tribalistic. A labyrinthian web of family relationships (largely the Potters) held together the various sub-groupings of radical city merchants, industrialists and engineers. Its influence spread far and wide in much the same way as the Tory Protectionists on Tyneside were later held together by the Armstrong faction. This north-east group sprang from the George and Robert Stephenson school; mostly they were engineers and later included Joseph Locke, Daniel Gooch and in a more distant way, Stuart Rendel. All of them entered Parliament as Coalition-Whig MPs, Armstrong himself being granted a peerage. Daniel Gooch, a protégé of both

Stephenson and Brunel, had a foot in both the Armstrong and the Manchester camps. In 1865 he took over the Chairmanship of the Great Western Railway from Richard Potter. He did so at a time when railway boardrooms and military engineering had become intensely political. Decisions were no longer based on engineering criteria but were Treasury orientated. Whitworth too found himself in the forefront of these most bitter controversies: he and Gooch had much in common – not surprisingly they became very good friends.[11]

RAILWAY LOCOMOTIVES, COMPOUND ENGINES AND STEAM VALVES

The more Whitworth became engaged in the affairs of Manchester the more difficult it is to understand how he found time and energy to do so much. By 1838 his centre-lathe programme was making tremendous progress and was at the heart of his workshop developments. Such were the profound design changes he envisaged one would have imagined him glued to his drawing board or patternshop. Not so. His additional interests stretched far and wide.

Among his Unicorn Inn-cum-Blackfriars Inn circle of friends were engineers building steam locomotives. Their whole topic of conversation centred on state-of-the-art engine design and the poor performance of their own locomotives. Joe himself had been tempted once or twice to get involved but his self-discipline held. In the end, however, there was an egoistic flash – or perhaps it was a natural desire to promote his own engineering image: something or somebody unwisely persuaded him to circulate his latest patent for a different type of steam engine piston and link motion.[12] He frankly believed he could assist locomotive designers overcome their problems, but he was soon out of his depth wrestling with steam. It was a chastening experience from which Joe learned many lessons: later on it even did him some good.

Although he was often accused of bombast and swollen-headedness Whitworth never behaved as though he was the greatest toolmaker since men first chipped flint – he retained too many good engineering friends for that to be true – but like all far seeing innovationists he had enough self-confidence to peddle new ideas. In this instance he had a bit too much self-confidence. He concluded that the locomotive problems to which he was listening could only be resolved by better *mechanical* design – in fact he seemed to rationalize practically every problem in a similar vein – but on this occasion he was facing a whole new speciality and like many other leading engineers throughout Europe he was blissfully unaware that the steam science then understood was minimal. Engine designers everywhere had to wait another decade before researchers found even primary answers to their steam problems. In the meantime, Whitworth plunged ahead with the most dubious design theories, some of which escaped universal ridicule only because other equally frenzied ideas were circulated at the same time by other engineers equally desperate to score a success. Most were as hare-brained as Joe's ideas, but considering the industry was little more than a decade on from Stephenson's *Rocket* it was hardly surprising.

The early pioneers had already made magnificent headway but at the time of Whitworth's 1837 patent excessive wear and the troublesome lateral shakiness of the locomotive still bedevilled progress: the latter difficulty sufficient on occasion to even derail the engine. Thermal efficiency was poor with too much live steam going up the chimney; the short stroke of the piston was unable to fully utilize all the steam the boilers produced. The valve-gear was inadequate for the job; the timing was crude with the result that incorrect steam cut-off points intensified 'big-end knock' and often jammed the motion. So what was the solution? What did Whitworth propose?

Towards the end of 1837 he submitted to the Patents Office a power-motion scheme which he described as his 'improved locomotive design', claiming it to be a plausible answer to current locomotive problems. Whitworth concluded his submission by arguing:

> The principal advantage of the apparatus I have described for obtaining a continuous rotary motion from the reciprocating action of the piston rod, is the opportunity afforded to increase the length of the cylinder and thereby of what is technically called the stroke of the engine. This applies more particularly to locomotive engines, the stroke of which has never, I believe, exceeded twenty inches whereas in the plan I have shown, the cylinder and stroke are six feet long. Owing to the extra length of the cylinder the steam may be worked expansively, so as to occasion a considerable economy of fuel and the wear and tear of the engine will likewise be diminished by the less frequent action of the valves.[13]

The design Whitworth had patented meant in fact an alternative to the camshaft motion accepted and used by every steam locomotive designer since Stephenson. But by extending the piston stroke to six feet – for reasons shortly to be explained – Whitworth recognized that an orthodox Stephenson camshaft motion would no longer be feasible. He therefore designed an entirely new system of his own. Even if the Stephenson system was modified it would still have required the camshaft to trace a peripheral radius of three feet. The overall height of the engine would have been truly farcical. He therefore replaced the camshaft with a flat rack and pinion drive.

To accommodate the extraordinary length of the pistons he devised two double-action 18-in diameter cylinders which powered reciprocally two 6-ft long twin racks: each rack driving a ratchet-controlled pinion thereby ensuring that each pinion could only power-drive in one direction. The ratchet drive he used was a sophisticated version regularly adopted for cotton machinery. It had an outer ring spur-gear carrying four integral spring-loaded pawls driving an inner ratchet-wheel – the two rack units synchronized to provide a continuous drive.

'That's it', he must have thought, 'the problem is solved'. But was it? Sadly not even his friend William Fairbairn gave his ideas a second thought, nor it seems did Joe's other Manchester colleagues who had first put the problem to him.

The whole business must have been a great disappointment and a waste. He had taken precious time off from his machine tool work. It was so unlike Joe. His attitude on this occasion was vacuous compared with the more rational methodical approach he gave his machine tools. Perhaps the explanation was that he, like everyone else, got caught up with the Stephenson steam hyperbole. It was the one single occasion in his life when he allowed headlong intuitive theories to rush him into something for which he rightly deserved the ridicule of his peers. Whitworth himself must have known his ratchet drive was a second-rate mechanism totally unsuitable for the job it had to do.

Though engineers at the time may have agreed Joe's long stroke engine would fulfil its mechanical function, it would have done so in a poor and rudimentary way. But on the big question of thermal economy, Whitworth was right to think about compound expansion though his conclusion to try a form of compounding by extending the length of the cylinder was a naïve interpretation of coffee-house steam theory.

As Whitworth saw the problem this was the only way forward for British locomotives. In reality though, no important advance was made with compound engines until a railway engineer named Nicholson built a three-cylinder compound locomotive for the Eastern Counties Line in 1847.[14]

Careful study of Whitworth's 1837 patent confirms that he was after the maximum utilization of wasted low-pressure steam but due both to his own and his contemporaries' lack of theoretical understanding he didn't realize that to achieve his steam efficiencies he would need to enlarge the diameter of the cylinder as the steam lost pressure. *He literally would have required a long tapered cylinder.* Quite logically, he had reasoned, that before any engine blasted 'good live steam' up the chimney (by working the piston a mere 2 ft) it would be much better to extend the length of the stroke – say three times – to 6 ft thus allowing the steam to fully expand before exhausting into the atmosphere. Whitworth's patent was simple and rational but *profoundly flawed* – it lacked his two major stock-in-trade basics – mechanical adeptness and theoretical erudition.

One other aspect of Whitworth's unresolved proposals, however, continued to occupy the minds of railway draughtsmen for many years: that was the capricious vagaries of link and valve gear. And although Joe's own suggested arrangement was never considered by many as a serious proposition he did in fact point future loco designers towards the use of worm and bevel gear systems for valve control and reversing. Indeed, had Whitworth's premature valve ideas been further developed by his close colleagues – perhaps Charles Beyer or John Ramsbottom – the scourge of early locomen (faltering starts and lateral shakiness) would never have persisted. Synchronized valve timing and flexible but precise steam cut-off points would have come much earlier, probably reducing the dreadful crudity which so bedevilled the early six-wheel locomotives, especially the Bury types built in Manchester prior to 1850.

In the case of Whitworth's simple cams, however, they were a particular favourite of his (shades of his textile machinery) though truthfully, the kind of valve Joe envisaged was a very different thing from the more modern sophisticated types which only appeared after some eighty years' progress. Back in 1838, however, the fitting of Whitworth-type valves was left to his two Scramble Club friends, the Peel brothers, but unfortunately they only ever built two locomotives (both were six-wheelers and both were fitted with gear operated valves) at their new works, the Phoenix Foundry in Swan Street, Manchester. Interestingly, members of the Peel family were long-established expert gear manufacturers and it would have been extremely rewarding had they added to their gear wheel specialities a further speciality like Whitworth's rotating steam valves. As things turned out their decision to close their Swan Street locomotive shop had more to do with their inability to make good boilers than with poor engineering or the fitting of Whitworth's valves.

By this time Manchester was fast becoming a locomotive centre of some importance. For a short time it equalled the north-east in output and prior to the new railway centre at Crewe, Manchester was the most influential. Talented young designers like Beyer were quickly into the lead. Fairbairn, however, was the first to set up a specialist locomotive department in 1837 and brought in men like Archibald Sturrock, a remarkable engineer who retired at fifty and lived a further forty-three years. And like most of the other Manchester railwaymen he was a Whitworth devotee having introduced Whitworth machinery both at GWR Swindon under Daniel Gooch and at Doncaster where he followed Edward Bury as locomotive superintendent.

Still in Manchester, at Sharp Roberts Co., Charles Beyer was asked to accept responsibility for their newly opened engine shop where he was lucky enough to be assisted by the young John Ramsbottom. At Patricroft, not far away, James Nasmyth built nine locomotives in 1839 followed by a further thirty-seven before the end of 1842. Two or three other Manchester foundries like Peel's and the Caledonian Foundry had joined the local locomotive builders but quickly pulled out once they realized how necessary it was to have highly talented engineers and draughtsmen in the leadership of their affairs.[15]

WILLIAM FAIRBAIRN

The employment of new superior supervisors was an entirely new experience for what was ostensibly a blacksmith-cum-foundry industry. It entailed paying much higher salaries: a phenomenon employers didn't much relish.[16] Even Fairbairn failed to comprehend the general salary drift and in consequence lost Archibald Sturrock after two years or so; a loss which would have had far more serious consequences for Fairbairn had he not employed two other very dependable works superintendents: one named Robert Smith and the other, a John Eliot, an exceptionally talented millwright. In regard to Robert Smith, he turned out to be an absolute life saver for Fairbairn in Manchester; he went on to successfully build six hundred locomotives at his Canal Street works alone. The second man, John Eliot, was grudgingly offered a partnership in Fairbairn's other interest – his Millwall shipbuilding company. Both Eliot and Smith in fact played a sizeable but unacknowledged part in helping shape Fairbairn's international reputation.

About the same time as Whitworth and Nasmyth opened their very small workshops nearby, Fairbairn had embarked upon his most audacious, historic scheme to prefabricate – kit fashion – small steam paddleboats mainly for use on inland waterways. The boats were between 100 and 250 tons apiece. Each section was built in the factory – closely supervised by two foremen – and then transported by canal for final assembly at the coast. Fairbairn's first experimental iron boat – fairly small, just 68 ft long – he named the *Lord Dundas.* It had a single paddlewheel located in the centre of the boat. The wheel was 9 ft in diameter and the boat was capable of 14 knots. And according to contemporary reports of his bigger vessels, they too were a remarkable success and further established that Fairbairn's own methods for rolling, shaping and riveting wrought-iron plate were far in advance of the world – let alone Britain. Thus he was able to earn the generous praise which accompanied his fine locomotive boilers and engine frames everywhere they sold both at home and abroad.

All this is an essential backcloth to the life and times in Manchester especially those experienced by Whitworth. Particularly so because he and Fairbairn – for the very first time together – were about to participate in certain literary (and to some extent scientific) gatherings. Consider too the motives which lay behind Fairbairn's actions which were equally absorbing. Why, for instance, did he slowly distance himself from Nasmyth and make almost a paragon of Whitworth? It is an interesting question. At first many observers thought Joe trailed along as Fairbairn's protégé; then they saw them together as two very close allies: finally whenever Fairbairn introduced Whitworth to an institute or to a professional group he would always present his friend as the one engineer, who in his opinion, was destined to raise mechanical engineering to some entirely new epochal level. Together they surmounted the toughest opposition; Fairbairn by his eloquent fair-minded persuasiveness and Whitworth by his blunt logic. Sadly, however, it didn't always work like that: when the eloquent fair-minded persuasiveness was absent the blunt logic made little progress – an opposite testimony perhaps to the long-held myth that Victorians liked their Lancastrians to be plain spoken and short. In Whitworth's case, they didn't.

Whenever Fairbairn travelled abroad he happily fraternized with royalty but in Britain, while in the company of either engineers or politicians, he constantly tormented himself with a totally irrational sense of inferiority brought on by his lack of a university education. It was both uncharacteristic and wrong. In fact he was a very well-read man; among the first three or four leading engineers of his time and because of his standing he could easily prevail upon others to follow his pacemaking trends. In that sense he was a natural leader, distinguished and recognized by his outstanding abilities: he was looked on as the doyen of Manchester's dissenting elite.

One other worrying self-doubt ran through Fairbairn's thinking: it was the 'London factor'. He was convinced that the government, the Admiralty and various ship owners ignored his well-researched brand of iron framed and plated steamships simply because he was tucked away in the provinces. It was an attitude he felt more than ever justified when years later he offered the government a Fairbairn marine engine (parallel motion) together with his patented shafting arrangements for screw propulsion. More likely he was tormented at the time by the frequent eulogies heaped by the press on such of his rivals as Messrs Maudslay and Field and I.K. Brunel. Fevered Scotsmen – particularly expat Scotsmen like himself, depressed during their most difficult years – were forever wrathful of the London clique, a communicable feeling perhaps which rubbed off on Whitworth from their earliest days. All in all the combined effect of this 'London thing' plus his 'so-called lack of education' drove Fairbairn to make the few bad errors of judgement which he lived to regret: the most bizarre being his 1836 decision to challenge the 'London factor' by himself building a shipyard on the River Thames at Millwall.

By the year 1840 Fairbairn employed over 2,000 men, two-thirds of whom were in his yard at Millwall. It was undoubtedly a colossal venture but never a triumph. Almost from the beginning of its very short eleven-year life the yard was beginning to slowly ebb away, so much so that, privately, Fairbairn soon recognized – after the first five years in fact – that premature closure of the plant was inevitable. Much depended upon his second partner and yard manager, Andrew Murray, and although Fairbairn borrowed heavily to fund the yard his decency and loyalty to his men was looked upon as a weakness and thoroughly exploited. A further weakness was obvious. By dividing his managerial control between two centres 200 miles apart, he finished up controlling neither. Not only did it dislocate the management of his Ancoats works but by being away from Manchester for weeks on end the town's cultural development – upon which Fairbairn had set his heart – also began to lose impetus. He had been so active in so many institutions persuading people to attend meetings and to do things, that once he himself was absent the whole movement became discouraged.

His Thames shipbuilding collapse wreaked havoc everywhere. The catastrophic closure at Millwall finally came in 1847. By this time Fairbairn himself was virtually drained – physically and financially – and maddened too for neither of his two sons proved to be talented shipbuilders nor exceptional managers. Ironically, the very same London people against whom Fairbairn had earlier complained were in fact the incoming management team taking over his yard. And as if to rub salt into his wounds, John Scott Russell and I.K. Brunel added an adjoining slipway to Fairbairn's original yard and found enough space to construct Brunel's majestic showpiece the *Great Eastern* – sadly to become yet another financial disaster from the very first moment the keel was laid – and for exactly the same managerial reasons which for ten years had bedevilled William Fairbairn.

The 1847 debacle, however, was not all disaster. Once Fairbairn had resumed full-time his Mancunian activity it is as fascinating as it is factual to learn how both Manchester's culture and Joseph Whitworth as a personality became more confident and adopted a more emphatic approach. But first, to learn more of how this happened let us for a moment return to 1835; that is two years after Whitworth first set up his own business. It was in this year, remember, that Fairbairn first started to build locomotives while simultaneously diversifying into ocean shipbuilding and steam engine manufacture at Millwall. He realized (because he was now so extensively involved in untried technology) that his kind of empirical method required a more scientific approach if his industry was to overcome the serious design problems it faced. Fairbairn himself needed to appoint competent researchers and persuaded men like Eaton Hodgkinson, the mathematician, and Bennett Woodcroft, the scientist, to act as his scientific advisers. He was, in fact, the first engineer to recognize science and engineering as inseparable parts of the same thing.[17]

While still in the year 1835 – despite his growing wealth – Fairbairn continued to live at Medlock Bank, a detached residence a little upstream from the more obnoxious effluents which dyeworks and tanneries still poured into the river. It was a comfortable house in which to live, big enough to enable his wife and himself entertain their friends. It was from here, almost a decade before, that Fairbairn, Richard Roberts and Thomas Hopkins convened a special meeting at the Bridgewater Arms, on 7 April 1824, to discuss the formation of a new science discussion group. Foreseeably the discussion very quicky gave birth to the Manchester Mechanics Institute. Disagreements between the leading lights developed: the same trend occurred not only in Manchester but elsewhere in the north. The 'Mechanics' movement was desperately needed but it sorely required coordination and a more practical theme and good leadership. More than anything perhaps it needed a sense of national reputation.

William Fairbairn knew exactly what had to be done to reunite the organization. His political antenna was improving and Fairbairn quickly diagnosed that the Mechanics Institute nationally still remained a series of disconnected parts. For him the only answer must be the launching of a magazine geared specifically to the Institute, not just to salvage the organization but to unify it and spread his own engineering gospel. The more he thought about it the more the idea raced through his veins. He lost no time calling together his advisers, Eaton Hodgkinson and the others – plus, curiously, James Nasmyth, by now a regular supper guest at Medlock Bank – to hear first hand his plans to publish a magazine. He would name the paper *The Workshop* and it would profile leading engineers, explain the latest workshop practice and propagate the theme that 'science creates wealth'. The paper would also campaign as tenaciously as it could to further Fairbairn's lifelong vision of raising the professional standing of the engineer to that of the lawyer and the surgeon.

The fact that he had invited Nasmyth and not Whitworth to join his editorial team proved a profound mistake. Fairbairn knew both of them equally well but presumably he and his scholarly friends considered Nasmyth's middle-class upbringing more in keeping with their task and as an entertaining raconteur Nasmyth was a delight. Within months the paper died. The principal reason no doubt was that Hodgkinson, Nasmyth and company never understood the purpose behind the Mechanics Institute nor could they themselves see any reason why they should interest themselves in the matter.

On reflection Fairbairn very much regretted that his magazine never really got started. In his autobiographical notes – as if to excuse its failure – he wrote:

> I was incessantly engaged in conducting my two large establishments in London and Manchester where I had collectively upwards of 2,000 hands employed. With such a business I could not have done much for 'The Workshop' if that publication had gone on. I confess that nature had endowed me with a strong desire to distinguish myself as a man of science. I was pleased to see myself in print and the only fear I entertained was the imperfections of style, and the great difficulty I had to encounter in expressing my ideas in a clear and perspicuous manner. This was a difficulty I laboured hard to overcome, and I have up to the present moment no clear perception whether I am right or wrong in any composition in which I have been engaged.[18]

In other words Fairbairn concerned himself more with grammatical refinement and correct punctuation rather than the quality of his ideas or his descriptive vocabulary. Elsewhere he had also confessed to experiencing an equivalent difficulty with his mathematics but he unhesitatingly overcame that particular problem by employing professional mathematicians and scientific advisers. How much more puzzling it is to understand why he was so reluctant to employ a professional writer, or even a diarist, to ghost-write his many engineering ideas and philosophical interests. It was a weakness which many of his engineering contemporaries shared.

Halfway through the year 1838 Fairbairn began to realize that his Medlock Bank supper guests didn't always understand – nor did they always share – either his evangelical mission, his morality or the purpose of his engineering crusade. He now felt an urgent need for a fresh approach and if that meant moving to a more suitable residence and making new friends, then so be it. Only recently had he familiarized himself with Whitworth's view that engineering progress was a far quicker way of liberating ordinary working people from their pitifully wretched conditions than, say, moralizing from a church pulpit. For the first time this new approach on the part of Fairbairn was discernibly closing the gap between himself and what he understood to be Whitworth's more workable, more nuts-and-bolts philosophy; a compelling belief that steam power combined with machine production would bring in its wake a more dignified existence for the great mass of ordinary people. Not that Fairbairn was moving away from his beloved Cross Street Chapel, or the Revd William Gaskell, or his Unitarianism: he wasn't. Indeed in a very real way, the longer he lived the closer to these he became.

Nevertheless, thought Fairbairn, if he was going to effectively convince the likes of the British Association and if he was to recruit behind his engineering campaign the rest of Britain's cultural élite – and maybe some government ministers too – then he would want to have by his side a very special engineer and one who was totally committed as well as being a very determined character. That very person he now honestly believed was Joseph Whitworth. And if all that sounds as though he had experienced some sort of biblical vision, or that he considered Whitworth pre-ordained, Fairbairn himself harboured no such nonsense. What had happened was that he himself had seen Whitworth's work and in doing so had actually been convinced of the man's great potential. He staunchly believed that Whitworth would deliver all the major innovatory engineering expected of him during the next decade or so and that he, Fairbairn, would give him every encouragement, plus as much practical support as he possibly could. He felt confident that together they could, within the time limits they had set for themselves, achieve their common objectives. The year was 1839 and their campaign was well under way.

It was William Fairbairn's intention to undertake a three-month business tour of Turkey and Eastern Europe during the second half of the year but before leaving Britain he was very anxious that Manchester businessmen plus the town's intellectual élite should get to know Whitworth much better. He didn't see himself as some crude lobbying campaign manager but honestly believed that he and Whitworth held in trust an obligation to Britain. In many ways it was also a two-way exercise in that Whitworth personally also wanted to explore for himself a cultural Manchester beyond the Scramble Club, his one source of intellectual and social activity. Thus he gladly took advantage of Fairbairn's shrewd scheming.

Soon after Christmas, on 22 January 1839, the two men attended together the Literary and Philosophical Society and Whitworth was elected a member. He enjoyed their meetings immensely, frequently attending, although throughout his lifelong membership he never actually delivered a formal lecture to the Society. Two months later, on 21 March 1839, the two men attended another foundation meeting. This time it was held at the York Hotel, Manchester, to set up the Institute of Practical Science, an exhibition-cum-lecture society which eventually became the Royal Victoria Gallery. Both Whitworth and Fairbairn, together with engineering friends like the Peel brothers later became board members of the Society under the chairmanship of Hugh Birley. They all worked extremely hard and each put in money to launch the gallery and to ensure that the scientist William Sturgeon became its first director; an event about which there is more to be said later.

Around this time another two local societies were given almost full-time attention by Fairbairn – himself being a better-than-usual geologist and also an astronomer: the two societies were the Natural History Society and the Manchester Geological Society. In particular, the Natural History Society had always provided a special interest for Fairbairn mainly because of its influential membership and the happy coincidence that so many of the members were personal Cross Street Chapel friends – probably at least half a dozen of them enjoying international reputations in their own subjects – men like Thomas Percival and Dr Edward Holme; plus obvious heavy-weights like Lord Francis Egerton and the Heywoods. It was exactly the kind of opinion-forming group Fairbairn had in mind for Whitworth but unfortunately Joe wasn't really interested. Once he had discovered that his 'favourite' *bête noire,* James Nasmyth, intended to play a leading rôle in both societies, Joe quickly concluded that their interests were not his forte: and to be truthful they never were.

Probably one of the most significant aspects to emerge from all this contrived pushing by Fairbairn was a fortuitous self-awareness on the part of both Whitworth and Fairbairn that each needed the other. As a partnership it was an act of astonishing benefaction which both men carried into their later years.[19] Sensibly, each of them recognized the other's attributes; qualities destined to emerge very clearly once Whitworth started to present his famous reports on matters like measurement and screw threads, his horse-drawn street sweepers and, years later, even his guns. But nowhere did their combined gifts manifest themselves more freely than when Whitworth joined his friend's five-year stint to campaign for a University of Manchester. It is often forgotten that in the five years prior to Whitworth joining this select band comprising the two Heywoods, Kennedy and Fairbairn, this small group almost exclusively funded the building of the Athenaeum in Manchester, plus two other splendid public buildings, while at the same time providing sufficient money to keep going the University campaign itself. It was a campaign which impressed Whitworth deeply to the extent that from the year 1840 he steadily worked towards his own ambition – not only to see the birth of a University of Manchester, but also for it to have a premier department of engineering.

In his own mind Whitworth recognized that had it been left to himself he most probably would not have made either himself or his ideas known to such an influential circle in so little a time span. He also acknowledged that neither would he have accomplished such a prolific and profoundly inventive decade had it not been for Fairbairn's persuasive encouragement. In regard to Fairbairn himself, he too reflected that his own vision for the future of the engineering story would never have been so convincing in the absence of Whitworth's majestic concepts and his incredibly beautiful and precise machinery. Of course they both became tireless self-publicists. They had to be in a world without easy communication. They both gave the impression of being a cross between propagandist and teacher; meaning of course that they wanted to both spread their message and influence public opinion while at the same time – more than anything else in fact

– they wanted to re-educate the engineering industry by demonstrating their own revolutionary concepts. Arguably they had at least one advantage. They both had served a trade apprenticeship becoming skilled manual workers, thereby understanding the special language of their industry – a facility which helped them overcome the opposition of endless generations.

The early Victorians attached great importance to age differences – at the time, 1839, Fairbairn was fifty years of age, almost fifteen years older than Whitworth, and employed some 2,000 men compared with the younger man's 160. Even so, on both counts and in boardroom terms, their mutual respect was unaffected. Indeed, Fairbairn saw Whitworth as a standard bearer – not in the bell-wether sense, meaning someone who leads a flock by wearing a bell around his neck – but rather someone who leads by the presentation of his ideas; by his engineering know-how and practical scholarship. Of the two, the Scottish Fairbairn was an accomplished speaker, a fluent lecturer, while Whitworth had a more mundane, earthy delivery blessed with a Lancastrian dialect. But intriguingly it was Whitworth whose imaginative, politicized ideas gave the whole business a sense of dedication.

In the end Fairbairn, a devout Unitarian lay preacher, came very near to acceptance of Whitworth's belief that only a science-orientated society with all its commensurate technology could possibly raise the level of conventional morality sufficiently to improve general living conditions. Admittedly, within the context of mid-Victorian ethics it was a difficult argument for engineers to advance. For Christians, particularly at that time, it meant some sort of hybridity, the joining of biblical teaching with the semi-secular understanding of science. But if working men and women were ever to learn that modern machinery and factory production was to be of immense benefit to themselves, then the acceptance of science and technology had to be preached from the pulpit. The fact that the established Church failed to do so, inescapably made the tortuousness of the transition that much more difficult.

To epitomize their personal attitude and philosophy both Fairbairn and Whitworth could best be described as 'intransigent futurists'. On the face of it the title sounds a bit far-fetched; but considering their attitude became so absolute the inscription is well adapted. It has to be recognized of course that to have developed such a commanding confidence in their own ability that they set out without qualm to guide the whole engineering industry – an industry so self-satisfied that it almost resented innovation – then to have coaxed it towards a new dawn in the way they did, was so pretentiously impudent that there must have been a genuine unity between the two of them, that is to say between Fairbairn's unswerving faith and Whitworth's mechanical genius. That in essence was the size of their professional alliance and the basis of their lasting friendship.

CHAPTER FOUR

The Inventor

An invention is anything not before existing

Nuttall (1887)

It is truly astonishing that prior to 1840 the 'science' of metrology was so haphazard – virtually non-existent. It still shocks that the era of precision is still so young – a mere 150 years. It is even more difficult to grasp that the Board of Trade became interested in these matters little more than a century ago. Until Whitworth, only time could be measured accurately, the length of anything else could not!

Admittedly, it is almost four centuries since Pierre Vernier devised his vernier system. Maudslay two centuries later converted it into practical mechanics: others proffered their own ideas. The fact is, it was left to Whitworth from 1840 onwards to mastermind the whole business. He introduced several revolutionary innovations: a one-inch standard, a micro-comparator, a system of length gauges, his ninety-one piece master slip-gauges and much more. He campaigned assiduously for a British standards system. Though it is now hard to believe, he persuaded Britain – and therefore the United States – to decimalize engineering measurement. In so many ways it was his greatest and most distinguished decade yet the radical changes he inaugurated still remain unattributed and largely uncelebrated.

It seems incredible that the man who literally taught the world how to measure things to within unprecedented fine limits should now be excluded from the credits. It was he who made the universal interchangeability of components possible. There is no other way of saying it. Whitworth created a new language of measurement by making for the first time a verifiable standard inch, then by dividing it 1,000 times he converted the words one-eighth of an inch into 0.125 in – thus inspiring a new decimal language – a technical esperanto nowadays used throughout engineering. In addition to this, Whitworth's own system of gauging and measurement triggered such a profound mutational change that engineering became a fundamentally different science within the same decade.

Avowedly, all this work is largely forgotten, what we must now do is quietly retrace his attainments over the years; his metrology especially. The expression 'forgotten giant' must engender for all of us a legitimate twinge of conscience. Remembered or not, the Whitworth years, the exciting 1840s and '50s, were memorable decades for engineers and if they are properly appreciated they still constitute a rich harvest for historians to reap.

The pace at which machine tool practice was changing during this period was quite startling, due largely to Whitworth's design neology, yet Whitworth's antagonists singled him out for attack. Of his innovatory outpouring his metrology alone compelled engineers generally to reconsider their methods. But strangely most engineering masters resisted these changes. Perhaps they resented Whitworth censuring their industry for its haphazard state of affairs. Some reacted by attacking Joe personally, labelling him a plagiarizer. It was perhaps understandable – an inverted form of self-defence – but hardly forgivable. As all would agree, no scientist or engineer starts from a 'black hole', from nothing: nor did Whitworth. Throughout these pages there are many examples of Whitworth's originality, but always a precursor of some sort, usually of the most tenuous kind, can be found somewhere. It is better that the argument is developed as each example occurs in the correct sequence – the question to be answered here is one of Whitworth's morality: was he guilty or not?

The filching of original ideas is a charge scientists have bandied against each other throughout the ages. In Whitworth's case the gentler term 'copier' was the more usual insinuation. Was it true? Generally speaking, no, particularly if taken in the sense that practically every engineering pioneer was preceded, one way or another, by Leonardo da Vinci. As was generally recognized nearly all practical inventions (particularly in mechanical engineering) usually delineated some aspect of earlier work but Whitworth's metrology, for instance, because of its precision and its new method, together with his usage of decimals, must be considered an entirely new concept. He should therefore be granted its originality. Indeed, careful scrutiny of the facts throughout this study, plus Whitworth's own reasons refuting the charge that he was a 'copier' all add up to the conclusion that he personally was more the victim of ideas-theft than ever he himself thieved ideas from others. Similar accusations were made against him all his life; the more colourful stories used by journalists appeared to have been stitched together by some Machiavellian seamstress. Not surprisingly they were repeated in Parliament. As a rule they were laid by fellow engineers or their patenting agents – even men like Brunel and Armstrong fired some pretty dubious shots across Whitworth's bow when it came to their arguing about gun design.[1]

Nowadays, modern writers compare Whitworth with Henry Royce (of Rolls Royce fame) as against say, Rudolph Diesel, the German engine inventor. Royce, it was said, was merely an improver of existing ideas while Diesel has long been recognized as an original thinker. Clearly, the reasoning throughout these pages is that Whitworth was more Diesel than Royce. We shall see. May it be stated, however, this defamatory opinion of Royce is not shared by the author. Royce was far more (as indeed was Whitworth) than a 'methodical perfectionist'; his aero-engines established Royce's pedigree.

Granted, an engineer who is also an employer – someone in Whitworth's position for instance – could always feed off an employed assistant but in Whitworth's case at that time the delegation of design responsibility was never his method. It is a criticism similar to that made against many engineering greats – particularly locomotive engineers – but in this context there can be little doubt that Whitworth himself was personally responsible for all his own design work. His so-called 'pig-headedness' – if accepted – is further verification; the way he announced design concepts *in advance* was yet another. His authoritative style when dealing with draughtsmen was also a sure sign that he was personally 'thinking through' his own work.

Here are some specific examples in terms of simple mechanics. The fact that most working components within any piece of machinery are 'pushed' rather than 'pulled' is one of several phenomena a modern machine designer can never ignore. Whitworth was the first to recognize the existence of such problems. Unlike his less talented contemporaries he is known to have modified his components to compensate for these behavioural hazards. He realized that if a shaft, for example, was being axially 'pushed' it would tend to buckle causing possible shaft-whirl and ovality in the bearings plus badly worn gears; in consequence he thickened up (contoured) shaft diameters midway between bearings. A revolving shaft made to carry an overhanging load would be another type of shaft he would design in exactly the same way. A lathe saddle based on flawed geometry would cross-wind if 'pushed'; much better if the lead-screw was made to 'pull' the apron instead. Vexed questions of this sort when put before Whitworth were given his immediate attention which again testifies his strict adherence to good mechanical practice. Original concepts are perhaps difficult to identify when, at a glance, machine pieces of all ages tend to look alike but of these difficult aspects the historic absence – in Whitworth's case – of vibratory chatter clearly shows him first in the field. Granted that if either his or other 1860s machines had been repaired or modified at some stage during their working lives the examination of original design is sometimes difficult but it can be done. Again in Whitworth's case a unique smoothness under maximum load was legendary, analysis indicating this to be down to his original design concept.

Whitworth went to great lengths to avoid mechanical imbalances: his harmonics and analytical geometry must have been exemplary though oddly enough few of his contemporaries ever followed his lead until many years later. Not that Whitworth himself understood one iota of this theoretically – and in fairness neither did any Oxbridge theoreticians at that time – but Joe had something almost exclusive to himself; he had an instinctive feel as to whether a mechanism would deliver the high quality performance he demanded.

It was typical of the man that at a time when all other makers were reducing the weight of their own machines Whitworth adopted a belt and braces approach by deliberately adding bulk. He used the sheer weight of metal to absorb any residual vibration and, the story goes, he personally spent many hours reshaping foundry patterns to give the ungraceful bulk a more elegant shape.

Very often Whitworth's claim to be the original inventor of his many innovations was challenged because he used the words 'effecting improvements'. This in fact was the exact formula demanded by the Patents Office following the submission of original work for patenting.

The following story illustrates how engineers tend to be disadvantaged by the use of these words. It is one of many. The story goes: two scientists roughly of the same period and of the same name: Sir Alexander Fleming, the Nobel winner who discovered penicillin as against Sir John A. Fleming, the now forgotten physicist-electrical engineer, who 'explained' equally complex phenomena. Both men are recognized internationally as brilliant scientists but the fact that they both *built upon or 'improved' upon* the work of their predecessors Louis Pasteur and Michael Faraday was never allowed to detract from the penicillin man's masterful attainments. For Sir John it was different. It was Professor P.M.S. Blackett who cheekily put forward this seductive comparison when speaking at Fallowfield, Manchester, about the poor treatment afforded engineers as against medicine when he suggested that it was Joseph Bramah and the plumbing trade, with their hot baths and flush-systems, who had probably contributed most towards the elimination of contagious disease. Who can say otherwise?

Here is another modern example of different principles being used for engineers as against the more glamorous scientists credited with making space exploration possible. Why is it that engineers are made to play second fiddle to the astrophysicists? Dr F.T. Bacon 'invented' the modern fuel cell. Though it is not denied that Sir William Grove discovered a formula for the gas battery in 1842, the late Dr Bacon's work in the 1950s was pure original brilliance. The astronaut, Neil Armstrong, said: 'Without Tom Bacon's work on fuel cells man's journey to the moon would not have been possible'. The point could not have been better put, but who else reveres Bacon's work?

Nowadays much discussion centres around 'intellectual property' and whether 'original thought' can be registered as a protected property. It was during Whitworth's period that the issue first arose: when a scientist 'discovered' a new chemical it would be patented but when some phenemonon was 'explained' like the sticking together of flat surfaces it usually ended up as a 'named' theory. As already mentioned, the work of Sir John Fleming became 'Fleming's Rules' but had Fleming been employed by a private company instead of a university, the same 'Rules' could well have been given the *company's name* and not Fleming's name: again, a positive disadvantage for engineers because of the phenomenal costs (therefore the need for international company funding) of engineering research.

In answer to the criticism that Whitworth didn't *invent* the Whitworth thread – he never claimed he did – he claimed he *discovered* it by practical experiment. As to the use of screws, many engineers, including Maudslay, preceded him in that they improvised their own threads as best they could. Whitworth himself determined the 55° angle and his threads-per-inch formulation by measuring the loads at which various other threads stripped. He then selected for his own thread the best angles and root depths.

Another illustration was the *sprung* carriage wheels he invented and patented in 1876.[2] This time the technical press couldn't wait to ridicule him: has Whitworth reinvented the wheel, they teased. The point was absurd. Goodyear invented vulcanization in 1841; Dunlop the pneumatic tyre in 1888; neither had re-invented the wheel but the world has rightly honoured them both ever since. Whitworth's *sprung* wheels however were not a success and he was sensible to let them fade away. The press was right to criticize but surely not to use that old parody about the wheel.

The press however were soon back on their favourite hobby horse. Without naming anyone, 'certain engineers', they wrote, 'lacked originality'. Some even copied other engineers' patents and 'sold their immoral replications to foreign governments'. Though not a criminal offence – editorials blazed – it was nevertheless downright unpatriotic. This wasn't aimed exclusively at Whitworth – that came later – but it was sufficiently close to be hurtful. The IMechE President, William Fairbairn, complained about this parrot-like behaviour while lecturing to his own profession. He was pointedly blunt about the hostility shown against certain engineers taking out patents for copied work. 'I myself could never knowingly take from others their original work and then claim its authorship for myself. That would be wrong and I couldn't live with such dishonesty but it is also equally wrong for certain masters to accuse others of infamy in this manner without themselves investigating the facts'.[3] That Fairbairn should have referred to this question at all during his own presidential year – the year immediately prior to Whitworth himself becoming president of the IMechE in 1856 – suggests that the question of disputed originality at the time was a popular theme especially as a topic of coffee-house gossip.

Tom Rolt, the engineer-historian, partially retrieved the record when he wrote: 'Notwithstanding the inventive achievements of Clement, Fox, Roberts and Nasmyth, there can be no doubt that it was Whitworth who succeeded Maudslay as the dominant figure in the history of machine tools'.[4] Rolt unfortunately then went on to mimic the more conventional platitudes when he coined his now much-quoted assessment of Whitworth the engineer. 'In machine tool history, Whitworth occupied the same position as Henry Royce in the history of automobile engineering. Neither man was an inventive genius but both possessed standards so exacting that even the best was never good enough. With unerring judgement they sought out the best features of contemporary design, improved upon them and combined them in one masterly synthesis. This is a conscious and deliberate process not to be confused with the kind of unconscious synthesis Henry Maudslay achieved when he built his first screw-cutting lathe. Works of the latter kind require inventive genius because the fact that they are combinations of preconceived ideas only becomes evident to the historian.'[5]

Although Rolt's judgement is profound it is precisely because we now have well over a century of hindsight that it is possible to understand fully the synthesis to which he referred. Granted, the synthesis he attributes to Maudslay should not include the preceding work of the French engineers Vaucanson and Senot, chiefly because Maudslay was probably not aware of their existence. It is therefore correct to reason that an 'unconscious synthesis' in this case does in fact establish Maudslay's entitlement to the accolade 'inventive genius'. In the case of Whitworth, however, the conditions are quite different. If the Whitworth 'synthesis theme' used by Rolt is to be considered in its totality then his machine tool mechanisms must be sandwiched between his metrology and his guns and the whole lot taken together. The fact that Rolt failed to do this partly invalidates his reasoning. To say that Whitworth was no more than a skilled improver – albeit in Rolt's view a meticulous and sometimes an ingenious improver – also miscarries because it excludes Whitworth's cardinal function during Britain's twenty years (1840–60) of world leadership in machine tools; a period followed by her equally rapid descent. This rise and fall was essentially a Whitworth rise and fall and had Rolt understood the significance of this period in terms of Whitworth's pre-eminence he surely would not have bracketed Whitworth with Henry Royce.

Although comparisons of this sort can often be invidious, Tom Rolt was not alone in linking engineers like Royce with Whitworth. As mentioned earlier, the name Rudolph Diesel should perhaps be substituted. Whitworth and Diesel had much more in common. Their research methods for instance were similar; systematic trial and error experimentation; the fact that Diesel completed each stage of his engine developments before proceeding to the next stage, was reminiscent of Whitworth. They each shared a perfectionist step-by-step approach which some writers complained was inconsistent with genius. Why?

If the question is posed 'what is the nature of engineering invention' as distinct from defining the incentive to invent, the answer most scientists would agree is the Whitworth gloss, that is to say, invention is 'eighty per cent perspiration – twenty per cent inspiration'. If the *incentive to invent* is questioned then the answer would seem the same today as it was for Whitworth – that if a combination of the best possible financial rewards are augmented with an overwhelming desire 'to leave for others a better world' plus a 'shot of egotism' then the same hard stimuli apply equally to the Watts, the Whitworths and the Wankels.

The intangible qualities 'personal recognition' and 'posthumous fame' defy assessment except to acknowledge that human ego being what it is, the quest for fame is more often than not a compulsive propellant.

Of the Manchester engineers during the 1850s the need to save labour and to eliminate 'high-wage' skill was for them 'the principle reason why gifted talents must concentrate on self-acting machines'. There were, however, other incentives. James Nasmyth, in a somewhat trivial effusion, said that 'machine tools never got drunk; their hands never shook from excess; they were never absent from work; they did not strike for wages; they were unfailing in their accuracy and regularity'. But towards the turn of the century the 'theory of invention' had shifted towards a much harder economic rationale. The majority of government and academic (engineering) studies usually concluded labour saving to be the prime motivator. This was far too simplistic a view. An American theoretician, Dr G.F. Bloom, argued that 'most invention is naturally devoted to saving labour because labour is so large an item in total costs and because the desire to make the job easier is the fundamental motive of invention'. Professor R.M. Solow, again in the United States, but echoing much British understanding, construed that 'during the period 1909–49 technical change was, on average, neutral as between capital and labour'.

Today's world however is a very different place. There still exists a need to save labour but present-day engineers see the nature of invention much more in terms of a collective progression rather than a singular genius. The whole business is still disciplined of course by the logic of its contemporary science but competitive egos will always race one another to win. As for Whitworth, he very much believed that the logic of engineering was man-made and not something which would look after itself, the automatic outcome of some natural selection.

The entire sequence of his *strategy for engineering* which he introduced during the 1840s was the carefully considered logic of new mechanisms, flat surfaces and precise measurement. His goal was the international interchangeability of components, a journey which contributed a veritable cascade of technical brilliance.

The fact that none of it could have much influence in the absence of government approval irritated Whitworth intensely. It was incoherent that the Board of Trade couldn't see the necessity to write his system of measurement into their legislation. The truth of the matter was that the government's scientific advisers thought Whitworth 'too big for his boots', They made him wait thirty-seven years before his work was finally recognized and stamped with the Crown. Now, with hindsight, it is possible to see the severe bruising this interminable bitterness had upon both British mechanical engineering and Whitworth himself. It was debasing and into the bargain, because the Board of Trade tried to justify their hostility by accusing Whitworth of dressing up old ideas, date-stamped the time when the plagiarizing insult first stuck.

It was this sort of vacuous anti-Whitworthism which the two doughty campaigners, Fairbairn and Joe himself, always expected their friends in high places would stop. But not so. First Prince Albert called upon the government to rationalize the whole business of interchangeable components by implementing the Whitworth strategy; but no action was taken. Some years later, Joe's friend, John Bright MP, was himself President of the Board of Trade from 1868 to 1870, but presumably his free-trade-non-interventionist politics also stopped him from taking action. Those advising the Department were determined not to legalize the Whitworth system of measurement.

From 1856 or so Whitworth was engaged in innovative gun design. The receiving brass-hats and War Office civil servants didn't like the recasting of established methods either and soon joined the Board of Trade in the mockery of the Manchester engineer. To them it was the best way of warding off change and to some extent neutralized the half-hearted demands coming from engineering for the part-recognition of Whitworth's mensuration.

It was a puzzling relationship; the *Engineering* magazine called it 'some sort of moronic perversity'. Whitworth himself seldom criticized the civil service publicly but he did let off one of his rare broadsides against the War Office following the annual dinner of the Foremen Engineers on 19 February 1870. He said:

> It is well known to you all that the War Department and the Admiralty of this country exercise control over mechanical operations of the greatest importance. In the Admiralty, at Whitehall, these mechanical operations have always been conducted with the advice of mechanical men; but in the War Department at Pall Mall, there is not a single person who has had a practical mechanical training to advise the Minister of War. The consequent waste of public money is truly deplorable, and this waste will continue so long as mechanical questions are settled by military officers instead of by mechanical engineers.[6]

Questions of this sort, especially the lack of experienced engineers employed by the Board of Trade, also irritated Whitworth. The fact that the Royal Commission, behind closed doors, twice rejected his system of measurement merely increased his depression. However, there was a good side: the effects of all this embitterment reinforced his campaigning zeal – he was in essence a campaigning man – and the negative attitude of all concerned made him even more determined to endow Britain with the world's best manufacturing precision. He knew that he would have to campaign hard. Nevertheless he was supremely confident that he could make and sell enough machine tools to fund his crusade, to mobilize opinion, enlighten his peers and eventually carry the government.

As a prelude to each stage of his campaign he shrewdly made available to the trade his most advanced machinery. His promotion of new machines was not by general advertisement but word of mouth and the odd press notice ensured for him a waiting list of impatient customers. As a sales strategy it worked like a charm. No manufacturer could have wished for more. Intriguingly his competitors did things very differently and commercially were not half so successful. They were unbelievably secretive and locked away their own experimental work in the most guarded fashion. Whitworth – always the most accessible teacher – bucked this trend by doing everything so openly.

He astounded the trade from about 1841 onwards when, with very few restrictions, he threw open his whole Chorlton Street works, virtually to any group of *engineers* who applied to visit. Internationally, he made it known to most leading engineers that they were very welcome to visit his factory and see for themselves the kind of progress his ideas made possible. It must have been a unique gesture in its day, and unusually altruistic, considering the vast advantage Whitworth's own machine tools enjoyed over his nearest competitors.

At the Chorlton Street works he had a special room set aside containing scale models of his machinery and his measurement equipment. According to the *Manchester City News*, Whitworth's guests would be met at the gate and taken up to the room where he would demonstrate his ideas in much the same way as he did at the British Association in 1840 at Glasgow.

'The careful preparation of plain metallic surfaces is crucial to all departments of manufacture. It is destined to prove of incalculable value in application. A true surface', he would stress, 'instead of being in common use is almost unknown; few mechanics have any distinct knowledge of the method to be pursued for obtaining it; nor do practical men sufficiently advert either to the immense importance or to the comparative facility of the acquisition. The valves of steam engines, for example, the tables of printing presses, stereotype plates, surface plates, slides of all kinds, all require a degree of truth much superior to the work generally done.'[7] And then, no doubt with a few extra words of encouragement, he would whisk everyone off into the most impressive classroom of all – his own tool and gauge workshop.

But not only did he have an inner sanctum at the works; he also carried on his travels a massive amount of tackle which always accompanied his carefully prepared lectures. His campaigns were such that on each occasion he was able to announce something new, his publications followed one after another in fairly rapid sequence. Whenever he and Fairbairn visited one of the many societies to which they had been invited Joe would always tell his hosts in advance the preparations he required of them. He deliberately made each lecture an occasion. He would have two of his employees accompany him, humping packing cases and boxes containing all his lecture equipment such as heavy gauges and comparators. It really was a travelling circus.

His five-year programme was extremely diverse and very hard work. He presented seven or eight major papers during the period, often accompanying them with practical demonstrations. He published the results of his research setting out a scheme for standard screw threads, to which he added – almost as a bonus – a more general toolroom code of practice. Not surprisingly, all this excitement and activity pumped still more adrenalin through his system. It gave him a new confidence and strengthened his resolve. Looking back over the period it must have been a joy for those close to him to experience these more optimistic outpourings, plus his new machinery – year after year – till it all finally emerged as one great manifestation; the two Whitworth Stands at the 1851 Great Exhibition. That, in short, was a kaleidoscopic view of his most prolific years.

THE TOOLMAKER'S BEST FRIENDS – FLAT SURFACES AND TRIBOLOGY

Henry Maudslay was the first engineer to be officially identified with the use of surface plates. To Whitworth must go the credit of making supposed flat surfaces optically flat and of perfecting so-called right angles by making them exactly 90° one to another. To him must go the credit for lifting the quality of work and measurement from that of a crude tape measure to the more sophisticated standards set by precision flats and length gauges.

Of the early surfaces produced by Maudslay's paste grinding techniques it was not only Whitworth who considered their degree of flatness and surface quality unsatisfactory, so too did other machine builders like Clement and John Bodmer. They themselves struggled for years albeit unsuccessfully to find a way of providing something better. But it was Whitworth alone, with almost masochistic delight, who long wrestled with the problem till eventually he found a way of making reference-standard surfaces.

Some years after Whitworth made this discovery, William Muir, a foreman at Maudslays and a one-time close friend of Whitworth, remembered that while he, Muir, attended London's Scottish Free Church every Sunday, Joe and his wife Fanny always took their dogs out walking. Far more to the point, however, Muir also noted that whenever they met in the street, Joe was always impatient to get back to his digs so that he could get on with his surface plates. And while none of those close enough to know Joe intimately during his London days ever recorded in detail what they thought Joe was up to, there is enough folklore – some of it originating with Muir – to suggest that Joe had concocted some kind of hand scraper which he was using at home as an alternative to paste grinding his surface plates flat – Maudslay fashion.

The most interesting evidence about this came from an experienced millwright who had worked alongside Whitworth at Maudslays. His name was John Hampson, a Yorkshireman, some years older than Joe. He well remembered 'the Sunday after Joe had succeeded he invited me to call at his digs – "Come to my house" he said, "I've something to show you"'. When the two of them reached the house, John Hampson followed Joe into the kitchen 'Aye! tha's done it', exclaimed John, genuinely thrilled for his Manchester friend. Together they stood and admired the finished metal surface. Some time later, when describing this new development to a journalist John Hampson explained how he had seen the perfectly flat planes on the kitchen table: 'I was as proud as Joe himself, and proud too that I had worked alongside him'.[8]

When Joseph Whitworth was asked by *The World* magazine (June 1877) what he thought of his old friend John Hampson, he replied, 'He was a good workman and a good fellow too, but he thought I was mad. He was kind though and took the interest in my work that a good workman always takes in anything difficult and doubtful. It was a long job. *Up to that time the most difficult planes were never true.*'

In his autobiography written during the year 1874, long after he had retired to Kent, James Nasmyth recalled his early days with Maudslay and the surface plates which were placed alongside each bench fitter. He wrote, '. . . by a few masterly strokes (Maudslay) could produce plane surfaces so true that when their accuracy was tested by another standard plane surface of absolute truth, they were never found defective; neither convex, nor concave nor cross-winding – that is – twisted'.

But was it ever so simple as this? The fact that Maudslay died in 1831, nine years *before* expert advisers were reluctantly called in by the Astronomer Royal in response to the launching of Whitworth's campaign for accurate datums and flat surfaces, must surely indicate that Maudslay had made little progress in the matter. In view of this and other evidence, it is hardly likely Maudslay preceded Whitworth in any aspect of this except in providing his men with reasonably flat plates – certainly not 'scraped' masterplates and gaugeblocks. Yet Nasymth was still able to write some thirty five years after Whitworth introduced the system:

> The importance of having standard planes caused him (Maudslay) to have many of them placed on the benches beside his workmen, by means of which they might at once conveniently test their work. *Three of each were made at a time so that by the mutual rubbing of each on each the projecting surfaces were effaced.* When the surfaces approached very nearly to the true plane the still projecting minute points were carefully reduced by hard steel scrapers, until at last a standard plane surface was secured.[9]

Not only does this recollection contradict other impressions, it is almost an exact reiteration of Whitworth's own exposition of his own method. If taken together with some other pieces Nasmyth has written it would seem that he had before him either a copy of Whitworth's lecture or the notes he himself made during his attendance at the British Association. There can be only one explanation. His purpose was to downplay any credence being granted his imagined arch-rival. Their irritability became a mutual resentment and remained as such throughout their lives. It all sounds so ridiculous but as a personal feud, the debunking part had the gist of a dedicated mission, with Nasmyth challenging practically all Whitworth's originality.

None of it espoused semantics – Nasmyth felt he was defending Maudslay's name. For him it was a very personal matter. Nasmyth had been introduced to Maudslay by his father and taken on as a young gentleman trainee, certainly as some would have seen it he went on to enjoy Maudslay's paternalistic coddling. For men like Whitworth and Hampson they were employed as 'hands' – a very different position – for them it was as bleak and as foreboding as only casually hired 'manuals' would understand. The truth is, Nasmyth probably resented Whitworth becoming a successful master; an aspect borne out some years later when his weekend chums, the Fairbairns, had switched their supper friends to accommodate Whitworth. Nasmyth couldn't hide his disenchantment; his relationship with Fairbairn was never the same again.

It would be an omission not to conclude Nasmyth's critical estimation of Whitworth without a more faithful denouement of his argument. First it has to be said that his critique didn't stop at surface plates; he went on to measuring machines, templates and gauges, cross-feeds and much else. Of course Maudslay was responsible for much of the original pioneering of these things – he was one of the world's great mechanical engineers and a prolific innovationist – but Whitworth was exploring new concepts on an entirely different tack. Certainly he was building on Maudslay's early success but in regard to Nasmyth's assertions about gauging surfaces and his debunking of Whitworth's other schemes on measurement, he would have been taken more seriously had he refuted Whitworth at any one of the meetings, like the British Association, at which they were both present. Or indeed had any of the other master engineers who earlier had worked at Maudslays as young craftsmen perhaps stood up at any of these lectures and questioned what was being said – but no – not a word of dissension was ever minuted.

The first highly publicized lecture Whitworth gave, entitled 'Plane Metallic Surfaces – why and how?' was at the British Association at Glasgow in August 1840. But before the end of the year, in Manchester, he delivered a further three lectures, this time emphasizing how gauging surfaces could be prepared and why they transformed machine building. In all four papers Whitworth announced that he had devised a new method of producing flat surfaces; describing how he did it, and why the universal application of this new technique was so important. He also explained how his method differed from that used earlier by Maudslay. By using a combination of three plates instead of two Whitworth claimed he had solved the problem of concavity. By rubbing each of the three plates against the other two in a strict five-way rotation, each time scraping away the coloured highspots with a hardened steel scraper (the process being repeated time and time again) until all three surfaces recorded a universality of evenly spread touching points, then – and only then – could all three surfaces be considered perfectly flat. The method was good then and still holds true today.

The reason it is necessary to make such a fuss about these basic fundamentals is the fact that Whitworth at all times was referring to something quite different from ordinary machined surfaces. He was the first to think about a flat surface mathematically – he was the first to make a planometer – that is to say he devised a mechanical instrument to prove that a flat surface, to be a *flat* surface, must live up to its mathematical definition. In fact before a precision thread could be screwed or a precise mechanism built any piece of gauge-standard machinery had to live up to the criteria set by Whitworth: each plane movement had to follow a perfectly straight line and be perfectly square in all three right-angled directions. By elevating the question to a much higher level Whitworth had technically placed himself ahead of his predecessors by many decades.

In the opinion of the late Professor F.C. Lea of Manchester, while crediting Whitworth with the origination of flat gauge-quality surfaces plus practically the whole of mid-Victorian metrology, he went on to record in general that the new accuracy of mechanical constructions, made possible by the creation of these surfaces, entirely revolutionized machine tools and the development of other sliding surfaces. The accuracy of the work turned out by lathes and planing machines and by many other types of machine depends to a large extent how near to a perfect plane are the sliding surfaces upon which all important parts of any machine move. Professor Lea went on to say:

> The production of a true metal plane surface was, however, not only of importance in machine tool development but also it aroused considerable interest among scientists. It was found for instance that if two surface plates were wiped clean with a dry cloth and carefully laid one upon the other, the upper one appeared to float on what was thought to be a film of air entrapped between the plates; and one plate could be made to slide over the other with the slightest touch. If the air was excluded, the plates adhered together so that considerable force was necessary to pull them apart.[10]

Dr Tyndall, the well-known British scientist, during a lecture on 4 June 1875, remarked that Robert Boyle had attempted to explain this phenomenon by the pressure of the atmosphere acting on the outside surfaces of the plates. Dr Tyndall disproved Boyle's theory by showing that the plates adhered together even when in a vacuum or, even more confusingly, when a 12 lb weight was attached to one of the plates, the plates still remained firmly stuck together. The mystery in fact was far more complicated than even Dr Tyndall imagined and it remained unresolved until modern physicists began to explain the phenomenon of 'molecular cohesion' – that is to say 'when two atomic orbitals overlap they coalesce to produce a single molecular orbital'. In other words: when two perfectly flat surfaces come together they stick together, in lay terms, by 'molecularly' becoming a single entity.

As a theory, it was at least a century on from Maudslay's surface plates. Young Whitworth, as a twenty-two-year-old journeyman working on the bench at Maudslays – even though he claimed to have been a well-read young lad – would at that time have been totally ignorant as to why his flat plates stuck together. The fact that they did lock solid was hardly the quality required for sliding surfaces. It was however when he began to experiment by scraping the surfaces that from a machine tool point of view he stumbled across a second important development: that by using a hand scraper to remove the high spots the very tiny hollows so created would retain a lubricant and thus form an oil cushion. And though *molecular cohesion* meant nothing to Joe he had at least discovered that by producing the plates his way and then by smearing oil across the surfaces, the plates would take on a beautiful sliding movement sufficiently precise for the very best of his machine tools. Professor Lea made the point: what sounded a very simple advancement had tremendous impact on the construction of machinery. As for Whitworth the tyro, he had given mechanical understanding to the Greek word *tribein* – to rub – a forerunner of the science 'tribology'. And to his everlasting credit he very generously kept faith with his industrial teaching campaign; quite happily offering free of charge his new '*tribein*' gospel.

He delivered one of these lectures at the Victoria Gallery at Manchester. It was reported in the *Manchester Guardian* on 9 December 1840, and sparked the best testimony any engineer in his position could have wished. It came in the form of a Christmas greeting dated 23 December 1840 and came from an ex-foreman who had worked at Sharp Roberts, but was now the superintendent of the locomotive department at the Liverpool and Manchester Railway. His name was Henry Dewrance and he wrote to Whitworth: 'I have this day taken out a pair of valves (got up with emery) that have been in constant wear five months, and I find them grooved in the usual way. The deepest grooves are one-eighth of an inch broad, one-sixteenth hollow, or out of truth. Those that were scraped are perfectly true and likely to work five months longer.'

The same meticulousness applied to Whitworth's methods for producing square gauging blocks. The method involved two surface plates and three rectangular blocks of approximately equal size and squareness. Placing the three blocks between the two surface plates, sandwich fashion, and scraping the high spots from the upper and lower faces of each of the three rectangular blocks until all three were brought to the same plane, then in a pre-set permutation he would subject all the other faces to the same treatment (each one in turn carefully scraped and matched to the other perpendicular surfaces). Then, and only then, would Joe pronounce all three blocks to be of gauge standard, perfectly square and good enough to use as reference blocks.

For most working engineers, having had their callipers and 'near enough' methods replaced by these new techniques, it required an entirely new attitude. Employers however became suspicious. They saw Whitworth's activities as injurious to his own interests, therefore highly suspect. Nevertheless, it was Whitworth himself who recognized the need for an engineering missionary and that was the rôle he himself had chosen. Having presented his ideas on plane surfaces, he was now ready to tackle the next really big question – accurate measurement. Not surprisingly, no sooner had he voiced his intentions than he was charged with wanting to spawn yet another cult. It was in a way true: not a personality cult but a cult of precision measurement.

With the coming of this new technology employers would be obliged to replace their old 'near enough' machinery with new machines equal to Whitworth's new standards. The market responded, not totally, but sufficiently to induce other machine makers to follow suit. Indeed, the professional audience Joe addressed in Glasgow, having witnessed a practical demonstration, must have pondered hard why such simple logic had been so long delayed. Joe as usual left with them a whole fund of valedictory homilies: perhaps not the most erudite but certainly the most quoted at the time. The first was a simple truism: 'It is plain', he told Glasgow and the others, 'that in machines intended to be used in reproducing other machines, errors in surfaces are of the utmost consequence for the original defects are propagated in an aggravated form'.[11]

So far so good. Whitworth's pleading to convince other machine makers of the importance of working from flat (plane) surfaces as their datum was beginning to get through. He felt satisfied that his message had been taken seriously. In the leading toolrooms particularly, the quality of new machinery was beginning to improve. Of course what he was doing was highly unusual. He couldn't escape the scepticism, the raised eyebrows. For a manufacturer to be offering help to his competitors was against all the market rules. Naturally, some manufacturers remained highly dubious. Nonetheless their later instincts were right to surmise that Whitworth's system of precision measurement would quickly follow his flat surfaces.

CHAPTER FIVE

The History of Measurement

When Whitworth first talked openly about the need for a standard system of precise measurement the majority of engineering masters simply brushed aside his arguments. It was, they said, an irrational complication and unnecessarily expensive. Reactions during the early 1840s assumed that Whitworth's plan would mean new precision machinery, improving skills, paying higher wages – a suicidal combination they thought, threatening possible bankruptcy throughout the industry.

Mid-last century, machinists in metal copied as best they could the model or pattern they were given. Drawings were intended to give no more than a rough indication of what was wanted.[1] Henry Maudslay and men like Joseph Clement had themselves been frustrated for years and tried desperately hard to do something about it. The progress they made and how they did it is difficult to assess because their methods and ideas were kept a secret for commercial reasons.

In the case of Maudslay he used his new measurement techniques within the privacy of his own workshop, making known just enough to improve the international marketability of his steam engines. Like Brunel and others he didn't generally believe in patents because taking out a patent publicized ideas, thus neutralizing any personal advantage. Long before 1828, Maudslay had already spent a great deal of time and money improving the accuracy and general quality of his lead-screws so that he could use them for the purpose of measuring length. In fact, about the year 1805 he made his first bench micrometer. And a beautiful thing it was too; probably accurate to within plus or minus five or six-thousandths of an inch taken over twelve inches. For the next twenty years or so he worked at it assiduously, achieving for that period unprecedented accuracy. But it was only 'accurate' if compared with Maudslay's own earlier standards and Maudslay's inch probably differed quite considerably from the inch being used in the next factory. Certainly it differed from the inch being used by Stephenson and other engineers in the north of England and in Scotland. There, the inch used was known as the 'long' inch as against the 'short' inch used in London. It was precisely this chaotic situation against which Whitworth was about to direct his missionary zeal. More than anything he wanted to promote a national standard of fine measurement (in other words a British Standards Institute) and a new decimal language to go with it.

Notably, it was at Maudslays that Joe first saw a bench micrometer, albeit a somewhat crude instrument by today's standards. It was his first experience of using a calibrated screw thread, a method he was later to describe as *end* measurement. He used the term to distinguish it from the then generally used rule and calliper method known as the graduated *line* system. Historically, the issue became a contest between a sophisticated optical *line* system and Whitworth's more advanced interpretation of the *end* method. It was in fact a sensory contest between a sole dependence on *sight* as against the more certain use of *feel*.

Not that Whitworth was unfamiliar with rough and ready rule and calliper methods. J.G. Moon, who afterwards became manager of James Watt and Co., served his apprenticeship at Maudslays around the year 1870. During this period he operated a centre lathe and remembered using a pair of callipers (the points were about a half-inch wide) made for measuring across the tops of threads. The callipers were stamped 'J. Whitworth 1830' and in the words of J.G. Moon, 'they formerly belonged to the great screw-thread reformer'.[2]

James Nasmyth, to quote again from his autobiography, described Maudslay's micrometer business very simply:

> Maudslay's love of accuracy led him to distrust the verdicts given by the employment of the ordinary callipers and compasses in determining the absolute or relative dimensions of the refined mechanisms which he delighted to construct with his own hand. In order, therefore, to get rid of all the difficulties in this respect, he (Maudslay) designed and constructed a very compact and handy instrument which he always had on his bench beside his vice. Maudslay could thus, in a most accurate and rapid manner, obtain the most reliable dimensions. He considered the instrument gave him the absolute truth – a sort of Court of final appeal – and humorously called it his Lord Chancellor.[3]

As a bench micrometer it was limited to measuring a maximum length of 8 in. He made a number of them, the last one about the year 1828. It was a superb piece of equipment.

Nasmyth recalled the frequent visits to the factory of two rather special guests who were also interested in measurement: a Mr Barton of the Royal Mint who Nasmyth described as being a 'special crony' of Maudslay's, and Mr Bryan Donkin, the engineer. Both were associated, said Nasmyth, with Maudslay's work when he tried to duplicate (using a lathe bed and a 2-in diameter lead-screw) the national standard imperial yard measure; Mr Barton being the custodian of these particular standards deposited at the Royal Mint. What Nasmyth meant, however – according to the earlier evidence published by the Royal Commission and by the Select Committee – was that Maudslay and Donkin had attempted to check whether their two-inch diameter lead-screw which earlier they had made at five threads to the inch did in fact measure exactly 180 threads when compared with the national yard standard.

Unfortunately, they were unable to make this comparison mainly because of the poor quality of the instruments available, either to read off an exact yard or to accurately measure their own lead-screw: and there, because Maudslay no longer wanted to continue, the matter rested.

Maudslay's thread work, however, had given him a great deal of personal satisfaction. He had constructed his first bench micrometer by making the most accurate screw ever made up to that time. In 1825, as already mentioned, he made an even better one which he personally used for checking work done in his own factory. Not surprisingly, within very few years of his death, writers began to credit Maudslay with the actual invention of the bench micrometer, an attribution not all technical historians now accept. Some, including James Nasmyth himself, named the seventeenth-century instrument maker William Gascoigne as being the authentic originator: the first engineer to use a screw to measure size. Sadly the man was killed at the age of twenty-four during the Civil War in 1644, so little is known about his instruments. The most likely contender, however, must be that great Glaswegian, James Watt (of instrument and steam engine fame) who, in about the year 1780, set about making a bench micrometer. For him, necessity really was the mother of invention. Watt desperately needed to improve the quality of his steam valve mechanism: a steel rule and callipers were no longer good enough. He intended the bench micrometer to be the answer. Fortunately the instrument remains protected in the Science Museum, allowing everyone to celebrate Watt's genius.

Twenty-five years after Watt, Henry Maudslay faced the same problems. What had satisfied the earlier man now became obsolete as much higher standards became a necessity for Maudslay. And so it went on. As each new development signified a fresh demand for better technology so the incentive for new inventions increased accordingly. Sometimes even one step by itself was big enough to set in motion an entirely fresh genesis.

Maudslay's bench micrometer for example, when compared to Watt's measuring instrument represented such a major progression as to confirm Maudslay not only equal to Watt as a leading pioneer but the genuine inventor of the modern bench micrometer. But the overall measurement situation had (post-Maudslay) reached an impasse. The Watt-Bramah-cum-Maudslay string of progressive improvements could no longer sustain its impetus. A brand new culture was required to envisage and construct an entirely fresh movement and to lift international engineering to a new level of advanced technology and fine measurement. It was not just a matter of improved micrometers: it had to be an entirely new concept. The expiration of the old order was inevitable, contingent as it was upon the next neoteric arrival, the big question being whether Britain could somehow produce an engineering genius of sufficient stature to show the way.

The fact that it did so was surprising in every sense except one: the place where it all happened: Manchester. The town by then was the world's most advanced engineering centre. But why was it left to Joseph Whitworth to provide the leadership? When he first realized it was down to himself to lead the way he was thirty-one years of age and had just celebrated his first twelve months at the Chorlton Street factory. Undoubtedly he already had loads of confidence. But in the year 1834 he really didn't know whether or not his machine tools were going to be the world success they became. For him to have then taken a decision to do all he could to perfect an internationally acceptable system of precision measurement was the first major test of his character but once he recognized the immensity of the job, his commitment became total and for life. Little did he realize, though, that it was going to take so many years of solid campaigning to have his ideas generally accepted.

Precise measurement, new quality gauging, decimalization, plus his proposed new standards for screw threads: when compared with any normal workload it would have been considered enough. But not so in Whitworth's case: in fact he thought of it in terms of his first decade only. Certainly he could never have contemplated it would be almost forty years before William Gladstone – then acting simultaneously as both Prime Minister and Chancellor of the Exchequer – agreed to amend the 1878 Act to legally adopt the Whitworth length gauges as official British standards. For Joe it was a lifetime. It took such a dreadfully long time his resilience must have worn thin on many occasions. Incredibly, he kept going.

The Birth of the One-inch Standard and Decimalization

Whitworth's early measurement techniques blossomed during the period 1834–6, he by then having built his first 36-in comparator. Recognizing there was little or no purpose in devising comparator equipment without first having an actual system of length gauges, he set about designing both from the beginning. His perceptive vision was such that he clearly foresaw the system he wanted. Not only that, he was confident that he knew how he was going to achieve the required precision for both the instruments and the gauges. The simplicity of the system was clear-cut but manufacturing the apparatus cost him three years' hard labour.

A comparator without length gauges is like a clock without hands: the length gauges are the essential module. Clearly Whitworth had long decided not to follow his predecessors in the matter of micrometers but first he would attempt to establish a set of nationally recognized measurement standards. The evidence of how it was done is remarkable. The fact that Whitworth first conceived his revolutionary system prior to 1834 means that he probably did so before he was thirty years of age, his system being well established within his own factory long before the Board of Trade first became interested in measurement standards.

Once he got started, however, the enormity of his task soon dawned. Nowhere in the world did there exist a national system of measurement, nor did he personally have any idea how government actually works, let alone how he was ever going to persuade the Cabinet to adopt a Whitworth system. In Britain, a standard yard measure of sorts did exist – but it was of sorts – even more surprising, prior to

Whitworth in 1839 the Imperial Yard Standard had never been divided into inches. *An authenticated one-inch standard just didn't exist anywhere,* hence the absurd 'long' inches and 'short' inches in use up and down the country.

The expression 'a standard yard measure of sorts' came about because prior to Whitworth it was just not possible to accurately duplicate any one particular yard measure. There were Imperial standards in existence, some at the Royal Mint while others were locked away in the Treasury, but no two were exactly alike. In all cases both here and abroad, length standards were either brass or gunmetal bars with small gold inserts across which were engraved lines indicating the authenticated measure. But while mid-Victorian microscopes could pick up a line fairly accurately, no machine at that time could accurately transfer the line somewhere else nor was it possible to convert the line into a gauge end-face; hence most engineers, as distinct from lawyers and astronomers considered the '*line system*' unsuitable for so accurate a purpose. Not that engineers knew the answers: they didn't. When asked by parliamentarians what alternative they proposed they shook their heads, the majority distrustful even of their own judgement for well over a decade. In truth, they were fearful of Whitworth: they felt comfortable with crown standards but flinched – for reasons bordering on avariciousness and jealousy – at the thought of Whitworth's own insignia replacing the crown.

Right from the beginning Whitworth had declared '*line measure*' to be the villain. As a precision system it was professionally agreed to be of little or no value to engineers; they had no way of adapting it for their own use. Joe's first task therefore was to convert the '*line*' system into some other method which could be readily available in the workshop. The choice before him was to introduce a new system of '*end measure*' – that is to say, instead of using '*lines*' to indicate length measurement (as in the case of foot-rules or simple callipers) Whitworth went for a system of 'pin' or 'length gauges' whereby the actual length of the gauge physically offered a very accurate standard of measurement. Unfortunately, good as his new method was (it is still in use today) in Whitworth's day it was bitterly resisted, particularly by Professor George Airy, the then Astronomer Royal (the man who in 1851 designed the House of Commons clock, Big Ben). It was on Airy's advice that a Royal Commission was appointed to review Britain's weights and measures. As a result the Whitworth system was systematically opposed for many years by the Treasury and other government officials. It was a curious coalition, mostly of lawyers and other non-engineering people who came together as though they each had some self-interest and therefore a need to unite against Whitworth's alternative ideas.

Typical of this unity, as also of the confusion, Professor Airy frequently spoke on behalf of Whitworth's critics. He had from the beginning set himself against Whitworth's idea of *end* gauges. In 1854, both the Standing and Select Committees taking the Weights and Measures Bill through the House of Commons examined the evidence. They again sounded out Airy's opinion following Whitworth's evidence to the Select Committee. This time the

Manchester man had accompanied his evidence with a selection of drawings showing his two comparators and yard *length* gauges. An expert sub-Committee then asked Airy if he could explain the variations in the length of the existing yard *line* standards and why Whitworth's new length gauge system was consistently accurate to within a 'millionth' of an inch, therefore so much better than the existing *line* method. 'Yes', replied Airy, 'I can state the differences exactly . . . and we may rest satisfied that we have overcome the difficulty'. He then went on to add: 'This is not a simple or abstract question. . .'. He explained that 'different observers (i.e. picking up a *line* with a microscope) *get different results*'.

'Upon what does this difference depend?' asked the Chairman.

'We do not know' replied Professor Airy. 'It is something in the vision by the sight of the microscope; we can tell no further. By varying the observers, the errors in *line* measures may be eliminated and unexceptional accuracy given the results.'[4]

His answer was an astounding piece of blustering bamboozle. Whitworth, when asked by the press what he thought of Airy's reply, kept his composure by conceding that had the Astronomer Royal been speaking before the advent of his own (i.e. Whitworth's) 'perfectly true plane surfaces' Airy may possibly have been right. Whitworth continued:

> That the Astronomer Royal does not believe in the existence of a true plane is quite evident or he would not support this standard bar of *line* measure in this way. I think it a clumsy way of doing the thing as I shall be able to show the Committee when I again have my apparatus here.[5]

Throughout this controversy the Americans were profoundly interested, some of them being present during Whitworth's evidence. Indicatively, the leading machine makers in America – the practical men – had been using Whitworth's gauges since 1850 and continued to do so until 1857 when the Washington Weights and Measures authority followed London and called in Professor Airy to advise them as to the method they should adopt. Without hesitation Airy advised them exactly as he did in London, to develop a comparison technique of their own master yard standards based on the *line* system. And with equal superficiality they accepted the advice given! Presumably in the United States, as in Britain, most academics simply accepted the microscope as the only satisfactory instrument available. Before the year's end they had recommended that each company should equip its 'standards room' with optical instruments in preference to Whitworth gauges.

The more generally quoted objections raised against Whitworth's pin gauges, or *end* measurement techniques, were chiefly that the accuracy of the gauges would very quickly be destroyed because many people would have to handle them in dirty conditions. The same points were raised time and again over a period of about forty years from 1840 to 1880. But had the Royal Commissioners seriously considered the matter they would have realized from the beginning just how silly these objections were. Even with the most excessive filth and heat variations, Whitworth's gauges would still have provided a far more accurate standard than any state-of-the-art engraving or even the most accurate *line* reading from the best possible scales of the day. Given the most powerful magnification there was still no accurate way of transferring the exact location of a line to any kind of gauging system convenient for use in the workshop.

Graphic confirmation of just how wrong both Airy and the American academics were – plus a description of the complexities and the cost of this work – was highlighted by Professor J.W. Rowe of Yale University. He referred to the fact that many years after Whitworth had pioneered his master length gauges the American machine tool company Pratt and Whitney was called in by the United States standards authority to sort out the confusion of measurement. 'The results were conflicting and very unsatisfactory', reported the Coast Survey. 'The length of the yard and its sub-divisions varied with the number of yardsticks.' 'Many thousands of dollars and three years of time went into this work.'[6]

Leading American machine toolmakers already used Whitworth-type gauges. For twenty years they had waited for the British Weights and Measures Department to make available London (master) yard standards. They waited a long time. Professor William Rogers of Harvard – engaged as an additional consultant by Pratt and Whitney – agreed with Airy of London about the need to use microscopes and to get rid of Whitworth's ideas. This particular American experience was an historic phase in international mensuration and we shall return to the matter.[7]

But the choice of the British standard (and therefore that of the United States) was always an arbitrary matter. When Queen Elizabeth I in 1598 randomly selected the actual yard standard from a number of brass bars offered to her she instinctively selected one on the basis it had a 'nice clean appearance'. Thus the making of history can never have been more simple – or so haphazard – considering that the bar she had chosen was between 0.025 and 0.030 in shorter than today's yard measure and quite different from the standard used in Henry VII's time. Incidentally, the gauge selected by the Queen was an '*end*' measure, i.e. a pin gauge of fixed length. In fact the Elizabethan primary standard of length continued to be an '*end*' standard until 1742 when the Royal Society converted it to a '*line*' standard; the Society felt compelled to do so once machine engraving and microscopes had improved so much. And it was under these fresh circumstances that the new standard became known as the 'Bird' yard; named after the instrument maker who had been given the job of making it. In fact, he made three such standards for the Treasury, all of which were bronze bars, into which he had mounted two gold plugs, each bearing not a '*line*' but a fine '*dot*', the distance between the *dots* defining the standard 36 inches. The Bird yard was thus legalized in 1824 after sixty tenuous years of royal wrangling and argument. Mostly these remaining (three) standards were kept in the Standards Room at the Jewel Tower near the House of Commons under the care of the Clerk of the House.

Henry J. Chaney, the Royal Superintendent of Measures, in his Treatise on the Standard Weights and Measures Act (1897) indirectly cleared up most of the doubts as to whether the Whitworth yard was actually a genuine Bird yard equivalent. It wasn't. And as it turned out, neither did it matter. None of the Bird (yard) standards, nor the subsequent Troughton standards, nor their Donkin replacements were exactly alike anyway. Again, it was Chaney who blew the story in a most interesting way. He wrote:

> In 1825 under the advice of various scientific authorities, brass copies of the new Bird Imperial standards were made and deposited at the office of the Exchequer. They became known as the 'Exchequer Standards' and placed in the custody of the Clerk of the House of Commons. None of them, it was later discovered, were accurate to within 0.020 ins. of each other. Yet despite this enormous discrepancy the Clerk in 1825 had two of them sealed up in one of the walls of the House of Commons: the particular wall on this occasion was the wall which separated the Lobby from the old Chamber. Less than nine years later, however, October 1834, the old House of Commons was destroyed by fire and the standards feared lost. Happily, still enclosed in their protective lead sheath, they were discovered buried beneath the rubble and immediately returned to the Crown instrument makers, Troughton and Simms, to be checked. Astonishingly they were found to be in good order; and with a requisite ceremony, both were suitably etched with up-dated crown markings and approved by the Privy Council.[8]

Professor Airy's Royal Commission, however, had earlier expressed a very different opinion. They had recommended that a new set of standards be made based upon a yard length midway between the Donkin and the Troughton models. It was of some relevance. In 1839 Whitworth had privately purchased both a Donkin and a Troughton standard yard measure. He then did exactly as Professor Airy (aided by Lord Rosse) did later: he split the difference between the two lengths and made that his master 36-in gauge.

When the National Physical Laboratories under fairly modern conditions (i.e. just before the 1914 war) compared these early Whitworth gauges with much later British standards they were remarkably close – a genuine, if posthumous tribute to Whitworth's work. Just how near they were to 0.9144 of a metre (the modern criterion) would have been interesting to know. Sadly, the official records have been misplaced.[9]

In regard to the more modern bronze bars made in 1845 by Troughton and Simms, Professor Airy granted them all the Royal insignia – master gauge status. It was in fact from this batch that the current walled-up parliamentary copies were taken. As with those of much earlier years the parliamentary authorities had again decided to do as the Clerk had done previously and have them properly entombed in a wall at the House of Commons: the actual ceremony being delayed quite some time due to unfinished building work.

The 1856 Weights and Measures Act however was clear. It specified that the standards must be taken from the wall and inspected every twenty years starting from the delayed second re-opening of the House in 1852. The first time this happened in 1872 they were re-interred under the blank window on the right-hand side of the stair leading from the lower waiting hall up to the committee corridor where they still remain. Henry Chaney continued his story: 'By a subsequent Act of Parliament, the "parliamentary copies" are required to be compared with each other once every twenty years and upon the last occasion' (Chaney wrote this thesis in 1908, therefore the occasion he was referring to here was the second exhumation of the bricked-up standards in 1892), 'Mr Speaker [Rt Hon. Arthur W. Peel MP] accompanied by the High Officers of the Board of Trade and the Secretary to the Lord Great Chamberlain met together for the purpose'. Presumably, with all the majestic pomp of a parliamentary procession, Mr Speaker, led by policemen and House messengers followed by the Clerk, the Serjeant, the Lord Great Chamberlain, the Astronomer Royal, stonemasons, plasterers and bricklayers, extracted the standards, examined them, found them unchanged and returned them to the wall. Henry Chaney describes the whole incredible business in the following way: 'The immured yard was placed on its eight rollers within a mahogany box, which was screwed down and sealed. It was then placed in a lead box which was soldered down. The two boxes were then placed in a further oak box before being returned to the wall.' Not surprisingly the Act is no longer obeyed, 1872 and 1892 being the only occasions the standards were taken from the wall and examined. (Perhaps as an historic gesture, as 1992 was the one-hundredth anniversary of the last exhumation, a couple of Whitworth's gauges could now be added to the mahogany box as a token of recognition).

At the end of his thesis Chaney concluded that all Imperial Yard Standards which still existed in 1908 were in fact derivatives of that particular standard originally selected by Queen Elizabeth I. Well yes, the evidence may suggest they were, but in a very indirect way. Even those sent overseas suffered all the ingenerate variations of their antecedents.

The task Whitworth had set himself in asking that his one-inch standard be accepted as the national standard was a formidable assignment. So much so, all the personal disadvantages he suffered (a lack of status and therefore credibility) were quickly brought home to him. First, he was reminded that he was not an Oxbridge scholar; he was both labelled and treated as a nonentity, an outsider in every sense. Culturally his awareness was that of a provincial, living as he did two hundred miles from the capital. He was, of course, comparatively young and virtually self-educated. His dream nevertheless was to provide for Britain a set of measurement standards – a realization that for the first time ever he would have to 'invent' a one-inch reference piece – and that he would also have to find a way of making the whole business of precise measurement understood. He was determined to make its terms of reference communicable. His initial strategy therefore was to go out and persuade the engineering industry itself to adopt his new decimal language based on his own model inch. And in doing this he did in fact have just one advantage: he knew from the start exactly the system he wanted. Already he had clearly visualized the only method by which he could make his set of standard slip and ring gauges without which no interchangeable system of measurement could exist. But looking back at the enormity of it all, for anyone so young, it certainly was some dream, some commitment, and in the end, some legacy.

For anyone in Whitworth's position, that is to say someone about to launch an entirely new system (whatever its merits) and to campaign for its adoption, it would inevitably mean facing immense obstacles. Whitworth's metrology in fact did require the endorsement of all three categories of the establishment: academe, industry and government, and if it was ever to become the officially authorized state system it would require a sizeable and well co-ordinated campaign. During the 1840s it would have been a unique undertaking.

Unfortunately at that time, Britain was in the grip of an overweening *laissez-faire* regime governed by an élitist Cabinet. The last thing ministers wanted was to be disturbed by innovation. One or two in both the Lords and Commons understood parts of the measurement controversy but didn't quite grasp that what was in jeopardy was a British capability to mass-produce interchangeable components – and in its wake of course the ability to make a major economic advance. Oxbridge classicists, by and large, were at cross-purposes with science and engineering and chose to keep out of it. Like certain government ministers and their autocratic law officers they were unable to see the need for legislation in terms of either a manufacturing advance or economic orderliness.

The engineering industry and its leadership – the 'influential kirk' as Fairbairn called it – comprised one or two leading members from each of the five science-based societies, preference being given to those who could use their ministerial contacts inside the House of Lords to pressurize government. It was a thoroughly unhealthy method of lobbying because it prevented the wider understanding of the issues and led to closet agreements. In the end it not only damaged Whitworth but seriously betrayed the best interests of all engineers.

In the beginning Fairbairn and Whitworth behaved like all novice lobbyists. They didn't quite know how to mobilize influential opinion, but as an employer whose stature was rising at a phenomenal rate Whitworth instinctively thought that the fewer decision-makers there were to persuade the easier it was to manipulate Cabinet decisions. How wrong he was. Of course, all Victorians thought like oligarchists: that government was a matter for a small exclusive class. For outsiders like Whitworth it was a bogus attraction. His real task was to get both his ideas and his colleagues out of the closet and into the open to achieve a wider understanding of the issues.

During the early days of his campaign – the first twenty years in fact – Whitworth would have been excused had he physically wilted. Thank goodness he didn't. He had powerful men like Fairbairn at his side and later his devotees included some very fine, courageous politicians both in Manchester and in parliament. He also had some unexpected allies like T.M. Goodeve, a barrister, and Professor C.P.B. Shelley, an engineer. And although they both knew Whitworth some years before they themselves came together in 1875 to write the story of Joe's 'length comparator' (at times incorrectly described as a bench micrometer): it is to them that we owe most of our knowledge of Whitworth's metrology.[10]

For Goodeve and Shelley to have written it up in such an authoritative manner must have meant that they were able to discuss in detail with many of Whitworth's contemporaries both his work and its problems. They were able to distinguish for the benefit of the lay person the kind of measurement which was dependent upon '*sight*' as distinct from Whitworth's '*end*' measurement which involved a sense of 'touch'. Descriptively they wrote about the methods adopted by the majority of workshops during the mid-Victorian years for measuring any object which had to be of a definitive size; methods which at that time depended upon the personal skill of the workman, his good eyesight and his being able to accurately set callipers from a steel rule. They wrote most perceptively:

> There was another difficulty experienced when it became necessary to compare work done at different places, for there was no such thing known as a standard inch, and it was by no means certain that the graduated foot rules, from which the measurements were derived, were exact copies of one and the same standard, or that the divisions on them were correctly given. . . .
>
> *Thus the whole subject of measurement remained in a state of uncertainty and confusion until Sir Joseph Whitworth applied himself to the construction of an 'end' measuring machine.* Before commencing that task he had satisfied himself that the only practicable mode of measurement suited for the workshop should be one founded on truth of surface and the sense of touch – the delicacy of the nerves of feeling being, in fact, a thing quite disregarded and neglected by all others who had applied themselves to improving mechanical measurement; and it has been in developing to the fullest extent the results obtained by the contact of surfaces which were almost ideal in their excellence that a system has grown up which stands quite alone and removed from all thoughts of rivalry or competition.[11]

Remembering that Joe commenced work on his first 'comparator' soon after he moved into his Chorlton Street factory he never let up until he was ready, towards the end of 1838, to purchase from Bryan Donkin and Edward Troughton the two standards from which he could make his first 36-in standard length gauge or his 'one-yard end-measure' as historians dubbed it. At that stage, one would have thought, such a feat in itself was enough to warrant comment, but no. It was long afterwards when the first press notices appeared. Whitworth had by then built for his own use an excellent conversion instrument sufficiently rigid to have it fitted with the finest microscope (see fig. 2), confident that it was capable of assisting the conversion of his newly purchased Donkin and Troughton 'line' standards to his

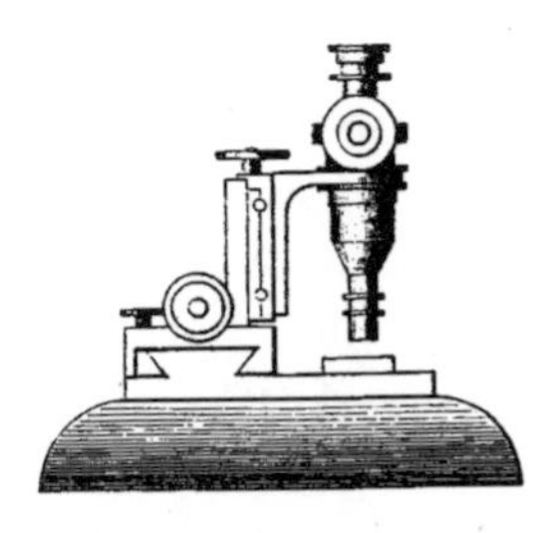

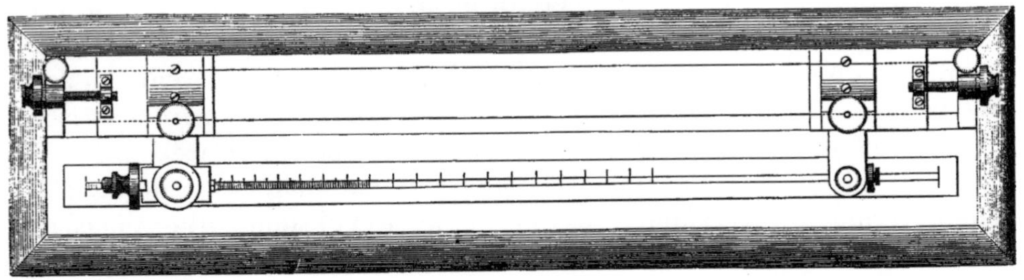

Fig. 2 Whitworth's Microscope Apparatus for the Comparison of Bars. This apparatus was made by Whitworth to transfer the Imperial Standard Yard (indicated by engraved marks) to his own Standard Yard pin gauges (end measure).

own 'end' standard pin gauges. In doing so he had first to overcome the same problems which had bedevilled the Crown instrument makers themselves. That he did; luck was with him all the way. He must have been delighted.

Within eighteen months, in late 1840, he surmounted his next most difficult hurdle. He successfully divided his 36-in gauges into three: each gauge being exactly '12 in long' and within reference standards of accuracy. Then within a further six months he had accomplished 'the impossible': he had accurately subdivided his 12-in gauges into twelve pieces exactly one inch in length. Engineering witnesses confirmed that when thirty-six of them were placed in line they measured (within the tightest gauging limits) exactly one yard; good enough to be used as international standards. Even then, sadly, such was Britain's industrial and political leadership, Whitworth's accomplishments were no nearer recognition. His work remained unappreciated. 'End' measure as a new technique was apparently unwanted by everyone except top-class engineers.[12]

When he and William Fairbairn attended various local societies during the 1840s, Joe could never resist talking measurement and gauges; the reaction he received from audiences was increasingly supportive. He was already working on new ways by which he could perhaps perfect his standard gauges. And although he was not yet ready to supply or advise those of his engineering colleagues who had factories near Manchester (about the wider application of his latest ideas), he was nonetheless anxious they should visit his factory to see for themselves. His enthusiasm never faltered. On 25 June 1841 he excited a Mechanics Institute audience by presenting an update of his measurement progress, so much so he was pressed by various questioners to again go for official recognition. This he did the following year after reading Professor (now Sir) George Airy's December 1841 report that the situation was wide open: the government, he said, was now ready to consider all suggestions, including presumably, the Whitworth system.

The Astronomer Royal clearly stated: 'We recommend that the existing Act be repealed and that the standard length be defined in subsequent enactments, either by the whole length of a certain piece of metal [i.e. the Whitworth system] or by the distance between two points or lines engraved [i.e. the existing line system] and that the yard not be defined by reference to any natural basis, such as the length of a degree of meridian or the earth's surface or the length of the pendulum vibrating seconds in a specified place'.

The clarity of the report was explicit. Whitworth must have been encouraged. The government, he assumed, was now ready to consider without bias an alternative system of measurement.

ROYAL COMMISSION ON METROLOGY

It was still not possible for manufacturers to make metal parts interchangeable in the absence of a workable system of measurement. Nor would such a system be universally accepted unless it was endorsed by the Crown. Whitworth understood this and was convinced by Professor Airy's report that the government at last intended to treat the matter seriously so he wrote to his friend the Prime Minister, Sir Robert Peel, in November 1842. He wanted to make sure he was going to be called before the Royal Commission to give evidence.

The Prime Minister, having read what Whitworth had to say, promptly forwarded the letter to the Chancellor of the Exchequer, Henry Coulburn MP, whose new Weights and Measures Bill it was: '. . . make sure Whitworth is called to give evidence', he scribbled across Joe's letter, putting the whole thing back in Airy's court.

This time, however, the Professor's Royal Commission included three newcomers known to oppose Whitworth's ideas. The Privy Council had appointed non-engineering scientists, Lord Rosse and Sir John Herschel together with the inimical Mr Sheepshanks. Unbelievably – but true to form – the four of them prattled on for eleven years no less (1843–54) surviving four successive Prime Ministers until finally in 1854 the Crimean War forced them to a conclusion and into print. When the 1854 report appeared they had apparently studied every aspect except Whitworth's end gauge system.

Joseph Whitworth felt angry and cheated. He had waited a very long time for Airy's report. And although the Prime Minister, eleven years earlier, had given him every assurance he would get a hearing, he knew that the Royal Commission contained no engineers who actually understood industry and its urgent need for precise measurement and the interchangeability of components. Assuredly, the report rejected the engineer's case but quite unexpectedly recommended that the Government put through another entirely new Weights and Measures Bill. Airy was determined not to be humbled by Whitworth. Because all five 36-in standards the Commission ordered in 1845 varied in length and because the Royal instrument-makers said that unless they used Whitworth's system they could not make five standards of precisely equal length, Airy recommended that the new Act should specify that each bar be numbered and stamped with the exact temperature required to adjust its length to the precision demanded. In other words, if one of the standards was assumed correct at 60°F, a slightly shorter measure would have to be marked, say, correct at 68° thus allowing the additional heat expansion to bring it up to the correct measurement.

In the wake of Whitworth's new system it was an absurd situation. But because this information now had to be put in the Act, Joe quite rightly anticipated that his parliamentary supporters would oppose the Bill. But no. The Crimean situation again confused the whole thing and it went through the Commons without debate.

When the Bill got to the House of Lords, however, their Lordships were not quite so obedient. They insisted that the matter again go before another Select Committee. They also wanted to question Airy on the way he had handled the evidence given by the German expert, Professor Bessel, very much a pro-Whitworth advocate. Bessel had told the Committee: 'The principle of *end* measure is more convenient than that of *line* measure for the production of extra copies of the standard'. 'Yes it is', replied Airy 'for commercial purposes only but not for national standards'. Bessel must have been flabbergasted. The very point he had put to the Royal Commission was that because the engineering world considered the Whitworth system best for industry the same system should be used for national and international standards. '*Line-measure*', insisted Bessel, 'was alright for steel rules and callipers and civil engineers using theodolites but unsuitable for the duplication of precise reference measurement'. Whitworth himself had made the same point many times; indeed, it was the very essence of what he was trying to do. As Professor Bessel said, 'There was no other way a standard yard could have been divided into 1.000 inch master gauges, except by using "*end*" measurement techniques.' It was the most important breakthrough made by the Whitworth system.[13]

From the time Airy's first report was published in 1841, *The Times* followed the whole saga with a great deal of misgiving but now (1855 and fourteen years on) they learned that a House of Lords Select Committee had at last agreed to take evidence from Whitworth; they rejoiced.[14] Not that Whitworth was allowed to give evidence in person without a great deal of argument. Ministers, merely for the sake of appearances it would seem, feigned annoyance. But Lord Hardinge and Earl Granville, the ex-Foreign Secretary, plus certain other Lords took up the fight seriously. Once they discovered that the Select Committee intended to ignore Whitworth and proceed to legalize the old '*line*' measure system, without hesitation they went straight to the Chancellor of the

Exchequer: 'Hear Whitworth out or lose your Bill'. It was a time-honoured parliamentary armlock and it worked.[15]

On 6 and 7 June 1855 Whitworth's men from Manchester repeated their committee room performance of fourteen months earlier, trundling past astonished policemen and along the Lords corridor with two or three small trucks loaded with measuring machines, carefully cosseted yard standards and a whole array of gauges. It was an impressive show and Whitworth carried the Select Committee hands down. Unusually so, one of the most compelling and relevant arguments in support of the Whitworth system came from naval engineers involved with the Cronstadt campaign and the Baltic fleet. The Admiralty, in the construction of their marine engines insisted on everything being made to Whitworth's standard gauges: thus emergency engine replacements during engagements were handled by a comparatively small battle workshop. And as *The Times* reported: 'A not very large floating mechanics' shop was quite sufficient to meet all the emergencies of the service in the way of damaged machinery for the whole of that mighty steam armada now facing the batteries of Cronstadt. Such a result would have been utterly unobtainable but for that extraordinary nicety in determining sizes to which Mr Whitworth has attained.'

The Times continued to be extremely supportive of Whitworth but even in unison with other newspapers and trade journals its influence was constantly marginalized by the élitist nature of the then parliamentary system. Unlike the somewhat unusual incident quoted earlier whereby Lord Hardinge and others came to the rescue of the Whitworth cause, political power and the Cabinet tended to remain unscathed inside the House of Lords precisely because the most influential voices in the Commons happened to be silenced by their *laisser-faire* beliefs. Even the most dedicated of parliamentarians judged the endorsement of Weights and Measures to be extraneous matter and none of their business. From an engineering and railways point of view, non-intervention under this free trade guise was a curse. Outside foreign affairs – and the Reform Act – the great Liberal free-traders recognized little or no rôle for Parliament. Engineers desperately wanted the law *now* to establish authoritative standards of measurement.

Although Whitworth still had to wait another twenty-five years for the final ministerial certification of his 'end' gauges, at least in the meantime he had been granted interim recognition as a consolation. As *The Times* explained following their 11 June report of the 1855 Select Committee:

> So satisfactory was Whitworth's evidence that we understand that the Committee have come to the decision of recommending that his standard yard measure constructed of the same length as that of the Royal Commission, be legalized as the secondary standard for comparison with local standards of measure throughout the country and that his [Whitworth's] standard foot and inch have the same sanction attached to them. No doubt this will now be effected by an amendment to the present Bill.

The Times should have known better. Yes, the Act was ultimately amended, but not until the year 1880.

Looking back over the years, some progress had been made but the situation in regard to the interchangeability of engineering parts remained very patchy. It was still very far from satisfactory. Certainly the pro-Whitworth Lords by their intervention had made the 1856 Act (which was initially drafted on Gladstone's instruction) less regressive. But let *The Times* finish the story. Lord Hardinge, for whom the paper later developed a passionate love-hate relationship because of his handling of the Crimean preparations did, on this occasion, earn valid editorial praise when he intervened on behalf of Whitworth. 'To legalize the best standards of measure that can be obtained is a matter of national importance', declared the paper, 'and we rejoice that even at the eleventh hour, steps are being taken to avoid in this respect (i.e. the omission of Whitworth's *end* measures) a serious legislative blunder'.[16]

The point was fully echoed by the engineering press. Professor C.P. Shelley summed up the position very positively: '. . . notwithstanding the efforts of the Commissioners to restore and reproduce a standard of length, there can be no question that, so far as it relates to the standards used by engineers, and which determine the lengths of an inch and a foot in our workshops, the practical standard has been originated by Sir Joseph Whitworth. The system of gauges, both external and internal, which he introduced has been universally accepted.' By everyone, that is, except the Board of Trade and the Government.

The above extract was published by Goodeve and Shelley in 1876 though it relates to a summary they themselves made some twenty years earlier in 1856. Overseas, Whitworth was increasingly considered the true originator of the mechanical comparator, precise *end*-measurement and modern gauging. Men like Watt, Maudslay and Roberts were themselves the inventors of some early measuring devices: ingeniously so. But none exactly preceded Whitworth's work because his basic intentions were quite different: he deliberately set out to revolutionize the then accepted way of doing things. Individual engineering companies – even the smallest – would no longer find it acceptable working to their own rule of thumb. Whitworth wanted to eliminate all self-perpetuating ad hoc standards of measurement and replace them with an internationally recognized interchangeable master standard – complete, of course, with all the practical machinery to carry it through. Engineers at last could then work to clearly defined precise specifications laid down by an international bureau of measurement or as Whitworth imagined it – a British Standards Institute.

Even by 1860 the battle was not yet won. The larger engineering companies, although they all professed tacit support publicly, privately pursued well-entrenched self-interests. Some saw in their own methods an advantage to themselves and at the last moment resisted Joe's overtures. The most prestigious firms like Maudslay and Field wanted to continue into the future in their own way, probably because men like Joshua Field felt they owed it to Maudslay to safeguard his legendary reputation. The fact remained, however, that the Whitworth system was unique in that it made possible not only accurate duplication of both the yard and metre standards, but allowed Whitworth (or his nominees) to provide length gauges to within tolerances considered impossible by his predecessors.

For a number of years however the periodic appearance of inferior non-Whitworth gauges sullied both his name and the crusade he waged. Naturally, when the victims of these anonymous gauges had their work rejected by the War Office – or some other authority – the contractors protested. 'Look', they said, 'Whitworth's gauge sizes are a sham'.

Quick to spot this enormity, both *The Times* and the *Engineer* rightly pointed out: 'The so-called gauges issued were never worthy of the name "gauge". In fact each succeeding gauge compounded the errors of its parent and quickly lost all semblance.'

The newspapers again defended him when a slightly different disparagement bubbled away overseas: 'Whitworth was not the first to either advocate or make interchangeable parts', asserted his discreditors. 'Eli Whitney was'. By 1860 however, the truth about all this became well known. Not only had Britain closely examined the so-called interchangeable muskets she had ordered from America and found them wanting, but three leading machine makers from America had visited Whitworth's factory to purchase his special gauging equipment. It was verification first hand that the Manchester man was pursuing objectives limited by far closer tolerances, therefore of a different kind.

This whole business had started when the Americans arrived in London for the 1851 Great Exhibition and made great play about the interchangeability of their small arms and other manufactured components. Until then little was known of either French or American engineering but once military contracts were placed a much more trustworthy historical record became available.

Eli Whitney, the great American originator who is usually credited with being the first engineer to achieve identical repetition of manufactured components is a case in point. Perhaps it is being a little too pedantic, but it really was early French clockmakers and silversmiths who were the first to make the effort. The French were using primitive die-sets prior to 1750: a die-set being the first technique for mass-producing anything exactly alike. In the same sense Whitworth was the first to mass-produce standard threaded bolts in 1836. Usually it had been taken as read that mass production as a technique started when Eli Whitney first secured a United States contract for twelve thousand muskets in 1798. On examination, however, Whitney's own guns plus an 1828 Congressional Report, plus the French evidence, plus Thomas Jefferson's own account all suggests that it was otherwise. Some still say the French came first. To epitomize the Jefferson correspondence: 'In 1785 a French gunsmith named Le Blanc convinced Thomas Jefferson [who was then American Ambassador in France] that Le Blanc could mass-produce musket locks'. Jefferson signalled Washington, 'Le Blanc can make every part so exactly alike that what belongs to any one musket may be used for every other musket. Furthermore', added Jefferson, 'he effects it by tools of his own contrivance'.[17]

But if Le Blanc preceded Whitworth why was it necessary for Louis-Napoleon (July 1857) to ask Whitworth if he would consider tooling-up the French armouries for the purpose of mass-producing interchangeable guns?

The Eli Whitney legend, however, is much more deep-rooted. The same American national pride that was attached to the first 'line-flow' system in 1873 or that which was attached to Ford's Model 'T' motor car applied to Whitney. Authenticity for the Whitney legend – they say – appears in Whitney's own correspondence. Just after the Jefferson incident Whitney wrote, 'I am persuaded to make the same parts of different guns, as the lock for example, as much like each other as the successive impressions of a copperplate engraving'. It was a marvellous aspiration. Had Whitney been able to do so and complete his contract in the two years promised, finishing his guns in accordance with his 'identical repetition' theme, he would indeed have been a genius. Unfortunately, his new water-driven mill at New Haven, Connecticut, had neither the machinery nor the tooling to deliver precision manufactured components – guns or otherwise – and make them all within so tight a specification. Indeed, in 1827 a team of experts summoned by the United States Congress to investigate the whole question of 'interchangeability' were not very impressed. 'Apart from the government armoury at Harpers Ferry', declared the investigators 'we know of no establishment where arms can be made so exactly alike as to interchange'.[18] And even at Harpers Ferry – twenty years on – it was still difficult to make rifle-locks within 0.002 to 0.003-in limits.

The Sam Colt armoury at Hartford USA was another prime example which deserves better historic scholarship (in terms of its technology, that is) especially as it brought together two of the world's most outstanding toolmakers, Francis Pratt and Amos Whitney (no relation of Eli) – later to start the brilliant Pratt and Whitney company. It was soon after the principle of *interchangeability* had again become the primary objective in the US that the then thriving Pratt and Whitney Company commissioned the already mentioned Professor William Rogers of Harvard University to advise them on the need for a higher standard of linear measurement. By now Rogers had been joined by another expert metrologist named George Bond. This time they only *partly* rejected the Whitworth system based as it was on 'end measurement' and advised a combination of length gauges including the old 'line-measurement' system for use as the United States reference standard. It was a curious compromise, considering Pratt and Whitney as a company had already fully adopted Whitworth and had acquired for their own use a full collection of Whitworth's master gauges.

Perhaps the decision was influenced by the Coast Survey Office in Washington whose original master yard standard in 1832 was defined as the distance between the 27th and 63rd inch graduations on an 82-in brass scale made by Edward Troughton. American measurement had not changed for twenty-five years. The Troughton scale had remained the US unofficial standard until it was replaced by two copies of the Imperial Standard Yard in 1857. Twenty years later (1877) Congress endorsed a recommendation that the US yard measure should henceforth be designated 'Bronze No. 11' and that the basic reference used be a compounding of the Imperial Yard in London and the reference metre kept in the National Archive in Paris.[19]

In the meantime the American machine tool industry adopted a very sensible down-to-earth attitude in regard to the question of work tolerances. They recognized that the quality of their machine room production was far less accurate than the impossibly tight micro-inch limits being debated in Britain so they settled for a more rational set of standards. From Whitworth's point of view the effect of this less exacting approach delayed the universal adoption by the New England machine men of his own end-measure gauging system. He had to wait in fact for the launch in America of the first Brown and Sharpe precision grinding machines around the year 1870 or so before his system was reintroduced to New England.

The American Civil War ended in 1865 and within ten years the American Society of Mechanical Engineers (ASME) reported the completion of the new Rogers-Bond comparator. It had a clever calliper attachment which worked in conjunction with a micrometer eye-piece. In terms of accuracy the comparator was considered to be in advance of all hitherto known methods (including Whitworth's) of comparing end measures with line standards. In consequence the toolroom end-gauges, which quickly followed, then became the basis for all Pratt and Whitney tool work. The ASME Report (1873) declared that Rogers and Bond were 'unquestionably' entitled to great credit for the manner they had solved the problem of exact and uniform measurement. Certainly they were entitled to something, but why no mention by the Americans of Whitworth whose system they so closely followed? When all was said and done the Americans attained no greater accuracy than the Manchester man.[20]

The lesson unfortunately was lost on Whitworth. He should have guessed soon after his British Association lectures that talking of gauging to 'a millionth of an inch' would sooner or later invite ridicule, particularly from fellow engineers in America. His comparators – or measuring machines as the press called them – from about 1842 onwards were no doubt beautifully made. Compared with any other measuring instrument anywhere in the world at that time Whitworth's comparators suffered minimal backlash (they had superbly honed threads) and were unbelievably precise; offering perhaps a feel, at best, say, of about 0.0001 in. Anything less than that was highly improbable. One-millionth? Ridiculous. Perhaps Whitworth considered he had no option but to dramatize his ideas to the 'nth degree if he was to achieve the greatest impact. It was absolute theatre: sheer illusionism; deep down he must have known it. He was far too good an engineer not to distinguish metrology from mythology.

Whitworth's comparators were designed and calibrated (theoretically at least) to read off six figures, but even today no screw thread mechanism will respond manually to margins so miniscule. In fact a solution to the problem of micro-inch measurement had to wait until 1918 when E.M. Eden and F.H. Rolt designed the Eden-Rolt millionth optical comparator at the National Physical Laboratory. Only then could toolroom gauges be checked to an accuracy of one micro-inch. Who knows, had Whitworth had his time over again would he have moderated his rash one-millionthism? More sensibly, he would first have assessed the accuracy bequeathed to industry by Maudslay, then declared to what extent his own mensuration would transform toolroom practice. He would have lost the impact of the word 'millionth' of course, but in the longer term he would have gained engineering credence.

Typically, when he went back to the House of Lords to give further evidence before their Select Committee on the Weights and Measures Bill, on 7 June 1855, he mischievously invoked his Royal Commission tormentors:

> I may mention that, in order to avoid any effect which might arise from a bias of my mind, I have frequently employed another person to set up a bar by a millionth of an inch at a time unknown to me, and looking myself to the gravity-piece, I have arrived at the same result. This experiment I made with my standard yard bar in the presence of Lord Rosse and Mr Babbage, at the Great Exhibition 1851.

The point need not be laboured. Whitworth's purpose was wholly honourable. He was endeavouring to persuade engineers to use techniques within tolerances generally thought impossible all through the mid-Victorian years.

SLIP GAUGES

Much to Whitworth's surprise his advocacy in 1856 of precision slip-gauging – in addition to his new measurement systems – met with the same hostility as before. This reaction was wholly unexpected because this time he was demonstrating how the machine tool industry could perhaps reduce its costs while perfecting new precision methods. Of course the new procedures he proposed required new skills – he realized that – and probably higher wages too but he still naïvely believed his colleagues would eventually see the benefit.

It was during Whitworth's presidency of the Manchester Mechanics' Institute that he explained how it was possible to combine the use of a flat surface with gauging blocks, a test indicator and other pieces of surface plate equipment not only to measure things but to accurately position the boring of holes in addition to locating other faces. This new all-in technique represented an era of innovation and transformed the situation. For many of his listeners it was a new toolroom culture tantamount to science fiction.

The fact that the trade generally remained hostile baffled Joe for some years. It was the same antipathy which dogged his military research but he always felt most of the innuendoes mocking his precision discipline emanated from his earlier campaign in favour of decimals. Many felt it was un-British. They suspected Whitworth wanted to go metric and replace the inch. Had the opposition been confined to Britain Whitworth would probably have handled it but the fact that a more generalized stigma spread overseas, even to France and the United States irritated him: for one thing it delayed recognition of his latest slip-gauge system and secondly it offended his pride. Even now, years later, both he and his friends still failed to see why his 'millionth' phraseology should have aroused such animosity. Maybe it was his triumphalist style – nothing to do with decimals?

Engineers throughout time have always reserved a natural antipathy for those of their own kind who tend to crow the loudest. Historians, on the other hand, aided by hindsight, would argue that this irrational humility has long been their downfall. Such was the dilemma facing Whitworth: indeed, he hesitated far too long before blowing his own trumpet. As late as 1865 engineering journals on the continent started to pick up criticisms by overseas buyers of British products, particularly steam engines, for being a miscellany of odd shapes and sizes. Quite literally, Britain had missed the boat. Whitworth had set out to solve their problem but the trade ignored his advice, sacrificing their own good name.

Fifteen years previously Whitworth had perfected his one-inch master gauges. What he was now offering was a major extension to this new system making it possible to master gauge any dimension between, say, one-tenth and one whole inch. First he had divided his inch into ten exemplary pieces and proceeded from there. He calculated he would need a set of ninety-one separate slip-gauges to gauge any dimension using 0.0001-in steps between 0.1001 inch and two inches. How he arrived at this number was not clear: a complete set of modern British or Swedish slip-gauges consists of eighty-one pieces including one and two inch blocks required for gauging up to four inches.

During the late 1850s the gauges made by Whitworth's gauge room were beautiful pieces of precision engineering. Unpublicized, the most remarkable compliment paid his work was the matter-of-fact way machine toolmakers and others began to quietly purchase them without questioning their uncertified precision. Both in Britain and abroad toolmakers ordered them, confident that they were absolutely correct. Forty years passed before a second proprietary name appeared in Britain but not surprisingly, once the competitor had arrived claiming as he did to be the first, trade journalists were quick to pronounce that Whitworth had been the originator.

Though Joe had been dead nine years before the question 'who invented slip gauges' ever came up, overwhelming opinion never hesitated to nominate his system as being at the very heart of the toolroom revolution from the beginning. Sadly it had to be posthumous and almost inaudible. His only slip-gauge epitaph – the early sales catalogues – remain to confirm both the name and the dates.

The news from Sweden fictitiously claiming 'an entirely new system of precision gauging' was surprisingly allowed to stand. The reason why the Sir Joseph

Whitworth company ignored this Swedish boast is as difficult to understand as was the company's long-drawn-out modesty in failing to announce its own gauging equipment. As it turned out, almost at the turn of the century, the chief beneficiary of this Mancunian self-effacement was a toolroom inspector working in an armoury at Eskilstuna, Sweden. His name was C.E. Johansson. The year was 1896. Johansson set up a workshop in his own home, surrounding himself with improvised machinery. The outcome was unorthodox but nonetheless successful. The Johansson gauge-blocks have now passed into our vocabulary, known internationally as *Jo-blocks*: an eighty-one-piece set of toolroom gauging.

Naturally, being forty years later the Swedish gauges were superior to those made by Whitworth. Both the quality of the steel and their precision reflected later technology but the basic system was indeed Whitworth's. If there is ever a renaissance in terms of invention and morality then colloquially, slip-gauges should be spelled '*Joe-blocks*'. As we know, Whitworth was frequently accused of copying but this is one clear example where the reverse is true. In this case he was again the victim of ideas-theft – not the reverse.

The question is asked, how precise was Whitworth's 1860s gauging?[21] The simple answer is, 'almost as good as that of 1910'. It was in fact the coming of ultra-precision grinding and lapping machines around 1920 which made the big difference. Corroboration testifying how good the Whitworth gauges really were can be provided in three ways. First, some of his gauges still exist; second, the close proximity between Whitworth and Johansson's earlier work was acknowledged by the National Physical Laboratory (NPL) and third, once the First World War had broken out the import of Johansson gauges into Britain became difficult. The NPL was therefore compelled to set about re-inventing a modern version of the Whitworth technique and for the next ten years the equivalent of Johansson's gauges were manufactured in Britain. Apart from easing supply one other good came of it. By using similar production techniques the modern experience at least confirmed that the pioneer's competence was all it had been claimed to be seventy-two years previously.

The United States suffered similar wartime restrictions to Britain. They too had to devise their own system of manufacture. They brought in their own expert, a man named Major Hoke who, in co-operation with the Pratt and Whitney company, evolved a 'new' method of accurately lapping the gauges. And as this work got under way, two companies in Britain quite independent of each other – the BSA Company and Pitters Ltd – joined the National Physical Laboratory in developing new grinding and lapping machines. The interesting thing here is that all four experimentalists in 1914 working quite separately both sides of the Atlantic, eventually adopted identical methods to those originally chosen by Whitworth in 1842. It was indeed an all-inclusive testimony.

To ensure accurate size and parallelism, the gauges were lapped in batches of eight and regularly interchanged; the rotational sequence being an update of Whitworth's original three-plate system. There was one other similarity. While in Whitworth's day fine precision grinding and magnetic chucks had yet to come, he had, nevertheless, constructed a most advanced (for his day) upright lapping machine based on the principle of two circular surface plates being made to rotate planetary fashion. In effect his techniques foreshadowed the ideas later developed first by Johansson, then by Hoke, ultimately to be perfected in the United States by the tooling monarchs themselves, Messrs Brown and Sharpe.

WHITWORTH REDEEMED

Reference has already been made to earlier spectrographic work, but no doubt it would help restore our historic perspectives if Whitworth's own contribution was briefly updated. It will be remembered that when Joe first put to the Astronomer Royal the desirability of replacing the use of the 'line' method of measurement by a system of 'end' gauges, Professor Airy rejected the idea. He asserted 'that factory filth plus repeated handling by hot grubby hands would destroy the accuracy of the standard lengths'.

Whitworth, on the other hand, suggested that his master length gauges be kept under laboratory conditions and that, if necessary, a yard reference gauge could periodically be checked against, say, a natural standard such as that proposed in 1827 by the Frenchman, J. Babinet. The Frenchman had suggested using a wavelength of light. Such a standard, he claimed at the time, would have been indestructible. Sadly, Babinet was too far ahead of his time. His ideas never really became a practical proposition until five years after Whitworth's death when the International Bureau of Weights and Measures made the first direct measurement of the metre in wavelength terms, that is by using *cadmium red* numbers, in much the same way at the spectrographic values of Krypton–86 are used today. In 1901 the Institution of Chemical Engineers combined with the IMechE and others to set up a joint committee from which developed the present British Standards Institution (BSI). Nowadays all scientific measurement is based on SI units (Système Internationale d'Unites). And while the SI (unlike the BSI) is not a direct descendant of Whitworth's dream, it is nonetheless a poignant vindication of the initial campaigning he did for both a British standard of measurement and for the international interchangeability of gauging limits.

Progress however, although slow, was inevitable. Airy's doubts from the mid-fifties were eventually swept away in 1893 when the International Bureau of Weights and Measures finally established the standard length of the metre based on a wavelength of (monochromatic) Cadmium Red radiation.

To summarize the British/American position, the British Treasury adopted the original bronze 'line' standards (made by Troughton) in preference to Whitworth's 'end' standards and incorporated them into the parliamentary legislation of 1856. Two of these standards were ordered by the United States the following year and in 1866 the American Congress adopted them as the official US yard standards. When, in 1893, the International Bureau declared to the world the scientific definition of the metre the USA was the first to issue a legislative order defining the precise ratio of its yard to the metre.[22]

British legislation was somewhat slower; parliament being tormented by the disinclination of the Foreign Office to go French for its definitions. While the Schedules to the Weights and Measures Act 1880 included by description the complete range of Whitworth's gauges (thus officially endorsing for the first time his whole measurement system) it wasn't until the Weights and Measures Act 1963 that the UK Primary Standard of the Yard was decreed exactly equal to 0.9144 metre. Needless to say, British scientists (being less inhibited than politicians) have quietly used the French (CGPM) optical wavelength since 1918 when E.M. Eden and F.H. Rolt designed the world's first 'millionth' comparator at the National Physical Laboratory. That apart, it all could have been so different, but at least Whitworth was redeemed – albeit many years too late!

Principally, because of its breathtaking accuracy, Whitworth's 'millionth' measurement technology remained suspect for fifty years. But was such scepticism ever justified? No, never, concluded metrologists at the National Physical Laboratories when, in 1967, they examined one of his 1855 measuring machines (see Fig. 8., p. 174) and found that the backlash of the whole micrometer system was no more than sixty micro-inches. Variations, in fact, of only four micro-inches were found in repeated forward settings. This same 123-year-old machine was again checked in 1978 (against a laser interferometer) and the error curve over one revolution of the micrometer screw (two hundred turns of the graduated wheel) was found to be quite smooth and amounted to just over 0.0001 in. The periodic error over one revolution of the worm (0.00025 in.) amounted to 35 micro-inches, less than 0.001 mm. [23]

With superb results like these it is little wonder that the late Victorians found Whitworth difficult to digest, let alone crown him father of modern precision.

CHAPTER SIX

Sparkling Progress

Leaving to one side their Scottish thriftiness, both William Fairbairn and James Nasmyth truthfully begrudged taking a cab for health reasons. They preferred to walk everywhere. Joseph Whitworth was the same; he too preferred the exercise every morning from home to the factory. And because most Manchester streets remained unpaved till 1860 or so, the constant mud alongside the road compelled all but the lame-footed to risk injury tip-toeing between the deeply rutted setts out in the middle.

William Fairbairn was frequently accompanied on his walk to work by his friend Alderman Hopkins, later to become Chairman of the Highways Committee or, as it was then still called, the Scavenging Committee. And because Fairbairn had fixed habits as to the particular places he would cross the road, he deliberately nudged his friend whenever they approached the clean bits. Hopkins quickly got the message. He repeatedly cursed the town's commissioners for their reluctance to 'get the damnable muck shifted'.

Alderman Hopkins was a decent man; a co-founder with Fairbairn of the Manchester Mechanics' Institute. But not always did he want the 'muck shifted'. Now and again his coal and chemical interests appeared to conflict with the town's interests. In 1840, Edwin Chadwick[1] had compared the expectancy of life for a factory mechanic living in Manchester with that of a mechanic living in Rutlandshire: in the first case it was seventeen years while in Rutland it was more than double – thirty-eight years. Why was this? A local physician, John Leigh[2] – the Manchester Medical Officer of Health – blamed, among other things, thick black air pollution from chemicals and coal burning. 'Their lungs are poisoned', he said. 'Not so', snorted Alderman Hopkins, 'coal burning is helpful. The hot smoke rises high into the atmosphere taking the filth with it, allowing the good country air to flow inwards!'[3]

Whitworth took a somewhat different view. Both he and Fairbairn later thought that chimneys could and should be filtered but street filth was, in Whitworth's opinion, the more important of the two questions. Among friends he posed one particular question: why not clean the streets by machine?[4] In reality it was a rhetorical question only he could answer. He was crazy even to have considered taking on additional anxieties but engineers north and south were increasingly worried about the malodorous mess they were contributing. Perhaps in some way he felt morally obliged.

Naturally he was not to know how close to international celebrity his other machine tool work was, nor indeed in what direction or to what extent this new interest in road sweepers would take him. For him personally the complexities were quite diverting and naughtily flirtatious. His subsequent negotiations with the Manchester Treasurer, for example (renewing his street cleaning contract), produced unforeseen consequences. The Treasurer's daughter, Mary Louise, played host for most of the talks – an unwitting harbinger perhaps of a new romance? But we shall see.

Whitworth habitually walked to the factory early. He regularly passed the early morning road-gangs (classed by the town as paupers but considered by many to be less than human) and noticed how they piled high the house garbage and horse litter just inside alleyways and undrained courtyards. The liquor seeped over the footpath. Not only was it a health hazard but a thoroughly unpleasant experience. The more he saw of it the more determined he became to find a mechanical solution until one day he let fly his critical irritation, justifiably so. The system was inefficient and expensive. The fact that the town had calculated that at least 4,500 horses were using its central streets made the need to sweep them daily an essential obligation.

By summer 1840 Joe was almost ready to finalize the design of the machine he wanted. But first he would get his friend Fairbairn to fabricate an experimental two-wheel iron cart. The outcome was very much as he had originally envisaged: that is to say, it would be a horse-drawn tank having a frame mounted at the rear containing pulleys and two endless chains between which a whole series of brush-heads would be fixed fairly close together. As the road wheels turned so they would drive the brush-heads round the pulleys and up an inclined ramp. The sweepings would be carried by the brushes up the slope and into the tank. And although he kept the design simple the machines apparently worked quite satisfactorily. The first sweepers he made had brushes 2 ft 6 in wide – four years later, 1846, he widened them to 4 ft – the whole thing being low-slung between two 6-ft diameter road wheels. At walking pace he quickly appreciated that the gear ratio between the road wheels and the revolving brushes had to be increased if the roadsweepings were to be effectively brushed upwards from the roadway and this he did. Total weight when empty was about one-and-a-half tons though later, wider, more sophisticated models must have exceeded this weight considerably once spring-adjustable brushes and such other refinements were added.

At first the newspapers were quite enthusiastic. Both Birmingham and Manchester – the towns where his partner Edwin Chadwick had chosen to carry out trial operations – reported local opinion very much in favour. Even more convincingly one hundred of Manchester's biggest merchants signed a statement in support of Whitworth's machines. They sent it to the town's commissioners, dating it February 1843.

> As inhabitants of the township of Manchester we are much interested in the trial now making under your direction of the Self-loading Cart. We beg leave to express our unanimous opinion of its success. (We speak) more particularly of the comfort and convenience derived from the superior cleanliness of the thoroughfares. We are desirous . . . of extending the benefit . . . especially as we understand it is also attended with a considerable diminution of expense.[5]

It was this latter point which appealed to their hard-headed instincts. Whitworth thought it would. In 1842 he patented his machine then finalized his ideas for a private leasing company to hire them out. The company involved three other partners plus himself and Edwin Chadwick, by now England's most famous sanitary inspector. In 1842 the Lamp and Scavenging Committee issued a report insisting that the streets were cleaner, tending not only to lessen the spread of infectious diseases but also that the machines were less damaging to the road surface. The Whitworth partnership must have been delighted. Support from the Manchester Council was not altogether unexpected, but was it truthful?

Their report was heavily biased in favour of the machines but of the evidence provided one would have thought that the existing hand-sweepers had won the contest hands down. But no! The Scavenging Committee then awarded all the contracts to Whitworth's private company: a familiar artifice it would seem, used throughout time. The Whitworth company had all along refused to sell outright its roadsweepers but hired them out at £33 per year on condition they were operated by the leasing company's own horses and employees. Probably it was the first leasing company to take on contracted-out services from a local authority. In 1846, Whitworth charged both Manchester and Birmingham £2,000 per year, everything provided.[6]

The workhouse masters in each town had previously press-ganged about two hundred and fifty men on a 'workfare' basis (that is to say, the men were allowed to eat and sleep at the workhouse only if they agreed to sweep the roads) thus an honest comparison with the Road and Street Sweeping Company was never possible. In reality though the controversy in the press was not about the weight of sweepings removed, nor was it about efficiency or cost; the real pressure came from those in the congregation who had a sense of moral probity and who wanted to see their so-called 'submerged tenth' actually working out on the streets. Revealingly, the Committee never dared challenge the workhouse masters as to how little they actually paid the poor souls using the brushes: who knows, it may have disturbed the pay-offs.

The matter festered on, having been put to the Manchester Board of Guardians on a number of occasions, the last time being January 1852. But typical of their furtive reputation the 'want-no-trouble' guardians long prevented their own so-called inquisitive troublemakers, Edwin Chadwick and his surgeon friend, E. Hodgson, from ever becoming visiting guardians charged with inspecting workhouse premises and accounts. When the names of the visiting guardians again came up, Hodgson moved a motion and Chadwick seconded, 'that the whole Board be included'. 'That's ridiculous' said the Chairman, 'there's no evil to inspect – and anyway, it's none of your business'. But Chadwick insisted, 'I do not see why one guardian is better qualified for the transaction of public business than another. The more the matter is thrown open to public scrutiny, the better.' The Board was only half-convinced – Mr Hodgson being the half selected to audit the books; Mr Chadwick being a director of Whitworth's Company.

For years pauperism had lain heavily with the conscience of the church, particularly the Unitarian Church. The Revd William Gaskell – Fairbairn's friend – took up the cudgels: what could these men do if they were excluded from street-sweeping? The *Manchester Guardian* replied to the question and would have none of it. 'The streets were much cleaner done by machines', the paper claimed. 'The paupers were too old and weak to be working in such cruel and dangerous conditions'. And if the work was degrading, well, 'Let free labourers apply and the denigration would vanish', wrote the editor.

Jane Carlyle, writing to her husband Thomas Carlyle in August 1846, after visiting the Whitworth works, instinctively wanted to defend Whitworth's rationale. 'Whitworth', she wrote, 'the inventor of the besom-cart and many more other wonderful machines, has a face not unlike a baboon; speaks the broadest Lancashire; could not invent an epigram to save his life; but has nevertheless "a talent that might drive the Genii to despair" and when one talks with him, one feels to be talking with a real live man, to my mind worth any number of the Wits that go about'.[7]

Thus, in a very laudable way Jane Carlyle had herself been caught up in the general controversy – her leading reference to the besom-cart underlines the seriousness of the topic – but her concern with Joe's likeness to a baboon and his Lancashire dialect was a direct throwback to the customary denigration reserved by classical scholars at that time for engineers. Happily the literary people she and her companions met in Manchester were more concerned with the underdog and life in the workhouse (thank goodness) but unlike most London literati they were not anti-machine as such. The great majority of young female radicals – like Manchester's Mrs Gaskell for instance, just two years before her *Mary Barton* was published – were slowly beginning to recognize that steam power and the new machine age could possibly be the beginning of a new social enlightenment capable perhaps of ridding Britain of its poverty and pauperism.

The fear that his sweeping machine removed less litter per square yard than the men using brushes started to appear in newspapers. The letter columns reflected Chadwick's earlier dismay. On 2 November 1842, in fact, Chadwick had written to Whitworth asking how they could explain this critical shortcoming. From the start expert observers had expected the machines to outperform the roadmen. Chadwick was worried. Twelve days later, on 14 November, Whitworth replied to his friend enclosing a printed table of the tonnages involved, padding it out with the most perfidious rigmarole. He wrote:

> The quality of the refuse collected from the streets will depend upon the amount of traffic and the quality of the foundations. We find where the foundation is made of soft material the quantity got off in cleaning is much less when the cleaning is performed frequently: the reason of which is that when the rain descends the water gets off and is prevented from filtering through the interspaces between the stones which would soften the foundations and again rise up from the pressure of the horses and carriages when travelling over the surface.[8]

This reply was unworthy of Whitworth. At no other time in his life did he resort to such irrational nonsense. It was so unnecessary. Above everything else Whitworth was a logician. For him to evade his partner's queries in this way was either fear of being second best or sheer pig-headedness.

Had Whitworth reacted sensibly to the poor showing of his 'besom cart' he should have jettisoned the whole project no later than summer 1843, but as it was he continued gratuitously to publicize one particular statement made in the Manchester Council report 'that his machine damaged the road surface less than handsweeping'. It was an incredible point to repeat. Indeed, on at least three occasions over the next ten years he exacerbated his position by adding 'my street sweeping machine tends powerfully to remove ridges and improve the surface'. It was such a fanciful slant that he actually converted whatever credibility his case enjoyed to one of total disbelief. Surely, his critics replied, 'revolving brushes – given a very lumpy surface – could do no other than fill in the ridges with dirt'.

Although this was a novel and somewhat lightweight twist to the debate, Joe still remained pugnacious and genuinely concerned for the roadmen right till the end. 'Hand-sweeping' he asserted 'perpetuated pauperism and exploited the poorest labourers', then, adding by way of advice, 'employ responsible men at decent rates of pay (and also by having men hand-sweep the footpaths) and in that way a better class of job and men would be provided'.

Midway through their eight-year road-cleaning campaign a nationwide scare concerning public health warned all authorities that they must clean the streets more efficiently. Not surprisingly the issue immediately prompted Edwin Chadwick to update the work he had been doing on road drainage. Around 1847 he came up with the most advanced ideas then known proposing that the newly emerging town authorities should build entirely new street drainage and sewage systems capable of taking away street refuse along with domestic and industrial effluent. He had first questioned Whitworth about similar schemes in his letter of November 1842 when he had requested from Joe his opinion concerning the use of sump-tanks below the roadway. Whitworth replied briefly but positively:

> With respect to the plan of getting rid of the refuse of towns by means of water through tunnels I think it an admirable plan for all matter soluble in water, but I should say with regard to the immense quantities of solid matter

> which are made in towns I do not at present see how such means could be rendered practicable.[9]

Then, as though searching for forgiveness, he ended his letter with a little Victorian flourish, usually reserved for very close friends: 'Believe me, Dear Sir, Yours Truly, Joe Whitworth'.

It was the start of a great deal more correspondence. Their cleaning company letters ricocheted back and forth: no longer about sweeping machines but now about possible new techniques for casting street grids and sluice boxes plus a host of related queries. And although there is no evidence that Whitworth had within his factory a foundry big enough to use either machine-moulding or a tramline for core-boxes or such other repetitious moulding techniques, it is known that his own pattern makers spent considerable time perfecting hollow-moulding methods in anticipation that cast iron street drains would be both permissible and in vogue before 1850.

Once the newly appointed Sanitary Commission (of which Edwin Chadwick became Chairman) got down to work, Chadwick put before them his theory that flushing street refuse through the sewers would assist rather than hinder the flow of domestic sewage. The Commission considered the merits of the matter but shelved their decision indefinitely rather than chance exacerbating an already critical public health situation. Both Whitworth and Chadwick felt dissatisfied believing the Commission far too timid. They decided to press ahead with their ideas and invited a Professor Clark, a pro-Whitworth expert, plus a Mr C. Holland of Sandlebridge fame, a consulting engineer experienced in hydraulics, to become partners in their Road and Street Cleaning Company. Their purpose was that this new team should work out the details for comprehensive town drainage. Charles Holland, being related by marriage to the Gaskells, presumably would have, in addition to his professional expertise, sufficient political credibility to allay any possible Manchester (or Liberal) reservations.

The Revd William Gaskell was himself an ardent member of the Manchester and Salford Sanitary Association. Also his wife, Elizabeth, was an enthusiastic helper devising many resourceful ways of raising money. By writing to her literary friends – the likes of Dickens, the Carlyles and Thackeray – asking them to declare war on the appallingly bad sanitary conditions and by referring to the shocking report of the (Chadwick's) Sanitary Commission, she would add: 'it tells one so very much one wanted to know. I want you please to write me a *WAR* letter.' Having then received what were tantamount to specifically autographed replies, she auctioned them forthwith in aid of the Association.

Politicians also figure prominently among the Gaskell targets. Fierce competition for the little money the Russell Government was prepared to grant town authorities caused serious resentment. Manchester fared badly: its two MPs, John Bright and Milner Gibson, were, for a time, the butt of much local criticism particularly from the likes of Mrs Gaskell and Edwin Chadwick. They could not understand the twisted complacency pedalled by Ministers when faced, as they were in Manchester, with such an appalling state of affairs. The local campaigners intensified their pressure but whether Milner Gibson in April 1848 resigned from the Government as a result is a moot point: he opposed Treasury policy certainly, but whether his Ministerial scalp should go to Mrs Gaskell and company is doubtful bearing in mind the unsettled state of the parliamentary Liberals.

Whitworth persevered. His factory was doing well. It was he who largely funded the work of Chadwick. These were especially difficult years and Joe was increasingly aware that engineering was relied upon by medical men to find a solution. The virulence of the Manchester typhoid outbreaks killed many hundreds. In 1849 alone there were 18,000 London deaths from cholera: a fact which in itself accelerated the appointment of (Sir) Joseph Bazalgette to lead the Metropolitan Commission for Sewers – a body which later included such engineers as Brunel and Stephenson. They constructed what was to become the world's most extensive labyrinth of underground tunnels and gullies. Unfortunately – with the exception of some grids and his less complicated street drainage components – very few of Chadwick's more advanced ideas were adopted by Bazalgette for London, nor, regrettably, by any other British local authority. Chadwick had to wait for Louis-Napoleon and Paris to recognize the true worth of his street system. Indeed, some little time after the Prince of Wales opened the London scheme in 1865 the Haussman reconstruction of Paris was amended to include Chadwick-type street-flushing systems, the visible efficacy of which still exists today.

Just prior to the opening of the 1851 Great Exhibition Whitworth made it known he fully backed the Chadwick syphon-traps, yet contrary to their more general public relations approach, they failed to exhibit a full range of their potential products, neither regionally nor, when the time came, at the Crystal Palace itself. Conceivably they could each have made fortunes yet there were no signs of personal problems between the two, in fact they continued to work together in close harmony. Only on one occasion did Chadwick confess to having naïvely leaked to the press some confidential information, but Whitworth forgave him and the incident was soon healed.

Chadwick's ideas were good. He wanted a combined drain, tank and sluice built into all street gutters every fifty yards or so. Roadmen with hand brushes would sweep the surface debris from the road into the gutter. Rainwater, occasionally assisted by roadside hydrants, would flush the muck down the grids and into the sewers; the extra water, in Chadwick's view, assisting the flow of sewage through the sewers.[10] Whitworth's sole responsibility in all this was the modernization of foundry techniques; the mass production of pumps and steam engines, the streets grids and all the other cast-iron furniture. But what went wrong? Why the business never materialized still remains a mystery. A little over a decade or so later other foundries were themselves casting copies of Chadwick's designs and making a lot of money.

ENTER MRS MARY LOUISA ORRELL (NEE BROADHURST)

Whitworth was anxious to get his hobby-horse – his sweeping machines – back onto the agenda especially with the Manchester Council. He arranged to meet the man with whom he had originally negotiated his first hiring contract, Daniel Broadhurst, the Manchester Town Treasurer. Broadhurst had been appointed in 1842 at the age of fifty-five. He was already a councillor and the two aldermen most influential in securing his selection were Henry Tootal (brother of Edward Tootal) and Richard Cobden. Indeed, Daniel Broadhurst had married a Tootal.[11]

But despite his influence, Whitworth's street sweeping contracts were not renewed. One councillor said they were 'no more than a whimsical crochet'. Manchester, like Westminster, again considered that men with brushes were the best street sweepers.

Notwithstanding his obvious disappointment, Whitworth's friendship with the Town Treasurer strengthened. Perhaps it was galvanized when Daniel Broadhurst introduced Whitworth to his recently widowed twenty-two-year-old daughter Mary Louisa. Her late husband, Alfred Orrell, the Mayor of Stockport at the age of twenty-seven, had six years earlier inherited his father's mill-owning wealth. Sadly, however, he had also inherited his father's weak heart and risk of a premature death. Indeed, exactly two years from the day of their wedding in October 1847, Alfred died leaving his young wife widowed – albeit a wealthy widow – with a twelve-month-old baby daughter.

Mary Louisa was no political innocent. For one so young she was already admired as an active Unitarian, steeped – no doubt due to her father – in Liberal radicalism. But despite her small child and the priggishness of Victorian society she insisted on being an outward looking young widow, attractive and extremely eligible in every sense. She very much looked to the future.

Her late husband Alfred, immediately upon his wedding day, engaged architects to build for him at Cheadle (a small prosperous village near Manchester) a substantial family residence which the couple named 'Throstle Grove'. His wife, however, no longer able to remain alone at the house following her husband's death, sold the place to a Mr Watts, a well-known Manchester cotton merchant. He immediately renamed the estate 'Abney Hall'. Meanwhile, Mary Louisa found a smaller, more suitable house at Rusholme, just a little distance from her father, Daniel Broadhurst, still living at Ardwick and also in the same close vicinity as Mr and Mrs Whitworth, both houses about the same short distance from Rusholme.

Just prior to the Great Exhibition the forty-eight-year-old Whitworth was obliged to travel the country a great deal. Nonetheless he and Mary Louisa found sufficient excuse to see each other occasionally. Possibly they couldn't avoid it: they both had friends mutual to each other. Not that Joe emulated her by actively cavorting around Manchester's young literati circuit, he didn't. But other more appropriate opportunities did arise. William Fairbairn a few years earlier had designed and erected for the Orrells, Travis Brook Mill (credited at the time with being the most modern, most expensive cotton mill then built), since which Fairbairn regularly invited Mary Louisa to the political-cum-Unitarian soirées he and his wife organized at their Ardwick home, The Polygon. Whitworth too occasionally attended.

One other beguiling feature of Mary's widowhood was the hideaway cottage she kept at Grasmere, a few miles north of Windermere. Once trains were running from Manchester the area became a favourite rendezvous. The Gaskells, the Chadwicks, et al . . . holidays there had all the familiarity of the Ardwick scene.

The sale of the Travis Brook Mill, of course, along with Throstle Grove, represented the bulk of Mary's considerable inheritance. Even if her other attributes were uncertain, her comparative wealth must have made her a prime attraction, eagerly pursued over the years by many would-be lovers yet clearly, for nearly twenty years in fact, she willingly waited for Whitworth, not knowing if they would ever be in a position to marry. Joe's wife Fanny (three years older than Joe) plus the absence of any divorce law, somewhat restricted their wooing to within limits set by the amount of deceit each was prepared to practise. However – leaving to one side his sly perfidy regarding Fanny – there must have been a more attractive side to Whitworth's character. His own potential wealth was surely not a factor. What else would keep Mary Louisa waiting for him? As we know, she had her own money. What else did Joe have? It was undoubtedly an intriguing duet, the story of which must wait its turn. Meanwhile the Tootals, the Chadwicks, the Fairbairns (all of whom knew Mary Louisa very well) along with Joe himself: they all came closer together in their lifelong mutual assignment; that of nourishing Manchester's influence and expanding its intellectual heritage.

NEW ERGONOMICS

It is difficult to imagine tourists wanting to include an engineering factory in their sightseeing itinerary, yet that is precisely what many visitors to Manchester did from the late 1840s onwards. They listed Whitworth's factory as their first choice. Not all were engineers. Then, as now, railway locomotives and big automatic machines evoked a romanticism satisfied only by a visit to the shrine itself – the place where they were made. In this instance, to see locomotives it had to be either Fairbairn's works or Beyer Peacock's; for pure novelty though, Whitworth's internationally recognized machinery was an absolute must.

Elizabeth Gaskell in 1864, when writing to a young friend, enclosed letters of introduction to William Fairbairn and Charles Beyer. 'The things best worth seeing in Manchester' she wrote (confusing their correct locations) 'include Whitworth's machine[ry] works Canal Street-Brook Street, or very near there. The rifle works which have made Mr Whitworth so famous, are out of Manchester and not easily shown. But these works, i.e. Whitworth's at Chorlton Street, are very interesting if you do not get a stupid *fine* young man to show you over, try rather one of the working men. [Try also] Sharp and Roberts, Bridgewater Foundry. Good to see the Railway-Engine line' – she was then referring to the loco-assembly line originally set up by Charles Beyer, whom Elizabeth Gaskell described in this same letter as 'a German, a very benevolent, eccentric old bachelor'. Certainly he was German and extremely benevolent but hardly eccentric. At the time she described him as an 'eccentric old bachelor' he was fifty-one years old, head of his own company, Beyer Peacock, and considered by many in 1867 'the world's best locomotive designer'.[12]

Most visitors arriving at Whitworth's Chorlton Street works would have been immediately impressed by the orderliness of the place. Whitworth didn't like jumble lying around. The *Engineering* magazine enthused about this, again returning to the subject June 1856. Quite simply it reported:

> Among the general arrangements of Mr Whitworth's workshop may be observed the high degree of concentration which exists in the method of placing all tools which perform analogous functions in the same locality, so that the workman has seldom any occasion to move his work any great distance through the shop until he has completed it.[13]

These words represent history in the making. Whitworth and his workshop foremen were laying the foundations of an entirely new science – nowadays called ergonomics – the study of movement, the relationship between factory workers and their working environment, particularly the engineering aspects.

Britain's leading engineers, especially Charles Beyer, unstintedly paid glowing tributes in their general recognition of Whitworth's new workshops. Even foreign trade journals despatched their best writers to assess the scene. Whitworth had resolutely pursued a building programme extending in a modern way the original buildings he first occupied in 1833. And to recall the sparseness of the property in those early days was to concede the incredibility of his achievements in less than a decade. Little wonder the paparazzi joined engineers from Leeds and London to view Whitworth's mechanical aids, especially his first ever power-driven gantry crane which ran the length of the main aisle.

The chief correspondent writing in *The Engineer* reported:

> On the ground floor there has recently been constructed what I may term a model workshop. It has an arched semi-circular roof of a rather novel construction. The beams have been so constructed as, without the aid of tie-rods or struts, to throw the weight perpendicularly upon the side walls, thus affording a clear and unobstructed span of about forty feet (42ft. x 102ft. long to be exact) under which a travelling crane passes, supported on ledges a short distance below the junction of the roof and the side walls.[14]

The construction of this roof started around 1841. Significantly Joseph Whitworth was one of few engineers prepared to invest considerable sums commissioning someone like Fairbairn to design and construct what was an extremely advanced glass-covered span roof. The advantages were obvious

Fig. 3 Whitworth's Chorlton Street Works, Manchester, c. *1849–50. Note long-bed lathe back gears (centre), 5 ft radial arm drill (right) and overhead gantry crane. Note too, Fairbairn's glazed span roof. This superb engraving was published in the* GNR Guide, *1853. Compare this with Plate 6, the same aisle sixteen years later.*

including the extra daylight it gained both summer and winter although the Manchester Gas Company laid its first gas main into the factory (providing both heating and lighting) the same year as the new roof was started (see fig. 3).

Once finished and talked about the Whitworth roof became famous in its own right. Technically it was a triumph. Although Fairbairn had Eaton Hodgkinson to advise him, the mathematics of cast-iron beams and trusses were still only vaguely understood. For strength it was a case of double the numbers and hope for the best – fortunately civil structures became less ecclesiastic, more science based, just in time for the 1851 Exhibition Building when the main Crystal Palace span was increased from Whitworth's 42 ft to a massive 72 ft. The commanding point about the Whitworth glass roof was the travelling gantry crane running the whole length of the aisle just a few feet below the roof. The combined weight – that is the gantry plus its maximum lift – would probably add to the supporting walls an additional loading of some 30 to 35 tons. Moreover, alongside the main aisle Whitworth had a first-floor machine gallery supported on cast iron pillars running the full width of the site.

Fairbairn's construction techniques and general cast-iron geometry was now copied by the best in Europe. Already he had perfected his own pre-fabrication methods: he would erect roof structures in his own factory, dismantling them before transporting each piece by rail for re-erection on the site. His team eventually became quite renowned, crowning their trail of glory with a superb 219 ft unsupported roof span covering the Royal Albert Hall – all of which was carried by rail from Fairbairn's in Manchester to its site in Kensington. R.M. Ordish, straight from his outstanding handling of the extremely impressive glazed roof of St Pancras station, worked closely with William Fairbairn in 1866 to ensure the ironwork success which made Captain Fowkes's Albert Hall such a triumph.

When Prince Louis-Napoleon first visited Manchester in 1839 Fairbairn brought him across to Whitworths to see the latest in machine tools. Unfortunately he was three years too early to witness the start up of the world's first *mechanically powered* gantry crane. John Bodmer had installed his own gantry crane over at Gaythorn a few years earlier but it was a manual block-and-tackle arrangement pulled by drag chains. Whitworth went one better; by 1842 he had working a fully mechanized 15-ton crane attracting to the factory not only leading engineers but a wide range of Britain's celebrities. The winsome gossip columns were colourful and somewhat exaggerated; nonetheless the more serious descriptive pieces concentrated on Whitworth's super steam-driven line-shafts, his powerful gantry crane and his new ergonomic workshop layout. Later on, his 'hydraulic hoist taking heavy machine parts up to the first floor gallery' was also a masterpiece, they said; naturally that too was pondered over many times.

Whitworth's single most important visitor turned out to be his German friend, Charles Beyer. He came across from Sharp Roberts, where he worked as chief draughtsman, to the Chorlton Street factory on 8 July 1842. It was a red-letter day for Joe; Beyer came to examine and record a most lucid appreciation of Whitworth's work. He had then lived in Britain for a mere ten years yet his splendid grasp of English plus his fine draughtsmanship enabled him to produce sketches and notes latterly considered by engineering scholars to be unique gems. Beyer was still only thirty years of age yet he was already classified among Britain's top locomotive talent. In his notebook on Whitworths he wrote:

> Those works appeared to me today a genuine pattern for any kind of machine-making establishment to arrange and conduct them by; our own (Sharp Roberts and Company) by no means excepted. The pains taken in doing work is as great as their means they employ as well as ways upon which they seem to proceed is judicious. The fitting and filing work generally is superior to anything I ever saw before. Their principal tools are lathes, planing machines and all sorts of screwing tackle generally; drills; and now they are commencing to make key-groove machines (1842). Having made several additions to their works since the erection of the main building they have laid down in the yard a turntable from which branch rails (radiate) for the better connecting of the different premises.[15]

Charles Beyer thus documented these revolutionary changes heralding an entirely novel, highly sophisticated approach to workshop design. He then went on to describe Whitworth's universal line-shafting and the power gantry itself: 'The continuous shaft which power-drives the crane runs the length of the workshop', he wrote before going on to explain that sliding along this continuously revolving shaft was a 'keyed bevel-wheel geared to which were the four flanged traction wheels' (two either side) running along rails twenty-odd feet above floor level. A main cross-shaft working both the traversing crab and the chain lift; each controlled independently of the other; each provided with a forward and reversing motion using bevel wheel clusters and double-faced dog clutches.

By far the most interesting feature however was the power take-off; a bevel gear heat-shrunk over a keyed bush (or sleeve) tapered at both ends. This bushed gear wheel travelled along the 3-in diameter shaft its whole length striking and tippling in turn each support bracket. The same system also applied to the smaller diameter cross-shaft supplying power to the crab. As each 'boomerang' shaped rocker-bracket supporting the power-shaft (by half-bearings) was knocked over it would pivot through 120°. It would thus replace each half-bearing in turn as the crab crossed the gantry unhindered. A crane driver stationed on top of the gantry controlled the whole operation by a series of levers and clutches. 'The way this enormous length of shafting was originally turned and a keyway cut along its extent deserves to be described', declared *The Engineer*, explaining that: 'The shaft was first turned in lengths of about 20 ft; five of these pieces were joined end to end. A number of lathe beds were then placed in line and the shafting turned between two headstocks.' The planing of the keyway was achieved by doing 20 ft at a time on a 40 ft planing machine – that in itself being a remarkable feat quite apart from having to perfect the joints.[16]

Whitworth's workshop innovations were powerful and convincing. He made no secret of any of them. Indeed, by invitation and press notice he actively encouraged both his competitors and other engineering establishments to copy them. Certain weaknesses remained, however, especially in regard to the crane. How to stop and start or reverse its movements proved an intransigent flaw. The same problem didn't inhibit machine tools quite so much because they were belt-driven but whenever the crane driver 'inched' his crane in any direction the gnashing of dog-clutch teeth was punishing. With a continuously revolving power-shaft some sort of friction clutch was the answer. Astonishingly, a practical solution stared engineers in the face for over forty years yet they could never see it.

At root, the problem lay in having a steam engine as a single prime mover. In Whitworth's case the whole of his workshop was supplied by continuously running line-shafts. Of necessity it meant the use of clutches for every single mechanism. The clutches were all beautifully made but their action was primitive. Free running or crossed-belt pulley systems were used in cotton mills and for some machine tools but they too lacked precision; their lack of positive engagement being too problematic for synchronized machinery. Dog clutches, the most popular of Victorian clutch designs, or even serrated plate clutches, both involved the most brutal mutilation of metal by metal and were so destructive of smooth running machinery that whenever it was required to transfer power from a running to a stationary shaft this kind of clutch was tolerated only because there was no other satisfactory option.

Despite many attempts a solution continued to elude the world's best engineers. The clutch had become the single most defiant design barrier of the nineteenth century. With all their mechanical ingenuity machine toolmen never came near to solving the problem. It wasn't in fact till the coming of the First World War that fibre clutches or electro-magnetic mechanisms made it possible to stop and start a machine in a precise manner or to change gear or to engage pre-optive systems while its driving shaft remained in motion. Soon after these well-engineered clutches and mechanisms arrived, in the late 1920s, great strides in mass production techniques and genuine self-acting machinery were quickly under way. A sixty-year design blockage had disappeared practically overnight.

In a curious and unusually myopic way the many practical clues which existed during Whitworth's time failed completely to point engineers towards constructive answers. Locomotive wheels gripping steel rails, for instance, or Beyer's use of soft-iron brake blocks meant little, even to those engineers working in search of a friction drive. Admittedly, frictional resistance is an extremely complex matter, but a rudimentary understanding was nonetheless visible to all. As to why friction drives were delayed until comparatively modern times is a puzzle. For all their Baconism neither Whitworth nor the others applied their 'scientific method'. They can't have done. From 1830 or so, machine builders understood the problem but merely incorporated 'serrated plates' for use as *friction drives.* Once the serrations had worn away the 'driving friction' would derive from two smooth plates – not very effectively – but had engineers softened (instead of 'remedially' hardening) the plates and had they loaded them with a powerful spring action, the history of machinery would have been very different.

This example is by no means hypothetical but rather it is a cogent illustration explaining that had Whitworth and his contemporaries worked from a stronger theoretical base they would have undoubtedly moved directly from 'serrated plate' clutches to 'soft disc' clutches. The outcome could not have been other than far-reaching. It was the one single mechanism Whitworth required so acutely yet he never got it right. The reason was the failure of empiricism, the much vaunted approach so beloved by Victorian engineers. Certainly suitable non-metal materials were available even in Whitworth's time but machine designers had to wait until long after his death before *friction clutches* became an essential part of a machine designer's handbook.

SCREW THREADS AND ALL THAT

Whitworth was increasingly aware that the rising expectancy of mechanical engineering would demand much of himself. The new technology had an imperative strength: he instinctively saw himself as central to its expectant theme. It wasn't a case of having 'greatness thrust upon him' but even the most casual survey of that going on around him posed the question; if not him – who else?

Going back over recent years, Whitworth had received a letter from the Institution of Civil Engineers dated 23 February 1841, confirming that they accepted him as an 'associate member'. He bristled at the thought that *they* had put him on probation awaiting proof as to whether he was a fully fledged engineer. He felt deflated. The letter explained he would not be granted full membership until he was judged a 'qualified' engineer or alternatively – as in the case of a junior civil engineer articled to a senior partner – he submitted an essay setting out an engineering thesis of merit. That was the rule. Joe hesitated; should he do what other leading mechanical engineers had done and follow the lead set by George Stephenson – just ignore the 'civils' qualifications and their associate membership?

Pragmatism and self-interest intervened. Whitworth desperately wanted to use the 'civils' platform to launch his national campaign for the standardization of screw threads. He somewhat graciously swallowed what pride he had, accepted the Civil Engineers 'associate' membership and within two months had delivered his paper on screw threads.

The aftermath which followed was a good indication of the professional resentment he suffered throughout his life: though it proved never to be a nemesis, it was nonetheless the pestilent envy on the part of his peers which rubbed against him continuously. They couldn't resist for instance muttering that Whitworth was by no means the first to call for standardized threads. Others, the late Mr Maudslay perhaps, had preceded him. Maybe he had, but Whitworth never claimed to be the first. Maudslay may have mentioned privately that a standard thread was required but there is no evidence he ever called for one publicly. As things stood, almost every big factory had its own system of screw threads. The situation was wasteful, said Whitworth; a uniformity of thread, if adopted, would benefit everyone, especially the railway companies and the steam packet people. All engineers would gain something. Specialist nut and bolt manufacturers could make sufficient sizes to supply the whole industry at less cost instead of every corner shop having to provide its own screwing tackle. It all sounded so eminently sensible yet the better-known engineers jibbed. If everyone worked to a uniform standard someone must compromise – why should it be they who have to compromise to suit the young Whitworth? Why shouldn't the trade adopt an alternative thread to that proposed by Whitworth?

When he first presented his paper setting out a table of uniform threads Whitworth readily acknowledged that his 55° angle and thread form was purely arbitrary. Pointing to the absence of any theoretical understanding he again acknowledged that pitch, shape and depth for each thread could not at that time be fixed by calculation. The fact that none of his ICE audience – which included the best engineering theoreticians – remonstrated against this, clearly indicated that engineering practice at that time was essentially empirical. This lack of recognized criteria, strength of materials and such like, applied equally to all their mechanisms, wormshafts and gear wheels alike. Considered in this way the ICE discussion about screw threads was an important piece of historic evidence which almost dated the precise time when machine builders departed their rule of thumb and turned towards scientific learning.

When questioned as to the suitability of his thread form he was asked whether it would suit both ferrous and non-ferrous metals? 'Not ideally', he admitted, 'there was a tendency to perplex in the choice of thread'. His own thread, he thought, would work best in cast-iron, less so for wrought iron and the more ductile non-ferrous metals. For the sake of simplicity, however, he advised keeping to one standard thread. His main concern was the retention of a proportional consistency between pitch and thread depth based on a 55° angle. For strength, he also wanted both the root corners and the thread apex to be rounded off.

By 1860 the Whitworth thread was in general use throughout Britain and the United States. Four years later a slightly different alternative thread was on its way. William Sellers, a Philadelphia engineer, preferred his own 60° thread-angle with a sharp cornered root and flat apex profile. He argued that in manufacturing a 60° flat-topped thread was more easily made and that for jig grinding of tools his 30° and 60° angles were reversible whereas Whitworth's 55° was a difficult combination (i.e. 55° and 35°). In William Sellers' opinion, his 60° angle would reduce the cost of threadmaking and provide greater accuracy. Thus the US government in 1868 adopted the Sellers thread as their standard coarse thread. Europe followed suit thirty years later when the 1898 Zurich Congress endorsed a metricated equivalent of the American system: in effect, they made the American (A N) coarse and fine threads the basis of a unified world system.

Very soon afterwards, academia volunteered the view that Zurich at least had finally brought some 'scientific reasoning' to the aid of thread design. But how wrong they were. The Zurich Congress did no such thing. The 'universal' coarse threads of today differ in angle only from their Whitworth origin: similarly today's BSF universal fine threads are almost of the same lineage as the fine threads Whitworth adopted for use with steel and brass in his own Manchester factory from about 1865 onwards. In other words, today's threads are very much direct descendants of those originally designed by 'averages' and 'rule of thumb' judgements; they are in fact virtually the same intuitive pitch and core dimensions as Whitworth presented to the ICE in 1841.[17]

On more general matters, however, London engineers – mainly leading civil engineers – were increasingly irritated by northern arriviste attitudes. The Lancashire men, like their Geordie brethren, openly bragged about their railway and machine tool success. In doing so they got the press and continued to attract widespread notice generating excitement throughout the 1840s. But to merely pass it all off as north-south pique – as some northern papers did – or just commercial sourness on the part of the southerners would be far too simplistic: it was in fact the beginning of a professional 'rift' between the licentiate civils and the 'unlettered' mechanicals. Needlessly alarmed, the London-based consultants feared their professional status would be undermined if the likes of Whitworth, the Beyers or the Broadbottoms were admitted into ICE membership. It was a frigidity of this sort which eventually aroused Charles Beyer to gather his co-mechanicals and convene a meeting at the home of J.E. McConnell. Their idea was to set up an alternative 'professional' institution in support of what the railwaymen euphemistically called 'proper engineers' – mechanical engineers.

Such a move had been inevitable for some time. After much canvassing a second meeting was called on 27 January 1847 at which Charles Beyer and his friends formally established their new Institution of Mechanical Engineers. George Stephenson was elected President; Charles Beyer a Vice-President; afterwards Beyer formally read out the constitution they had agreed, part of which read: 'by a mutual exchange of ideas respecting improvements in various branches of *mechanical science* [engineers might] increase their knowledge and give an impulse to Inventions likely to be useful to the World'.

To have been present at this inaugural meeting would have been privilege indeed. Predictably, part of the discussion centred on the use of the title 'Engineer' – the historic misuse of which has bedevilled the profession ever since – its capacious use being applied to all and sundry whether lathe operator or steam mechanic. Beyer was also keen to exemplify the term 'engineering science' – he appears to have settled for the words 'mechanical science'. Professor Eric Laithwaite, pioneer of the linear motor, recently commented, 'one still sees [the term] "engineering science" which always reminds me of describing Fido as an animal dog'. Theodor von Karman, a pioneer of jet propulsion, explained that 'a scientist explores what is, an engineer creates what has never been'.

The word *engineer* comes from the French *ingénieure*, but the term 'engineers and scientists' implies there is no science in engineering. Such a conclusion would be ridiculous. William Fairbairn, himself an ICE member, thought John Smeaton FRS was the first engineer to use the title 'Engineer' when he compiled a report on the building of a Staffordshire canal in 1761. Others have since elaborated on this and suggested that Smeaton did so to indicate he was also a builder of machine tools. If this latter point is correct, it would seem Smeaton used the title to indicate that he was both a civil engineer *and* a professional 'mechanical engineer'.

Those engineers of today who seek the underlying reasons why engineers generally are so undervalued should heed the Manchester pioneers. Charles Beyer, the key participant at the 1847 inaugural 'mechanicals' meeting realized even then that 'builder of machine tools' was not only an inadequate definition, it could also be professionally ruinous. In his view there had to be a distinction between Fairbairn's millwrights, Whitworth's fitters and professional mechanical engineers. This wasn't just a meaningless class distinction; for Beyer it was an essential qualitative distinction. How right he was!

A works technical school, the first in Britain, was opened by Charles Beyer inside his own locomotive works on 19 January 1856. A 'works soirée' was organized to mark the official opening. Joseph Whitworth was the honoured guest, attestant to the message delivered by Charles Beyer that higher technical knowledge was not only a prerequisite of better locomotive design but a fundamental necessity without which mechanical engineering would never equal the professionalism of the law or medicine.

Beyer, himself a product of the German Dresden Polytechnic, thoroughly understood the prize to be won – the personal respect, the much sought-after professional esteem; all of which would belong to engineers if the words 'scientist' and 'engineer' became synonymous in the public mind: the very reason in fact which persuaded his fellow countrymen, the Germans, via Charlottenburg, to grant their professional engineers in 1899 the title of Dr. Ing. Had Beyer's close associates been more supportive they would no doubt have led Britain's legislators along a similar path thirty years ahead of the Germans. Sadly it was not to be. As it was, he himself demonstrated his total commitment; firstly by providing a technical college inside his works gates and secondly, by contributing more towards the endowment of Owens College and its engineering faculty (later the University of Manchester) than even its chief benefactor, John Owens himself.[18]

On the subject of Whitworth's membership of the two institutions, it is interesting that the Civils and the newly born Mechanicals agreed that he should become a full member of both their institutions on the same day, 11 January 1847. Presumably this was a gesture requested by Whitworth himself; a symbol of equality between the two professions. The fact that such a thing was conceded was a clear indication of Whitworth's professional standing. As we now know, he behaved in exactly the same way as George Stephenson before him and refused to submit an essay expounding his engineering intelligence. For that he had been made to wait almost six years from the day he first applied.

But 'all's well that ends well'. In December 1855, Whitworth was elected by the ICE a member of its Council while in the following year, 1856, he was elected President of the IMechE. Recognition indeed!

THE INFLUENCE OF WILLIAM MUIR

Typical of his new approach in wanting to recruit the best professional help, Whitworth persuaded John Aston, a Manchester-born solicitor, to oversee the legalities arising from his fresh patentable ideas. As things turned out, John Aston not only became a very loyal family and business solicitor, he also established an international reputation as a practitioner in patent law.

Aston's advice and his personal friendship proved invaluable. A man of great intellect: like his father he was both a poet and a writer. Almost as soon as he was appointed he was called upon to act internationally on behalf of the Whitworth company. He also developed what seemed a fascinating sideline. He defended

Whitworth with great sagacity: whenever hostile letters appeared in the press, he responded in the most entertaining way. Two years younger than Whitworth, he and Joe travelled the country together. Privately, they probably shared each other's fun; no doubt each other's heartaches too. Undoubtedly the persuading of Aston was one of Whitworth's most inspired acts. Not only did they form a very special friendship which lasted some forty years, but Whitworth knew he had recruited an adviser of unmistakable professional competence. When the time came for him to enter the league of big armament manufacturers he did so with a commanding confidence he otherwise would never have accomplished.

Once over Christmas, with the new 1840s beckoning, his next priority was to assemble a truly professional drawing office. He wanted the best possible design talents yet he was far from prepared to grant them free reign. Even when his overtures to certain leading draughtsmen were well advanced, he still betrayed, not for the first time, a lifelong reluctance to delegate full design responsibility to his senior employees. By today's standards his attitude against design delegation would be impossible yet mid last century, before the days when scientific method replaced instinctive judgement, innovative engineering was usually down to one man. In this case: Whitworth himself.

Come 1840 then, his first choice for a works director would be someone he considered capable of combining works supervision with the rôle of chief draughtsman. The man he eventually chose was a person he got to know best during his Holtzapffel-Clement period in London; a man named William Muir.[19] A nephew of the great William Murdoch, Muir was three years younger than Joe. He was then currently employed by Bramah and Robinson, the famous locks and hydraulics people, newly relocated at Pimlico in London. Not being one for 'messing about' Joe straightaway offered Muir a handsome contract if he would become his works director to include responsibility for his new-style drawing office. It was a primary condition of employment that new machine design would be strictly controlled by Whitworth himself: all this was very plainly agreed by their handshake. Muir accepted, agreeing to start work at Chorlton Street in July 1840.

In keeping with Joe's ambition to attain the highest possible design standards, it was also agreed between the two that Henry Goss, a leading draughtsman from Sharp Roberts, should also join Whitworth's staff as an assistant designer under Muir. Whitworths at that time, now towards the end of 1840, was still a comparatively small firm employing a works staff of some sixty-odd people. Happily, but indicative of the personal loyalty within the firm, Joe's existing supervisory staff, John Booth and John Wild, plus his existing chief draughtsman, Francis Wise, all agreed to remain with the firm and to accept what was for them a secondary rôle working within the new Muir hierarchy.

Some historians refer to the period 1840–43 as the Muir period. They also point to it as the time when Whitworth's most powerful creativity first evolved. The fact that William Muir managed his factory throughout this period offers some credence to their view that Whitworth's genius at that time was Muir orientated.

The Scotsman's particular style of management must also have worked well – at least outwardly because the Whitworth company had built such a legendary reputation during the period. But all was not well. After exactly two years the partnership between Muir and Whitworth came to an abrupt end in June 1842. What happened? Strangely enough, though they parted company amid much huffishness, their personal relationship remained amicable. According to Samuel Smiles, the engineering biographer, Whitworth considered Muir 'clever and persevering, an outstanding inventor' and in terms of worldly wisdom 'a Nathaniel in whom there was no guile'. But something more than a personality clash had arisen.[20]

Muir's own sketchbooks – in much the same way as those of Charles Beyer – were helpful in that they explained the dispute in engineering terminology. While working for Whitworth, Muir confirmed he had worked on knitting machines and had drawn a full set of detailed drawings for a road sweeping machine. He also made a beautiful scale model of the sweeper for exhibition purposes, a ruse which had significantly helped its sales promotion. Samuel Smiles also hinted that Muir had gathered together from other leading engineers a whole collection of differently pitched screwed rods in preparation for the elaborate experimental work he carried out on behalf of Whitworth. No doubt the nationwide contacts Muir had previously made when selling Holtzapffel's machine tools enabled Whitworth to claim that before he reached a decision about the actual form of his threads he had actually tested screws used by the majority of Britain's largest engineers. When eventually Whitworth did announce the final details of his 'Universal Thread' he emphasized the importance of the experimental work done yet pettily omitted to mention William Muir's contribution. When further sketchbooks drawn by Muir during this same 1841 period were seen to contain other memoranda relating to '*fine* screw threads', they were earmarked, no doubt, for the day when he himself would be manufacturing 'fine thread fasteners' suitable for instrument-makers – an expanding line of business Muir established in 1847.

But why did the Whitworth–Muir partnership end so abruptly when clearly had it continued it would have been the most creative combination in the history of British machine tools?[21]

Towards the end of Samuel Smiles's biography of Muir, he suggested it was an 'incompatibility of temper'. There was probably much more to it but first here is an abridged version of Samuel Smiles's story. 'Early one Saturday, Whitworth was impatiently waiting to take up to London one of his small knitting machines. He requested that Muir oversee the completion of the work the following day, Sunday. Because of his religious beliefs Muir refused, promising only to work until Saturday midnight. Thus', wrote Smiles, 'matters were brought to a head.' The story itself was probably true; when Muir himself became an employer he never allowed his men to work on the Sabbath. But to provide a much better understanding of Whitworth's view we should perhaps flesh out his engineering relationship with Muir in a little more detail. Destined to become one of Manchester's biggest machine tool makers Muir's engineering credentials were never in doubt. His sketchbooks impartially prove an invaluable source, sometimes critically examining Whitworth's 'sequence of innovation' as if exploring the engineering differences between himself and his earlier partner.

One of the simplest, yet most telling, examples of this work concerns Whitworth's screwing machines. Muir himself did some work on the development of the die-head, noting in 1841 that he considered it wrong for the dies themselves to advance towards the centre at 40°. He wanted to modify the design but Whitworth wouldn't hear of it: they disagreed. In 1862, however, Muir decided 40° was the correct angle after all. At the South Kensington show Muir exhibited his own 'Britannia' screwing machines which used die-heads copied exactly from Whitworth's 1841 model.

Equally important, the sketchbooks also verified the range of experimental work he himself organized towards the end of the 1840–42 period. He recorded the work he did on a 6-in screw-cutting foot lathe (later discontinued) and a new type of universal boring bar (the forerunner possibly of Whitworth's gun-barrel horizontal borer). He also sketched what some would call the greatest machine of all, Whitworth's (1841) big planing machine which Muir later confirmed as Whitworth's exclusive design.

Finally there was – in Samuel Smiles's opinion – 'Muir's, *not Whitworth's*, most brilliant invention of all: the radial-arm drilling machine'. Certainly in its day it was a brilliant piece of machine design but exactly opposite to the citation handed out by Smiles: by general consent it was Whitworth's work – not Muir's. Smiles's mistake probably embarrassed Muir more than most, knowing as he did that the particular modifications, which on this occasion made this machine special, were actually designed in 1845, three years after Muir had left Whitworth's employment.

To be fair, one of Whitworth's best ever draughtsmen and a contemporary of Muir, Francis Wise, once confirmed that Muir did contribute towards the reconstruction of the earlier Whitworth drill, the 1838 radial-arm machine. It was largely a generative process, work on the machine continued for ten years. Ironically, it was probably Muir's 1842 experimental work which set Whitworth off in search of improved screw feeds and grooved power drives; thus years later not only was his radial-arm drilling machine awarded a medal at the 1851 Great Exhibition, but it went on to establish the most significant landmark in the history of radial-arm machines. The praise it received was international. The fact that William Muir pressed hard for the machine to be fitted with his favourite rack and pinion movement is one of those historical quirks. Had Whitworth agreed, his celebrated drill would never have been noticed. As it was, the very system Whitworth insisted upon – the comparatively smooth precision screw feeds – triumphed: his radical-arm drill became a world trend-setter. Under these circumstances exhibition journalists were justified not to include Muir in their credits.[22]

Nor were these matters just semantics. Whitworth considered all rack systems were flawed mechanically – only to be used when forced by necessity. But once Muir was free of Whitworth he very soon reverted to his preferred rack and pinion assemblies, again proving their differences were questions of professional judgement. Harking back to the broken partnership, it wasn't an 'incompatibility of temper' as Smiles hinted, it was a matter of basic mechanics. Even the more distant question of working on the Sabbath was soon forgotten; a mere hiccup among many.

Throughout the mid-Victorian years the rack versus lead-screw controversy emerged with yet another closely linked, equally profound problem: the optimum shape of gear teeth. Again Whitworth played a prominent part in both these questions, his radial-arm drill again illustrating as clearly as his other machines the amount of thought he put into gear design. He led by example: not just in machine tools but manufacturing machinery and cotton too. Naturally, power transmissions aroused great interest in the trade press, none of it hesitant when it came to criticisms about the extra cost of Whitworth's machines. It was he who was making waves and offering new ideas and he looked to the press for support but sadly they gave him little or no encouragement.

Indeed, as if to emphasize their price criticisms they implied that Whitworth was neither the inventor, nor even an improver, of the radial-arm drill. Not the inventor of it, no; he never claimed that; but certainly he fundamentally redesigned the basics far beyond its original function. Robertson Buchanan's *Practical Essays* published in 1841 included drawings of the earliest machines showing the elementary base from which Whitworth subsequently created the modern drilling machine. From later drawings collected and published by George Rennie, it would appear an even more convincing supposition that Whitworth was in fact the sole innovator of practically all the radial-arm *improvements* which followed the early 'swing' drilling machines used by boilermakers in the 1830s.

He designed his post-1845 machine to be heavy enough to perform both cylindrical boring and radial-arm drilling. He gave it a 4-in diameter telescopic spindle-barrel squeezing a grease cavity between the double bearings. The radial arm itself which carried the spindle-saddle was for the first time mounted in trunnions, its vertical slideways allowing the arm to move smoothly up and down its rotating column. He incorporated feed screws and key drives throughout although his dog-clutch combinations tended to make the housings awkward and bulky.

One other machine tool figured equally in the divergence between Whitworth and the other makers, including Muir – the vertical slotting machine. Principally the argument was again about the use of a rack and pinion downward movement as against Whitworth's vertical worm-screw. Messrs F. Lewis and Company of Manchester built the first upright pedestal slotting machine in 1835 using a crank and slotted-link drive complemented by a worm-geared rotary table. Even today this machine remains the most popular basic form for less sophisticated machines; the one improvement added by Lewis in time for the Crystal Palace Exhibition was a copy of Whitworth's own quick-return motion. Tit-for-tat, Fred Lewis pooh-poohed any complaint coming from Whitworth about this copying by pointing to Whitworth's own cheeky replication of almost the entire Lewis slotting machine less than four years after it was first marketed.

Perhaps mindful of these wider accusations Whitworth quickly followed up his first slotter with a second machine of entirely different construction. Its unusual appearance being best explained by its curious origin: it had been originally intended for use as a hub-press and keyseat broaching machine, big enough for locomotive driving wheels. Whitworth added a slotting function thus converting it to a heavy-duty dual purpose slotting machine, hence the hybridity of its composition. Once fully developed, it thus became a machine of amazing potential. At the 1851 Exhibition foreign machine makers were able to see it alongside Whitworth's other great innovation, his horizontal slot milling machine – a sight of such animating stimulus as to inspire a few years later the first glimmerings of what today is a combined vertical mill; a slotter-cum-horizontal plano-miller; feeds and face plates et al – machines which today are perfected in one great universal creation.[23]

Full credit should be given to Frederick Lewis of Salford for having pioneered the crank-operated slotter but its hybrid screw-operated sister machines should undoubtedly be credited to Whitworth. Incredibly the early work by Lewis was ignored altogether while Whitworth's later machine was the subject of much criticism. Fortunately American historians with an interest in technology wrote very differently: they carefully studied the genealogy of both machines alongside others before properly accrediting both Lewis and Whitworth with their due attribution.

When Charles Beyer first saw Whitworth's hybrid vertical slotting machine during a visit to the works in 1842, he dubbed it a failure. He sketched the machine in his notebook – perhaps in disbelief – showing two 8 ft vertical columns between which vertical slideways worked the toolbox up and down. He titled it a 'key groove machine' below which he wrote: 'Compared with (Whitworth's) other tools, it appears a complete failure. The tool, which has a stroke of 28 in, is worked by a vertical *lead-screw* placed at the back.' He then went on to complain that the cutting-tool was cantilevered too far out from its power-source, the lead-screw, for it to be a competent design. It was in fact the one feature which achieved for Joe universal acclamation. What Beyer criticized the trade applauded.

Beyer's criticism, however, was misplaced. Eight years later when the machine appeared at the 1851 Great Exhibition the jurors awarded it maximum points for reasons the exact opposite of Beyer's. They applauded the way the cutting tool was *tucked in* close to the line of the power-feed – it was in fact the principal reason why Whitworth had chosen 'a nut and lead-screw vertical movement' in the first place. Before leaving the subject, however, Beyer later quoted John Booth, Whitworth's works superintendent, who verified that Whitworth 'put considerable stress upon the unformity of cut', a feature later mulled over and praised by trade journalists when they came to emphasize that the machine had 'a surety of touch and a positiveness immediately the compound feeds of the machine were engaged'.

Some years later at the 1862 South Kensington Exhibition, the new jurors, when evaluating other vertical slotters on show wanted it known that in their opinion the best system by far was Whitworth's vertical screw-feed. They rejected both the Lewis and the Muir crank and cam-slot mechanisms. They recorded the very objections about which Whitworth and Muir had disagreed and came down in favour of Whitworth. Their report said of Lewis and Muir ' . . . the ram very much overhangs the slotted-disc by which it is driven, which also overhangs its bearing without affording any assistance from an upper bearing to reduce the leverage strain'.[24] In other words (in regard to Lewis and Muir) the actual cutting tool is unavoidably cantilevered so far out from the power-drive that it constitutes a serious design handicap. But even if this report still didn't do Whitworth full justice, the fact that the world's best machine makers by the 1880s accepted Whitworth's lead must surely endorse the master's design philosophy. Certainly his clever, robust screw-feed combinations with their co-ordinated power-feed rotary tables made fine machines, the basic elements of which are still discernible.

Towards the end of William Muir's period at the Chorlton Street factory both he and Whitworth agreed that a new first class foundry was mandatory. In fact, within two years it was fully operational, producing castings with a greater accuracy in rounded shapes and wall thicknesses than most of his competitors could achieve by machining. These splendid results confirm that Whitworth and Muir must have employed some highly skilled pattern makers and moulders. Thus, from the time Muir first became manager in 1840 to the time when the new foundry could take on outside jobbing work midway through 1844, the company had grown quite sizeably from just over 60 men to a workforce of around 172. This total apparently included many men who became the envy of other machine builders, innocently the best poaching material; machine fitters reputedly trained by John Booth personally. There was only one way Whitworth could have held on to them: the technique was the same then as it is now, he must have paid them more money.

Nonetheless, as settled as things appeared to the outsider it was obvious that Whitworth was working towards a radical overthrow of existing methods. He was particularly keen for his own company to review any of its own hidebound design weaknesses which he considered bad mechanics. Some of these outdated practices which the wider industry tolerated remained custom and practice purely because a lack of theoretical understanding drained confidence from new ideas. Whitworth wanted his second decade at Chorlton Street to set the trend. He wanted to give the industry leadership. He wanted personally to emulate his more academic brethren and play a bigger part in Manchester's learned societies. But he knew only too well none of this was possible unless he himself could show by example and create the actual technology while at the same time ensuring a highly profitable company to fund his endeavours. He realized the necessity for a strong economic base and it was towards this end he carefully calculated his next moves. Now that we can look back nearly 150 years it is possible to see the great transformation Whitworth envisaged. The replacement of what was then little more than a crude rough and ready engineering industry, revolutionizing it with a much more precise technology clearly owed much to the genius of Whitworth. A few mocking cynics have been heard to say 'hardly ever single-handed' – well, of course not – yet the changes he brought about by his unaided advocacy of the drawing board, fine measurement and well-designed machinery, were of such magnitude that the grudging, very often disputative recognition offered him was perverse in the extreme.

Not that this kind of shabby treatment was restricted to Whitworth alone; the very talented design engineers he employed over the years suffered an equal pettiness by association. Perhaps it was that Whitworth himself was jealous; that he harboured some vengeful spite and deliberately played down the work of his own men like William Muir and Henry Goss. It is difficult to say. Apart from the gnawing rivalry between Nasmyth and himself there seems little evidence that Joe ever deliberately denigrated, either individually or collectively, the design work of either his own or any other drawing office. Indeed, his constant campaigning to stress the urgent necessity for training highly skilled draughtsmen was always forthright and open. He went out of his way to congratulate others on their success.

Whitworth's one salient, idiosyncratic flaw we know about, a tendency which threatened to drive to distraction his own senior draughtsmen, was that he frequently withheld until the very last moment the completion of his design specifications. Maybe he was acting out a not unknown phobia – it can be the only explanation – that if his draughtsmen knew too much they may have absconded, their heads full of his best ideas. It was all so contradictory. Other commentators have suggested he convinced himself all draughtsmen were dedicated saboteurs working to undermine his best projects. Surprisingly, for an engineer of his quality, he forever failed to instil into the minds of his men a good draughtsman's trained approach 'to first distrust all ideas until they are proved sound and feasible'.

The Whitworth company, however, made a point of employing good draughtsmen and good pattern makers, but proportionate to the size of its workforce, it never employed enough. It was a weakness and the draughtsmen themselves knew it. Perhaps by way of redeeming himself Whitworth became a founding father of the Manchester School of Design, preaching most fervently that the old methods of chalkmarks on the floor must henceforth be replaced by pencils on the drawing board. His workshop gospel spelled out the lesson that only by understanding the dialectics of good design would national progress be made. In that he undoubtedly was a Baconian fundamentalist. Nonetheless it was still the opinion of many that had Whitworth used more often the pulpit offered him by the Mechanics Institute and later by the IMechE. his influence deservedly would have been far greater.

As late as the mid-1850s the use of linen drawings in factories was still a novelty. The few that did circulate were certainly beautiful works of art: fine lines, coloured in light and dark washes to emphasize round solids. Very few dimensions were given therefore no tolerances were required. The drawings were intended purely as pictures for workmen to copy as they would copy a model. But once Whitworth's own drawing office was established, he encouraged his men to work to given dimensions. He specifically instructed that first-angle projection be used.

Some years later, shortly after he became a member of the British Small Arms Commission, he insisted on including in the Commission's report a proviso that henceforth government contract work be checked against templates and gauges and that each gauge used should be numbered on each drawing. By 1846 his own men actually went further. It was then that he laid down that his staff work to three-dimensional (first-angle) line drawings and that they checked each piece they machined with Whitworth's own 'go-no-go' system.

Each stage of development from templates to systematic drawing practice readily slotted into its successive position. First came the plane surfaces and the measurement, then the gauges, finally the drawings to co-ordinate the whole thing. Whitworth created both the means and the language: he created an entire system.

According to William Muir, towards the end of 1842, Whitworth was producing some fifty tons of machinery per week. Just after the 1851 Great Exhibition, his manual workforce rose from 277 to an astonishing 636 in just over two and a half years. It was a phenomenal rise – almost wholly due to the international reputation he had acquired following the Great Exhibition – a surgency which lifted his machine output well over 200 tons per week. Not all machine makers enjoyed this kind of success; most, like Nasmyth, did very well but none secured the future by investing in proper, well-funded research. In truth, neither did Whitworth.

In 1838, James Nasmyth wrote, 'These are glorious times for engineers. I was never in such a state of bustle in my life, such a quantity of people come knocking at my door . . . the demand for work is really quite wonderful'.[25]

But sentiments such as these were deceptive and short lived. By denying themselves consistent investment in research British engineers denied themselves a future. The price they paid was extremely damaging. In 1877, F.B. Norton, an American, patented the first synthetic grinding wheel. It was a brilliant advance and snatched from Manchester the well-deserved leadership of the new era which Whitworth had created in Britain. The Americans then held the upper hand in precision machine tools and high speed steels. The superbly rich work contributed by Brown and Sharpe, Pratt and Whitney and a host of others verified their primacy.

The story of poor Henry Barclay working away at Stourbridge, England, twenty-five years earlier when he struggled hard to pioneer vitrified grinding wheels (but was starved of research money) proves the point. Little wonder the critics complained that British entrepreneurs lacked entrepreneurial vision!

CHAPTER SEVEN

A Tour de Force

> The true epic of our time is not Arms and the Man but Tools and the Man – an infinitely wider kind of epic
>
> Thomas Carlyle

'Precise knowledge concerning mid-Victorian machine building remains elusive', admitted Professor F.C. Lea, a leading Whitworth scholar. 'Contemporary opinion tended to shift according to fashion'.

Although much of the injustice suffered by Whitworth stems from this paucity of knowledge, the same grievance also applies to some other machine makers. This chapter attempts to overcome these shortcomings by including within its scope the broader canvas of his dissimilar yet equally massive work on both gearcutting and hydraulic forging.[1]

The engineering basis upon which Whitworth established his early machine tool reputation unifies around three areas of machine practice: planing, centre lathe turning and gear cutting. Drilling and boring holes should also have featured quite prominently early on, but because he decided to soft-pedal both his initiatory work and the selling of these heavy duty drilling machines he was never given credit for the development of the modern radial-arm drilling machine. Of those that were sold during the 1840s some were partly copied by others, but not exhibited until much later. The first the public saw of them was at the 1851 Great Exhibition.

It was a much regretted period of self-imposed anonymity, thankfully short, when some of his best work on both upright and radial-arm drilling machines was about to become influential. What matters here is not his personal anonymity but that the development of his radial-arm drill with its mitre-gear clusters, telescopic shafts and castellated clutch assemblies helps authenticate the actual technology threshold from which Whitworth launched his more advanced mechanisms. It helps because Joe, in much the same way as his Manchester contemporaries, appreciatively built upon Clement's earlier gear and clutch arrangements. Our purpose therefore is to separate what was new from what existed; to credit Whitworth only with those advances which resulted from his personal invention and skill.

The most advanced machine technology available in 1830 was almost wholly embodied in three pieces of machinery. The first, a bolt threading (pump-

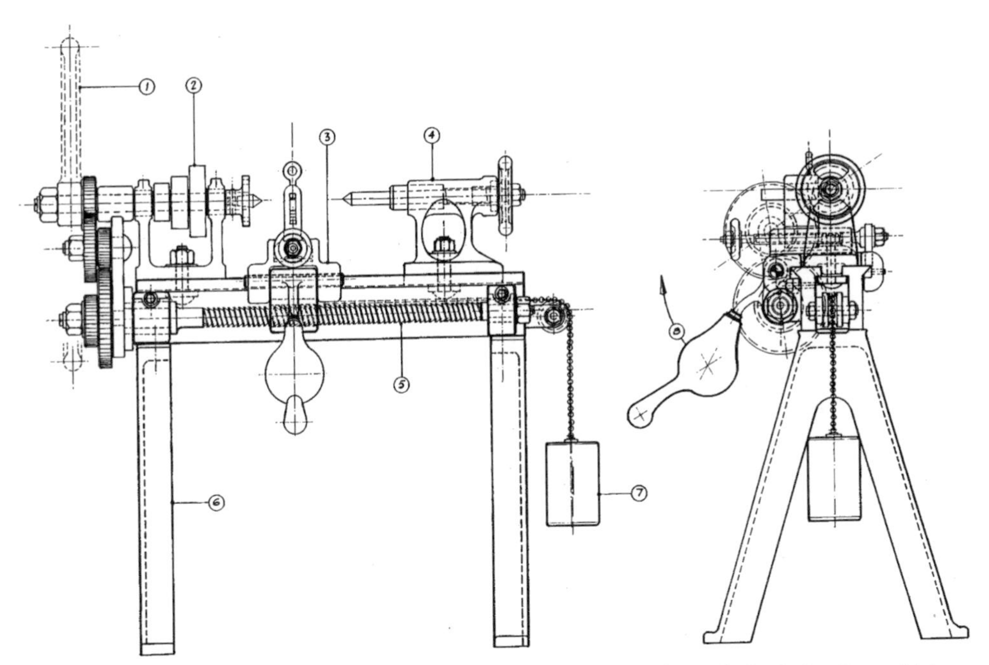

Fig. 4 Clement-Maudslay bolt threading lathe, c. *1824–8. State-of-the-art lathe design from which Whitworth developed the modern lathe*
1: optional handwheel for manual operation mounted on extended shaft with flywheel; 2: stepped pulley for endless belt-drive from overhead line shaft; 3: saddle with manually operated fixed cross-slide and tool-post (cross-slide fixed at 90° to bedways); 4: tailstock with cylindrical barrel and screw-fed dead-centre poppet; 5: buttress thread leadscrew mounted in single bolt plummer blocks outside bedways; 6: Richard Roberts cast trestle type inverted 'V' legs; 7: weight suspended on chain attached to saddle for return of saddle to tailstock; 8: dumb-bell handle. (Hinged to lift half-nut to engage/disengage power feed. The screwing of bolts is from right to left. When the full extent of the threaded part is reached the dumb-bell handle is lifted: the power traverse thus disengaged, the weight will return the saddle and tool-post to the tailstock ready for the next cut.) This drawing is approximately to scale.

handle) lathe first constructed jointly by Clement and Maudslay around 1824–8. This particular machine tells most of the story. Two other machines of about the same period, a centre lathe and a planing machine, both made by James Fox of Derby, complete the trio. Unfortunately, the Clement-Maudslay 'pump-handle' lathe (see fig. 4) no longer exists (except in photographs) but the actual work of James Fox still does exist both here and abroad. Some excellent descriptive writing by engineering journalists contemporary with Clement, Maudslay and Fox also endures, from which it is still possible to construct an accurate picture of what was then the most advanced mechanical engineering available to Whitworth.[2] That was his inaugural base. The verifiable developments down to Whitworth which occurred during the following twenty years flowed from then onwards from his own drawing board and pattern shop. It was this inventive work which, in the main, composed a brilliant inventory of his more outstanding machinery and for which he should be recognized.

It was a great pity that Whitworth never had an Olympian outlook otherwise he would have carried far more easily the fame so rightly his. Of course, a person could flaunt both a monumental ego yet pretend to be demure (as some have suggested) yet these were both genuine aspects of Whitworth's so-called complex character. The trouble was he was far too modest following the launch of his great planing machines in late 1842. It was then he needed some ego.

Both his 30 and 40-ft machines were considered by French and German pundits to be his *tour de force* yet only two technical writers in Britain, D.K. Clark and Robert Mallet, came out passionately in support – the remainder of the trade press were politely cynical. Whitworth got the message. To improve his machines he not only jettisoned from his post–1842 planing machines many of the well-publicized features which previously had attracted the press, but he also dropped what some journalists had called his 'more lucent inventions'. One such gimmick, his 'facing-both-ways' cross-beam toolbox – nicknamed by magazines as his 'Jim Crow' because it turned through 180° enabling it to cut in both directions – later embarrassed him to such an extent that he would only make them to specific order. At that time Whitworth thought any feature which cut out non-productive 'idler' time must be an adroit move. It was only his later experience which taught him that it was just not possible to stress-load a planer type machine in both directions without sacrificing the very qualities for which he was searching – fast metal removal and good finish.

Appreciation of this complex stress-cum-torque problem (though not necessarily because of his improved theoretical knowledge) swiftly guided him towards a genuine world first: his brilliantly smooth 'quick-return' mechanism. At the core of this new system lay a wormshaft which replaced the more usual rack and pinion drive; the work-table being propelled back and forth by disc-pawls engaging the wormshaft. His single-belt drive consisted of three pulleys: two driving pulleys either side of a free running pulley. The two drivers were linked by two-speed teleshafts to a central bevel-cluster so as to provide a quick return stroke; the two driving pulleys having integrally cast fast and slow gearing. The teleshafts were hollowed out to provide grease lubrication. All in all, this self-contained mechanism (like his centre lathe power cross-feed) rightly secured for Whitworth international acclaim as a designer of exceptional originality (see fig. 1).

Apart from cheapness, most machine-makers other than Whitworth fitted rack and pinion systems to their planers largely because they thought them safer (less damaging to the machine, that is) in the event of an accident. If the machine operator failed to adjust the table-stops correctly and the table overshot the intended work-stroke it would cause the toolbox to crash quite disastrously. A 'rack' system would minimize the damage by allowing the table to 'jump' out of the guideways and free itself from the power shaft. The absolute simplicity of the system was an additional bonus enjoyed by the maker when he came to assembling the machine.

But simplicity and cost-cutting were not Whitworth's principal aims. He went for quality. By using open disc-pawls instead of a closed worm-nut, however, and by carefully positioning his shaft-bearings his favourite wormshaft transmission also became 'fail safe'. The trade journals were right to point this out. His unique worm-drive also eliminated the other major defects associated with the rack arrangement; its shuddering imprecision for instance plus the poor quality of its machined finish, generally described as the 'ripple-effect' – a notorious fault – generated by all rack systems, especially most early machines. Obviously, the wormshaft design was more expensive but Whitworth had a waiting list for his planing machines precisely because of the vastly improved machined surfaces they produced, the very qualities his competitors claimed engineering firms didn't want.

The American engineer, William Sellers, was still grappling with the same problem twenty years on. His eventual solution (heralded as 'beautiful' by the American press) was to have a worm-drive (a spiral pinion) meshing at 30° into an epicycloidally generated rack: the motion being assisted by a fly wheel; otherwise the machine was not dissimilar to Whitworth's. Sellers patented his design in 1862, verifying perhaps that the Americans were moving ahead of Britain in machine technology. Although his machine sold well it never quite equalled Whitworth's for smoothness. The other top American builders who had remained loyal to the original Whitworth design based their own planers on a new wormshaft, split-nut arrangement.

Reverting to Whitworth's own work, however, his progress can only be described as phenomenal. Unbelievably, he had progressed from a tiny 2-ft 6-in treadle planer – almost a toy by comparison – to a 40-ft (wormscrew traverse) planing machine in less than eight years. Judged by any known engineering performance, this was a remarkable progression probably unequalled. Not only did he screw-cut a wormshaft 40 ft in length, he also machined guideways of much greater length, incredibly using machines only half their length. It was reported that he excelled at improvization – a grotesque understatement – when in reality he engineered to within unprecedented limits absolutely superb components. One outstanding example stood above all others: within one setting, he actually machined a flat surface of well over 200 sq. ft – a monumental achievement, either then or fifty years later.

Clearly, neither a machine table 40 ft in length nor an even longer machine bed, nor indeed, a wormshaft of similar length, could have been made in one piece. Of his big planers only the vertical pillars or the cross-beam itself could possibly have been made in a single casting. This elemental necessity alone must have caused Joe considerable difficulty when finally he assembled the finished machined pieces. The wormshaft, because of its enormous length and weight, was supported on four pedestal half-bearings fastened to the machine bedplate: another remarkable feat. It was enough to tax the ingenuity of a modern machineman, let alone a man making a machine this size for the first time ever in the early 1840s.

Altogether Joe had ten planing machines in his own factory, the biggest of them accommodated in a newly erected building, the huge work pieces being transported between departments by a tramway across the yard. When Charles Beyer visited the Chorlton Street Works in August 1842, he particularly noticed these fresh arrangements. He immediately clarified his earlier sketches with the following comment: 'They have but few [referring to Whitworth's ten planing machines], the larger ones, three in number, are fine and the largest, 40 ft in length, is a splendid machine. Like everything else, they [Whitworth's] make their guideways with judgement – the breadth as well as vee-angles according to the size of the machine. All their tables have dove-tailed grooves running the whole length. In planing the vees of the beds they put two [toolboxes] on the cross-slides and plane the two vees at the same time'.[3]

The Joseph Whitworth company – as journalists were saying of his Chorlton Street Works at the time – now represented 'a gateway, opening up a whole new machine world'. But as Charles Beyer and some other Manchester engineers were the first to see these colossal machines actually working it is not surprising that Whitworth's machine fame at that stage centred more on these giant planers and their 1842 quick-return power transmissions rather than his less obvious, but more influential power cross-feeds and lathe lead-screw (clasp-nut) actions. Incredibly, he continued to work on all these things simultaneously in addition to his legendary work on gear cutting as early as 1843. He even found time to initiate some experimental design work ranging from horizontal boring, punching and shearing to a universal shaping machine; the very stars in fact of his machine galaxy, all destined to outsparkle the rest eight years later at the Great Exhibition.

The *Engineer* magazine, once the chief advocate of Whitworth's work, particularly his planing machines, suddenly became hostile (January 1863) and set about Whitworth with mesmeric zeal. As an appetizer they led with 'Whitworth's duplex lathes are but little used' before savaging the reputation of his by then famous planing machines. The *Engineer* wrote:

> The screw drive [power wormshaft driving the planer] as applied by Mr Whitworth, was an expensive affair and its working was attended with considerable friction. No other toolmakers, we believe, now use it, the rack [and pinion] being every way preferable. Mr Whitworth's reversing or 'Jim Crow' toolhead, was another feature against which something might be said. It would not plane down into deep grooves; it would not work up to a shoulder . . . it lacked strength in the return cut. Mr Whitworth also adopted inverted Vee-slides until his customers refused to have them when he then resorted to the hollow Vee-slide.

After listing a number of other critical points the *Engineer* then concluded their 'slaying of Whitworth' with a monumental injustice, albeit softened by patronizing praise.

1 Joseph Whitworth, pictured at the time the press first noted his lathes and planing machines, 1846.
Photo: Science Museum

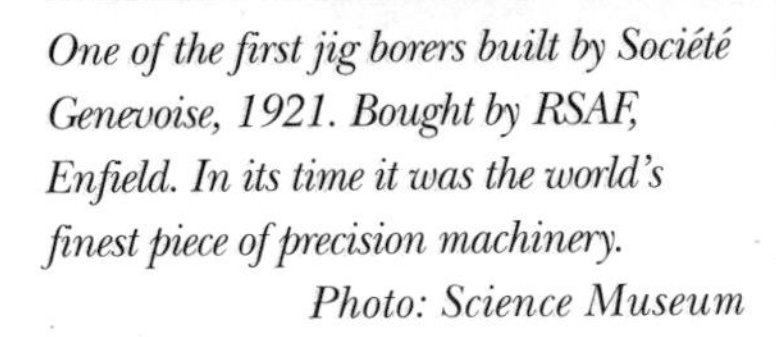

One of the first jig borers built by Société Genevoise, 1921. Bought by RSAF, Enfield. In its time it was the world's finest piece of precision machinery.
Photo: Science Museum

2 Early planing machine built by Whitworth, 1842 (see fig. 1, p. 62). Fifteen years later he converted one of these machines into a precision plate drill by replacing the 'Jim Crow' tool-holder with a drilling spindle. The location of each hole was achieved by the use of pin-gauges and toolmakers' 'buttons'. Although Whitworth had perfected a lead-screw and a 'graduating engine' by 1856 both he and his successors failed to visualize a possible jig borer. How close he came – see inset.
Photo: Science Museum

3 13 John Street, Stockport (built 1800–1805). Often misinterpreted as Whitworth's birthplace. His more likely birthplace, Fletchers Yard, could be entered via the iron gate and house passage to the left of number 13. John Street was made up and named in 1828.
Photo: Stockport Central Library

4 Soon after returning to Manchester in 1833 Whitworth found accommodation in the Castlefield area, at the back of Deansgate. It would probably have been a house similar to this (9 Worsley Street, Castlefield, built c. 1815–18), from which he could walk along the Rochdale Canal towpath to his factory in Chorlton Street.
Photo: Author's Collection

5 Whitworth lived at 62 Upper Brook Street, Manchester, from c. *1839 until he removed to The Firs. The house shown here is in Wilton Street (less than 80 yards from 62 Upper Brook Street). Both houses were built* c. *1805–10 and were very similar in appearance. Part of this house was subsequently occupied by one of Whitworth's managers.*

Photo: Author's Collection

6 Whitworth's extended fitting shop, Chorlton Street, 1866. Note the continuous line-shaft driving the gantry crane and note through the gap (top left) his second new machine shop. This picture was taken a mere 33 years after he started – an incredible progression ahead of the world.

Photo: F.C. Lea Collection

7 Small centre lathe built by Whitworth 1843, fitted with dividing head. Basic design patented 1835 (small treadle lathe). Various improvements made 1837–42 including swivel cross-slide and modified toggle activated half-nut on leadscrew. The 1851 version was awarded a Gold Medal at the Great Exhibition.

Photo: Science Museum

8 Armour plate milling machine (with independent steam engine) 3ft 6ins diameter multi-tool facing mill. Made by Whitworth. Machine similar to this first used Thames shipyard for armour plating HMS Warrior, *1860. (Table traverse confirms this machine was made in 1862.)*

Photo: IMechE

9 Horizontal boring and facing machine with short traversing spindle and external tool slide made by Whitworth. Universal boring-bar support with hand and power feed not shown. Larger travelling-column type machine appeared about 1870 which dates the machine pictured here c. *1863–4.*

Photo: IMechE

10 Radial arm universal drilling and boring machine made by Whitworth. The gutband (spindle feed) dates this ingenious machine 1862 as shown at the South Kensington Exhibition. (See fig. 3, p. 126, for the first of this genre.)

Photo: IMechE

11 Twist Drill Department, Openshaw, Manchester, showing Whitworth fluting machines first made at Chorlton Street, c. *1875. Whitworth invented the twist drill to assist in drilling rifle barrels from solid bars.*

Photo: Author's Collection

12 Gauge room, Openshaw, c. 1912. These Whitworth lapping machines were probably more than forty years old. They were also used for setting broaches and key drifts.

13 The tool and gauge room at the RSAF, Enfield, seen c. *1925–6. This (Whitworth) layout is exactly as it was laid down in 1885. The line shaft was put in in 1892 to replace the shafting originally put in by Fairbairn (1852). Each toolmaker has his own surface plate.*

Photo: RSAF Enfield

14 The American Civil War 1861–5. There remain seven breech-loading and five muzzle-loading Whitworth 12-pounder Hexagon rifled field guns in the USA. This photograph taken 1863 of a Whitworth 12-pounder is hexagonally rifled from muzzle to breech. The Whitworth 12-pounder field gun shown (inset) stands in the National Park, Gettysburg Battlefield, USA. The Confederates purchased from Whitworth the equipment to manufacture their own supply of hexagonal shells but failed to use it, relying instead on unsuitable substitutes, hence their failure.

Photo: RAI, Woolwich

15 Whitworth 12-pounder (2.75 inches A/F) breech-loading rifle (BLR) on standard field carriage taking part in gun trials, Southport Sands 1863. Sir John Burgoyne is 3rd from left and 3rd from right is Joseph Whitworth. His best shot hit the target at 4.7 miles.

Photo: Manchester Central Library

16 Whitworth 12-pounder (2.75 inches A/F) breech-loading rifled (hexagonal bore) field gun (1863). See cartridge case and shell (probably supplied by the Manchester Ordnance and Rifle Company) standing below carriage.

Photo: RAI, Woolwich

17 The Firs, Fallowfield, Manchester, in 52 acres. It was in these grounds that Whitworth built a shooting gallery half a mile long to carry out his early experimental gun work. On this lawn he organized a number of IMechE gatherings, the first in 1856.

Photo: M.J. Harris

18 The Firs, stabling and carriage mews. Whitworth was a keen horseman and raced trotting-ponies. His stable-yard, originally built for Ardern's Guest House, covered ¼ acre and was entered through an arch at right angles to this wall. It was demolished 1885–8.

Photo: M.J. Harris

19 The house provided by Whitworth for his estate manager, Joseph Dawson. Dawson managed both The Firs and Stancliffe, naming his house on the estate at Darley Dale, Fircliffe.
Photo: Author's Collection

20 Church Road, Darley Dale. Stancliffe estate workers' cottages. Local folklore has it that 'Whitworth requested no front doors to stop gossiping.' Not so. They were typical model cottages by George Dance. Even without water-borne sanitation they were considered 'advanced' for their time.
Photo: Author's Collection

The one surviving piece of the original 17th-century house – the south facing gable end and rooms shown here. The small conservatory, seen right, is a modern replacement for the iron veranda which led to the winter garden.

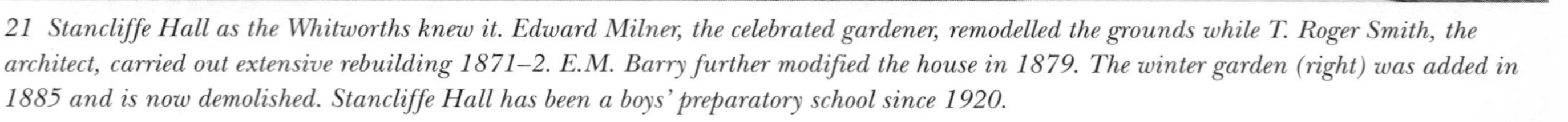

21 *Stancliffe Hall as the Whitworths knew it. Edward Milner, the celebrated gardener, remodelled the grounds while T. Roger Smith, the architect, carried out extensive rebuilding 1871–2. E.M. Barry further modified the house in 1879. The winter garden (right) was added in 1885 and is now demolished. Stancliffe Hall has been a boys' preparatory school since 1920.*

Photo: Estate Agents, 1897

22 The uncomplicated entrance to Stancliffe Hall. Interiors by John Gregory Crace described as 'elegant classicism' (1885).

23 Stairway. The baluster lantern posts suggest a Pugin image – probably also designed by Crace. The spacious landing is just visible.

Photos: Author's Collection

24 Stancliffe Hall West Gate and Lodge (1872–3). The lodge was reputedly designed by T. Roger Smith, a beautifully proportioned house, most decidedly not a gate-keeper's cottage. In Whitworth's mind, he probably saw it as a residence for a college principal when the Hall became a college.

Photo: Courtesy of Terence Kilburn

25 The Whitworth Hotel (left) and Institute (right), Darley Dale, shortly after its opening in 1890. Sir Joseph wanted a college for Darley Dale but Lady Louisa wrote 'Our scheme includes an hotel and refreshment rooms and we hope, large and convenient school buildings'.

Photo: Courtesy of Whitworth Institute, Darley Dale

26 A view of the parsonage from the site of the Whitworth family grave, parish church of St Helen, Darley Dale. Whitworth wholly disagreed with the rector, the Revd Frederick Atkinson, about education in the village. Lady Louisa held the peace. Whitworth wanted a village college.

Photo: Author's Collection

27 A full-length portrait of Lady Louisa Whitworth by L. Desanges, c. 1871. Both this and the full-length portrait of Sir Joseph (see jacket) were probably wedding portraits and now hang in the Whitworth Institute, Darley Dale.

Photo: Terence Kilburn

28 Sir Joseph Whitworth FRS. An engraving from a photograph by Elliott and Fry, London W, 1882. 'His later years were embittered by a sense of the injustice done him by the British Government', C.P. Scott, Manchester Guardian, *24 January 1887.*

> In mechanical arrangement the planing machine owes little, if anything that is useful to Mr Whitworth, but on the other hand where he was not entirely successful as a designer, he was eminently so as a maker, or, if we may employ the term which best expresses our meaning, as a workman.[4]

Not that Joseph Whitworth would object to being called 'a good workman'. He wouldn't. But for the *Engineer* to divorce his name from the design legend of the modern planer, and by rubbishing his quick-return wormshaft drive and his other machines, is to replace history with a whole series of crass misconceptions. No less misjudged was the *Engineer's* reference to Whitworth's introduction of 'inverted-vees'. The fact that his customers objected to them in no way justifies their criticism. In this case, the customer was wrong: modern machine designers now use 'inverted-vees' (as did Whitworth's contemporary, James Nasmyth) for the very same reasons Whitworth explained at the time. Joshua Rose, writing in *Machine Shop Practice* (May 1880) about Whitworth's early machine tools, especially his screw-drives and power-mechanisms, said:

> His machines could master the heaviest cuts without the slightest tremor. *They were as near perfection as possible due largely to Whitworth's magnificent sense of design* and his insistence on the highest quality (close limits).

Whitworth probably more than any other machine builder suffered a disquieting press capriciousness: one moment it was Hallelujah,[5] the next day he would be flattened; his critics dousing him with anything they fancied except logic. Typical of the absurdities raised, the *Engineer* (23 January 1863) went back thirty years to chastise Whitworth: 'Richard Roberts assures us that he still prefers the chain to either the screw or the rack'. Well – he would, wouldn't he?

As Whitworth made headway it was a natural progression that he should increase the size and capacity of his machine tools. It compelled him to make his bigger machines in small sections bringing the castings together for the first time during their final assembly. This required the accurate pre-positioning of dowels or 'fitted' bolt holes in much the same way as increased speeds and feeds compelled him to reconsider gear design and the insufficient strength of his power-transmissions. Convenient or not, his design schedule was thus regularly extended to include many more unexpected additions, like special-purpose machines for the drilling and reaming of these newly required 'interlocking devices'.[6]

While the origin of the modern jig boring machine is open to considerable conjecture it could perhaps be that Whitworth's own new-found need for precision drilling was its nineteenth-century beginning. Of the few known contemporary references which pin-point his use of a 'table drill' all suggest he converted one of his own planing machines by replacing the cross-beam clapper-box with a drill spindle. In the beginning he used a system of length gauges and toolmakers' 'buttons' to accurately locate hole positions but later on there is some evidence to suggest he actually calibrated the lead-screws to position the table or adjust the cross-beam saddle. Both Beyer and Mallet wrote in cryptic language but if they meant that Whitworth calibrated his lead-screws for his 1847 converted planing machine then it would have had a remarkably prophetic similarity to that of a 1927 Société Genevoise jig borer (see Plate 2 inset).

Confirmation that Whitworth developed the idea of using special lead-screws for the accurate location of machine work-tables can be gleaned from the notes left by Charles Beyer. Shortly after he opened his own locomotive factory in 1854 Beyer asked Whitworth to build for him a 'dividing engine' for the purpose of calibrating his own special steel rules (Patternmakers' Contraction Scales as they were called), which Beyer had invented to enable his pattern-makers to produce accurate castings to a specific size. The special lead-screw by which the carriage and engraving tool was moved along a modified lathe bed was then made by Whitworth to the most exacting limits: it had a pitch accuracy within 0.0005 in at any one point along its entire 36-in length – or so Beyer claimed. The method Whitworth used to achieve this unprecedented precision was probably an advanced variation of the system first announced by John Bodmer in 1841. Whitworth continued with this work until in the end he had perfected a series of master lead-screws: good enough presumably for use as national standards.[7]

Though there is no reason to suppose that either Whitworth or Joseph R. Brown at Providence in the United States were aware of the other's work, both were developing almost identical 'dividing engines' simultaneously. Joe Brown, founding partner of what was shortly to become the world famous Brown and Sharpe Manufacturing Company, progressed more rapidly than Whitworth, not only perfecting his own linear measurement but adding to his 'dividing engine' a splendid calibrated ring for making accurate index plates. Brown was thus able to build both a milling machine and a gear hob equipped for the very first time with a satisfactory (self-acting) indexing mechanism.[8]

One other interesting toolroom event arising from Brown's new-found ability to calibrate lead-screws occurred the following year, 1855, when the first Brown and Sharpe hand micrometers arrived in Britain. Even though they were not freely distributed the 'awesome' idea of having them available on the shop floor quickly established a basic difference between British and American engineering employers. The British were none too keen; they thought the more skilled their employees became by measuring their own work with a micrometer the sooner they would demand higher wages. American employers, on the other hand, actually wanted to pay their men more money for higher skills, an attitude which took them into world leadership by the 1870s, never to look back.

The first screw-pitch 'correcting lathe' in Britain was invented by Maudslay, the second was shared between Bryan Donkin and Bodmer. Whitworth learned from all three and some ten years after Maudslay he contrived yet another giant step forward by designing a somewhat modified version of Bodmer's original mechanism. Whitworth modified one of his own centre lathes to automatically adjust the cutting tool axially once the machine detected a lack of pitch accuracy in the thread being cut. It was in principle the same system later adopted by the Swiss perfectionists, the Societé Genevoise company. This particular feature, when allied to their unique wear-adjusting vernier scales, became the nucleus of the Société's superb 1927 jig-borer.

Historically, all the machines must be judged against the best engineering standards in their own time. The Société Genevoise 1935 Hydroptic jig-borer with its hydraulically operated worktable and optical scale-reading system undoubtedly remains the world's most impressive machine. Even so, considered in their mid-1850s setting, Whitworth's uniquely calibrated machinery and the accuracy of his superb lead-screws required equal ingenuity in their making to any of the mechanical gems which have arrived since.

It would be an interesting piece of research to discover just how close Whitworth came to making the first lead-screw jig-borer prior to Genevoise. Arguably it would be the one test to prove Whitworth's worth. Fourteen years after his death the Armstrong-Whitworth Company presented to the National Physical Laboratories a special lathe, the lead-screw of which had an intrinsic accuracy of 0.0002 in over its screw length of 53 in. By using a sophisticated version of the correction attachment previously mentioned the machine gave results accurate to 0.0001 in at any one point.[9]

Hobbing Gear Teeth

High on the list of Whitworth's own priorities in 1842 was his determination to improve the quality of gear wheels. Even gears manufactured on his own machines were wholly inadequate for the speeds and feeds he himself envisaged. The task however proved a much more complex business than he himself contemplated; he admitted his ingenuity had been stretched in all directions. From the day he patented his first gear hobbing machine in 1835 he recognized it wasn't just a matter of more accurately spaced teeth, but one of redesigning the tooth profile to facilitate both extra strength and less wear once the gears were made to take heftier and faster power feeds.

To some extent he was now technically out of his depth but he realized from reading John Hawkins, Britain's leading theoretician at the time on gear transmissions, that a strengthened *involute* profile was a must for speeded-up spur-gears running between parallel shafts and that something similar to a helix tooth was an essential development for worm-drives; but no gear manufacturer, including Whitworth, knew quite how to replace with a fully self-acting operation the hitherto manually operated (and therefore comparatively crude) gear hobs.

John Hawkins persuaded most engineers that there was such a thing as a fundamental law of gear-tooth action. That the comparatively smooth transmission of power, the avoidance of vibration and noise and the severe scuffing of one toothface by another was a question of getting right the rolling contact between gear teeth at pitch-point. Whitworth himself had fully understood these strictures having observed by experiment just how much the earlier gear teeth of the 1840s slid about, chattered and dug into adjacent teeth, but he was sensible enough to realize that he himself could only do a limited amount to improve teeth durability. To concentrate on improving the poor quality of the cast iron was a start but not enough. What he determined to do was to improve as best he possibly could the tooth action itself by redesigning his own gear hobbing machines. Ideally he aimed to hob gears from steel blanks.

Two centuries earlier, a British professor of geometry, Robert Hooke, had written about the principles of gearing and transmissions. He introduced the idea of helical gears and universal joints. Cycloidal teeth came a century later when C.E. Camus in 1752 extended his own theoretical work. It is interesting that though the quality of gear wheels and gear systems has advanced out of all recognition, mechanical engineers still repeat today what Hooke and Camus once said and even what Whitworth was still saying in 1862, 'that the improved mechanical efficiency of machines still depends upon a further improvement in gear manufacture'. Only one other English toolmaker at the time of Whitworth – prior to the 1862 South Kensington Exhibition – made gearing his special concern. Frederick Lewis of Salford in Lancashire exhibited excellent gear hobs at both the 1851 and 1862 exhibitions, otherwise most British gear machinery remained little more than simple gear shapers.

Whitworth's inspirational nostrum in this regard centred on making his own universal dividing head self-acting, an integral part of his gear cutting machines. For him it was a judgement at the very heart of any gear making strategy, a conclusion readily borne out by Joseph Brown's brilliant universal machines in the late 1860s. And although Whitworth's best gear work didn't come until 1856 – three years after his trip to the United States and a possible meeting there with Joseph Brown – there is little or no evidence he was ever influenced by his American visit. As things turned out, the design qualities of his gear work never equalled in mechanical ingenuity his other mechanisms. Gear technology – transmissions generally – was profoundly culpable as a central weakness of Britain's machine design and manufacture. The fact that Britain failed to retain its world leadership can be traced in part to this particular aspect. In Whitworth's case his work on gears was considerably weakened by his diversionary interests, especially his military work. It was a fearsome mistake considering that internationally no more than five or six machine tool engineers were capable at that time of overcoming the complex design problems which bedevilled the development of both hobs and gear-generating machines.

By 1861, Joseph Brown and Lucian Sharpe, aided by Frederick Howe, were determined in their efforts to make gear cutting and worm transmissions an accomplished task.[10] The fact that no specialist in Europe seemed capable of reaching the same perfection unquestionably hampered British machine design in a wider sense. Much blame for this must rest with Whitworth, though it should not be overlooked that it was he who clearly led the way for over a decade. At fifty-eight years of age Whitworth himself was still indefatigable and inventive and backed by an astutely perceptive design staff but he failed to see the extra-special importance of his gear work. Having led the way with his universal gear-hobs, his location mechanisms and new type dividing heads he literally snatched defeat from victory when he turned away towards military weapons and hydraulic forging presses. How wrong he was not to encourage his drawing office to take his ideas to the next stage we shall never know. Regrettably, neither of his two original *universal* gear cutting machines have survived – nor their workshop drawings – but there are reprints of some early illustrations with sufficient detail for us to recognize the mastery of both machines.

Clearly, during the second half of the 1850s, machine tool design underwent a whole gamut of mutational change; the surprising fact is that some of the modified constructions remain in evidence today. Certainly Whitworth's second and third series of gear-cutting machines came well within this designation; the basic, if somewhat primitive, synchro-mechanisms are still there for all to see. Both these series of machines were genuine hobs in that they both used side-and-face cutters, shaped exactly to correspond with an 'involute' gear tooth. Whitworth, in fact, never built a gear-generating type machine: an understandable omission considering that gear-hobs (let alone machines like hypoid gear generators) never really came into their own until 1895 or so. It was really Whitworth's own synchronized indexation systems which merit special recognition, though he never quite succeeded in perfecting their conversion from manual to power operation.

The official catalogue published during the 1851 Great Exhibition described his second gear-hob as 'Whitworth's Self-acting Wheel-cutting and Dividing machine'. The catalogue gave a whole list of special features which commenced: "for (cutting) bevel, spur and worm (gear) wheels, with headstocks and dividing wheel, moveable horizontally for different diameters of wheels, cutter frame with universal adjustment, self-acting traverse for cutter, self-adjusting driving pulleys, change wheels for all numbers up to 100 teeth by 40ins. maximum wheel diameter'. The arbor carrying the hob was mounted vertically and could be swivelled through a 60° arc: the whole thing designed to slide along guideways similar in style to a heavy duty lathe bed.

Whitworth's 'third series' gear hob – highly commended after the 1862 South Kensington Exhibition – represented some twelve years of development work. In appearance, the machine was dwarfed by its huge diameter index plate, a quite different configuration from its predecessors. In some ways this latest machine reflected the imaginative brilliance of Whitworth's new management team led by Gledhill and William Hulse but paradoxically, it also portrayed a design team – including Whitworth himself – who were needlessly stressed (as already mentioned) by too many projects running simultaneously. According to the 1862 Exhibition jurors, however, this particular gear-hob was far ahead of its competitors, being the first hob in their opinion to have a 'self-acting' indexation system. Historians, with hindsight, know that it wasn't. Had the

Americans, Brown and Sharpe, exhibited at South Kensington the latest of their own machine tools the jurors would have seen at first hand just how advanced the American milling machines and gear-hobs were, not only equal in design to the Whitworth machines but actually poised to lead the world with their three-dimensional worm-drives and 'universal' attachments. Even more aggressively – once F.W. Howe joined Brown and Sharpe as their works superintendent in 1868 – the now legendary machine tool company left most competitors a long way behind with their own special brand of superbly engineered machine tools.

The excellence of the American challenge confirmed not only the fine qualities of Whitworth's work but also laid a comparison by which the work of the burgeoning Manchester machine builders like Craven Brothers could also be measured. Gear manufacturing had long been identified with Lancashire companies, so perhaps it wasn't surprising that engineers from most European countries descended upon the 1862 Exhibition in search of Manchester ideas anticipating that they would get an insight into the future of gear cutting. But despite Whitworth's remarkable progress they seemed disappointed. The critics gave his latest hobbing machine almost a 'thumbs down'. They latched on to its one important frailty; the gear-blank itself lacked precise location as it automatically clicked round to each tooth station. The fault was puzzling because pitch imprecision was the one weakness Whitworth's design team had set out to avoid.

The Americans were the first to overcome the problem, but not until 1873. Prior to F.W. Howe leaving the company, Brown and Sharpe (due largely to Howe's three years' personal contribution) were able to build both an automatic gear hob and a universal milling machine, both to the meticulous high standards which finally established the company's reputation. This seemed yet another illustration how engineering invention remains dependent upon the work of an inspired individual, the downside suggesting that Whitworth was beginning to fade and no longer inspired his drawing office staff.

In Whitworth's case his uncharacteristic 'compromise' design work was symptomatic of the rapid mutational changes occurring throughout the period – the basic reason why possibly he had been pushed prematurely into launching a fully automatic machine. In all probability his draughtsmen at this time (three years earlier he had been embroiled in some quite radical managerial changes) were 'hooked' as draughtsmen say, on universally power-driving a machine which had till then been indexed manually. It was a bad mistake. Instead of starting afresh by scrapping the old manual design they endeavoured to mimic it: merely exchanging crank handles for powershafts. The real alternative they failed to see was the use of segmental gears and a precise worm-unit feeding a multi-station indexing system.[11] His own (and in consequence the team's) judgement was at fault; he simply missed the boat; otherwise the admirers of his new gear-hob would not have been put off. The power-driven dividing head was a diversion. Had he kept to a manual crank-handle the press would have recognized the true value of his otherwise trendsetting hobbing machine.[12]

This analysis is thoroughly straightforward and valid. It is not a question (as the *Engineering* magazine suggested) of bogusly criticizing Whitworth for failing to get right a technology not available to him. The technology *was* available. For some dubious non-engineering reason he allowed himself to be distracted at a most critical time from his far more important machine tools. He himself had already manufactured some of the world's best worm-gearing and manually operated dividing heads; the leading machine makers supplying the cotton industry had been regular users for some years of Whitworth cam-plates and segment-gears. In terms of know-how Whitworth was almost alone among machine makers in having the potential to develop the most difficult self-acting mechanisms capable of taking the industry into its next phase. The fact is that in the end he was faced on the drawing board with a dilemma; either to go ahead with premature concepts and try to make them work, or play safe and revert back to his more reliable manually operated system. He chose the former and although mistaken he deserves some credit for risking his reputation in an effort to make progress.

THE CENTRE LATHE – THE BIRTH OF THE MODERN MACHINE

Just before the 1851 Great Exhibition the demands of manufacturers pushed existing technology towards goals the rate of innovation could not sustain. The sheer frustration experienced by machine designers to deliver new plant and equipment capable of providing a much higher rate of production triggered a whole series of incoherent adaptations. The majority of Whitworth's competitors manufactured machines which offered little more than cosmetic modifications to satisfy the market.

There were unexpectedly a number of historic engineering landmarks which stood out like beacons when Crystal Palace eventually opened. Exhibitors had learned about the final decision to go ahead with the exhibition only since June 1850. The real epoch-making machines, unveiled for the first time once the royal opening ceremony was complete, must have been built in secrecy: the press was taken by surprise. Whitworth himself was in the forefront exhibiting no less than twenty machine tools plus his own pièce-de-résistance, his new micro-measurement and gauging system. Having survived a very tough period, his managerial changes alone must have been severely disturbing yet he was still able to deliver such credible results. His drawing office and new management team must have been proud, considering that within the Whitworth Stand were five award-winning lathes comprising the most comprehensive lathe capacity known in Europe. Though considered a miniature, his small treadle-lathe was judged the most beautiful, perfectly balanced piece of machinery in the whole Exhibition. Alongside this little one were the great epoch lathes, one of Whitworth's long-bed lathes, an equally long duplex lathe 36 ft between centres with four traversing toolposts, two either side plus two heavy duty gap lathes; one designed to machine two 8-ft diameter locomotive driving wheels simultaneously while they were mounted on their axle.

The firm also exhibited fifteen other machines, but it was mainly the lathe section which the design staff treasured most because it was work they had commenced after William Muir had left Whitworth in June 1842. Henry Goss had then become chief draughtsman but he remained in the office little more than two years before Muir offered him far more money if he became Muir's own head of design, working for a new company which Muir had established in 1845. Needless to say, when Henry Goss left Chorlton Street he left Whitworth facing yet another quandary: whether he should bring in a fresh chief draughtsman or revert to his original design staff who had remained loyal to him throughout. He chose the latter, recognizing the rising talent of his twenty-five-year-old cousin, W.W. Hulse, an enthusiastic engineer whom he had invited to join the company two years earlier as a trainee general manager. Francis Wise, who had been Whitworth's senior draughtsman since 1834 then took over the reins in the drawing office, assisted by John Wild, while the ever-present, very able John Booth continued to superintend the whole works. This was the team, under Whitworth's leadership, who in less than eight years provided Britain with the brilliant array of machinery now exhibited, eventually to be either scorned or envied by engineers everywhere but certainly not ignored.

Described by the *Mechanics* magazine during the years prior to the Great Exhibition as being someone in 'frenetic pursuit of logic' Whitworth was reputed to preface his own reactions to problems with either 'let us try' or 'it is only logic' – certainly his engineering brain at that time was at its most prolific. On occasions his judgement was perhaps obscured by over-work; many years later a period of sickness suggested he suffered severe stress symptoms – but generally he kept up a relentless momentum. His design technique always retained a self-possessed coherence, yet apart from his gear-hob mechanisms which were far too ambitious for the time, he was always sufficiently flexible to re-think 'design blocks'. Evidence of this was the training and encouragement he gave his cousin, Billy Hulse. With Joe's support and good wishes he eventually left Whitworth's employment in 1862 to join his brother, Joseph Hulse, in establishing a new company Messrs J.S. Hulse & Co., Ordsal Works, off Regent Road, Salford.

The two brothers developed confidently, building some of the biggest, most memorable machine tools of the last century, especially their long-bed heavy duty centre lathes, all of which were essentially Whitworth in design. As the *Practical Mechanics Journal* reminded its readers in September 1862, 'The very fine machines of J.S. Hulse Co., an offshoot from the establishment of Mr Whitworth, exhibits a selection of cutting tools of various kinds which are generally, in design and manufacture, fair representatives of the school they spring from'. The Hulse brothers were, in fact, the epitome of Whitworth's attitude towards management and design but it was their lathe work particularly which followed so closely the work of their mentor which finally crowned their reputation with such glory.

Like all time-served artisans Joe loved to reminisce about his earlier skills.

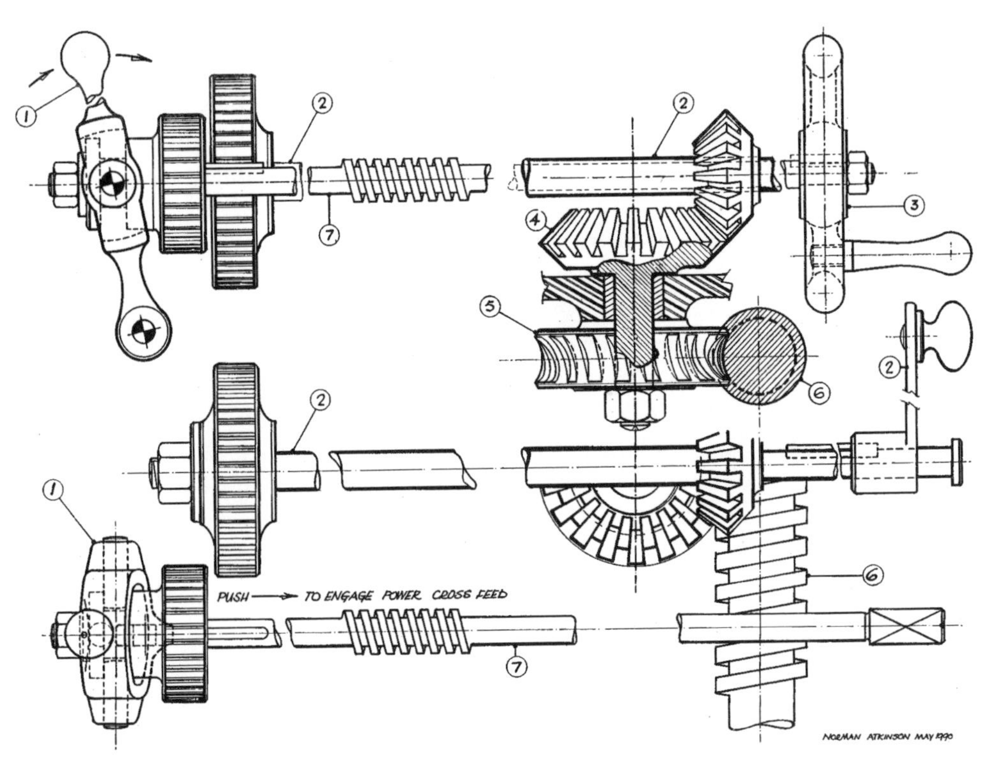

Fig. 5 Whitworth centre lathe – power cross-feed. A schematic arrangement of Whitworth's combined power cross-feed and longitudinal manual-power traverse, 1835. 1: push–pull stirrup hand lever. (Push to engage power cross-feed) (2); 2: primary cross drive shaft; 3: Handwheel attached to power shaft (2) revolves when leadscrew revolves. When leadscrew is stationary, handwheel can manually operate worm-wheel; it then functions as a rack and pinion longitudinal traverse (5, 6); 4: bevel gear keyed to stub shaft and wormwheel; 5: wormwheel with combined function; 6: tapered turret thread leadscrew (when stationary acts as rack); 7: cross-slide leadscrew. Whitworth later added an additional rack and pinion hand traverse on all lathes over 5ft.

Referring to his final two years in London (1831–3) he often remarked how pleased he was to have worked for both Joseph Clement and John Holtzapffel. He referred to Clement in particular; the man largely responsible for the final improvements to the 'pump-handle' screwing lathe, but by employing Whitworth at that time, he probably bequeathed to Joe a singularly rare understanding of the most advanced 1830 lathe mechanisms then available (see fig. 4). Apart from the square-section powershaft introduced by James Fox in 1820 the 'pump-handle' lathe represented the most advanced technology at the time Whitworth moved into his Chorlton Street works. For the previous fifteen years lathe design had made little or no progress simply because machine makers were baffled as to how they could stop-start the saddle traverse without stopping the lead-screw. In the end they gave up. They were again stumped when faced with the problem of how to simultaneously power-drive the saddle traverse while stop-starting a power cross-feed from the same lead-screw.

It remained for Whitworth's innovatory know-how from 1835 onwards to provide the answers. He led the way forward to a new era of genuine *universal* centre lathes. Once he had incorporated his two quite revolutionary cross-feed and traversing-nut mechanisms into his lathe design his work really did represent 'crossing the rubicon'. It was largely thanks to Whitworth – albeit capitalizing on the work of his predecessors – that the modern lathe became customary around 1842. Referring to the machine tools which existed prior to Whitworth, J.W. Rowe, Professor of Machine Design at Yale University, said:

> In none of these machines was the slide rest combined with change gears and a power-driven lead-screw. It was these improvements which raised the device from an ingenious but cumbersome mechanical movement to an instrument of precision and power.[13]

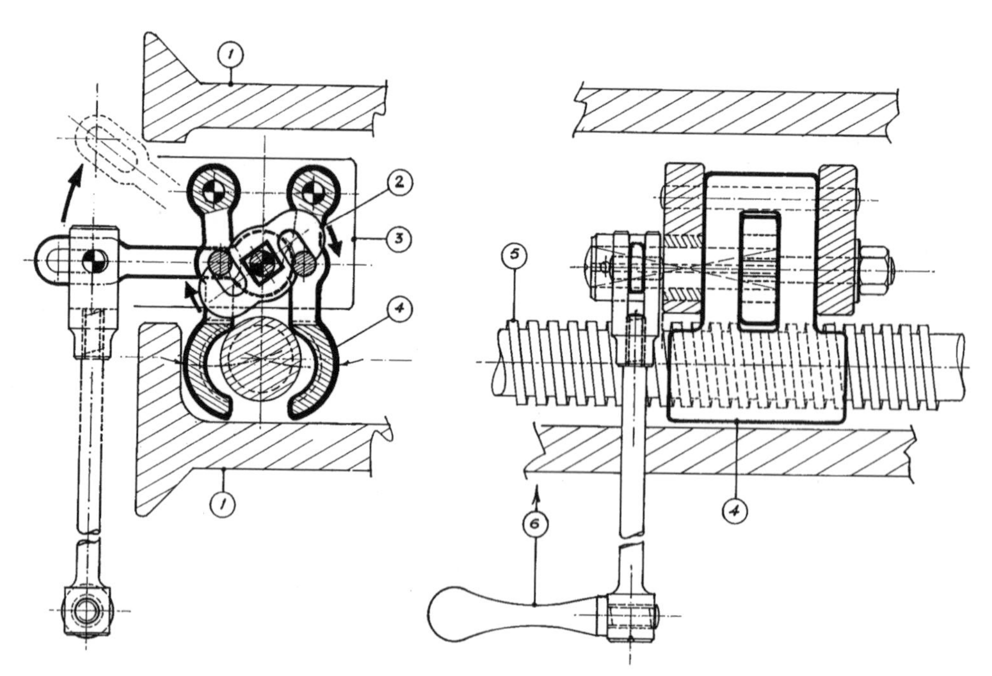

Fig. 6 Whitworth centre lathe – longitudinal power traverse. Detail arrangement of Whitworth's clasp nut and toggle action. He sometimes simplified this arrangement by using half clasp-nut and single toggle lever. 1: cast-iron (webbed box-section) lathe bed; 2: double toggle latch mounted on square stub-shaft operated by push-pull lever in front of the machine (6); 3: integral part of saddle casting; 4: split clasp-nut (hinged) open and closed by toggle latch; 5: square thread (longitudinal) leadscrew; 6: operating lever: push to engage power feed, pull to release.

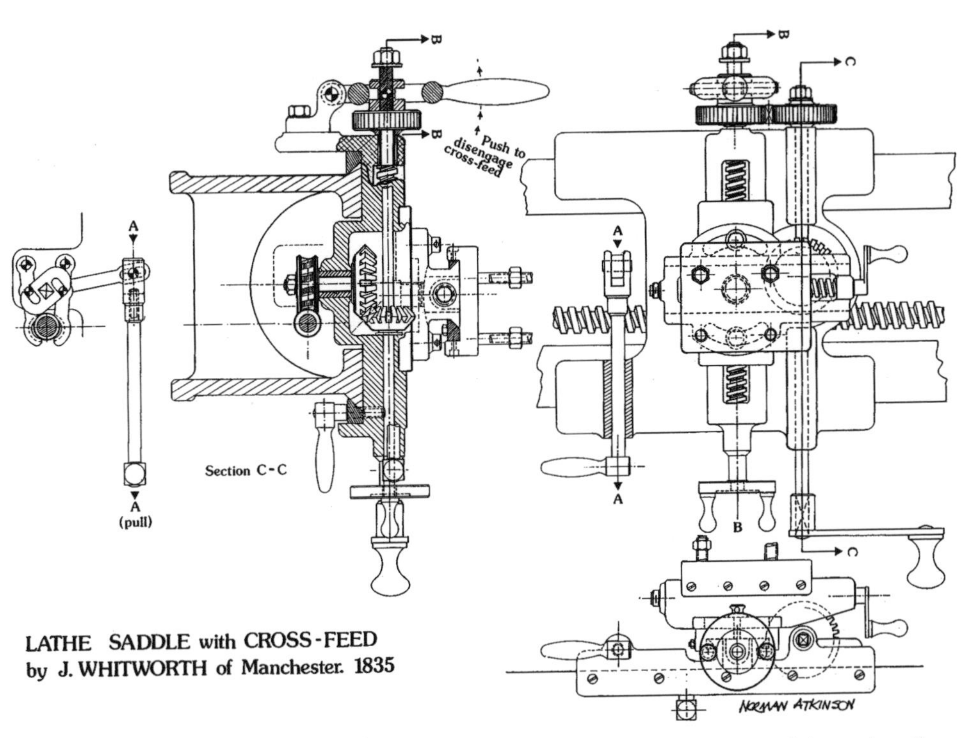

Fig. 7 Whitworth's introduction of a combined power/hand longitudinal traverse (via toggle action split-nut) and power cross-feed with hand-feed toolpost (60° swing) represented an epochal transformation. His new lathe then remained state-of-the-art until modern capstan lathes and automatics came in at the turn of the century.

Retracing the lathe's development, it was Joseph Clement's idea to fasten a 'pump-handle' to a traversing 'half-nut' thereby making it possible for the first time to engage-disengage a power-traverse by raising or lowering the handle. It was as rudimentary as that. But it worked. Once the half-nut was lifted from the lead-screw the saddle was then free to return to the tailstock by virtue of the weighted linkage. Whitworth replaced this manual arrangement with a toggle-action split-nut (see fig. 6), again replacing this experimental work later on with a different type cam-action. He also designed a wormwheel and bevel-gear mechanism to power the cross-feed which required the wormwheel to fulfil a dual function. When the lead-screw was stationary and the wormwheel turned by a handwheel it acted as a manual quick traverse in much the same way as a rack and pinion handwheel system. These were fundamental innovations first introduced by Whitworth to fit his small treadle lathes but by the year 1842 he had developed the most sophisticated power-feeds capable of power-driving facing-cuts 9 ft in diameter (see fig. 7).

The emphasis was now on swift metal removal and increased production. The kind of heavy lathes Whitworth pioneered could be ascertained by the work they were called upon to do. Much of it, as required by the railways and big marine paddle engines, demanded power, rigidity and higher speeds to take full advantage of better cutting tools which were then becoming available. Again it was Professor J.W. Rowe who best described Whitworth's work in this regard when he summarized Joe's post–1842 strengthened lathe beds: 'He made the bed of the lathe its foundation . . . an open box section with integrated guideways braced by cross-ribs for strength and rigidity'.[14] As most engineers at the time agreed, Whitworth's heavy duty saddle had a much reduced tendency to cross-wind under the strain of the heaviest cuts – proof indeed of a machine's rigidity.

Careful scrutiny of the engine and millwright jobbing work undertaken by Whitworth during the early 1840s shows that it required a variety of heavy duty lathes, gap beds and extended bar lathes. Only Murdoch and Maudslay had previously attempted to build machines of this size but now the large diameter steam cylinders, cranks and paddle shafts necessitated entirely new type machines and boring bars. Accurate finishing and parallelism were now essential prerequisites. Everything was getting bigger and more accurate. Atlantic marine engines and the like faced draughtsmen with an entirely different set of problems. They literally had to design a new generation of tool-feed mechanisms based on the idea of big heavy castings held stationary on a bedplate while they were machined. Whitworth was the first to respond with a hybrid machine: in appearance something like a cross between a horizontal borer and a plate-facing lathe. The emergent alternative was Bodmer's vertical borer with its large revolving bedplate-cum-table.

Robertson Buchanan and George Rennie described the machine they considered to be the first of these new hybrids and said it was built by Whitworth.[15] They calculated his machine would take a cylinder 7 ft dia x 10 ft long or a shaft up to 3 ft 10 in dia x 19 ft between centres. For the internal boring of large cylinders the workpiece was clamped to the bedplate while a horizontal boring bar carrying a fixed cutting tool was made to revolve while traversing to a maximum length of 10 ft. In the early days the boring bar was advanced forward and backwards by rack and pinion, supported at one end by the headstock tunnel, while a pedestal bearing providing tail-end support was placed between the extent of the cut and a belt-drive.

Within two years of its 1839 introduction this somewhat crude concept underwent fundamental modifications. A more sophisticated facing lathe-cum-universal borer began to emerge; ideas which were soon to influence Whitworth's other heavy duty lathes. In this particular instance the updated boring bar he developed contained an internal lead-screw to provide the tool traverse – the bar itself being a slotted tube along which the cutting tool traversed the length of the cut. While the original machine had a detachable tunnel headstock, his latest machine with its new boring bar allowed the lathe facing plate and orthodox headstock to remain in position permanently; there no longer being a need for the boring bar to penetrate the headstock.

All Whitworth's lathes were now subject to far heavier loads and he paid special attention to the bearings. Charles Beyer in 1842 made sketches of them. Not only were these new bearings used for the machines described above but were specially adapted to suit his much bigger lathes from the early 1840s onwards. Hardened thrust plates had also become necessary once Whitworth introduced live centres and carriers. His common shaft bearings he made from brass with locking collars for adjustment. For his shaft bearings, now having to support far heavier loads, he designed tapered shell bearings (case hardened) again with locking nuts so that the diameter of the bearing could be adjusted to take up any slack due to wear.

The earliest of these machines came off the drawing board about 1839; the long-bed centre lathes were the first to be sold but were very soon followed by his duplex gap lathes. The centre lathes were equipped with compound swivel tool-slides, taper turning attachments and additional screw-cutting facilities. They had two-speed power traversing in both directions safely controlled by a strengthened lead-screw disengaging nut. Their extra big saddles could also be moved along the bedways by a rack and pinion handwheel mounted in the centre of the apron. One other small but important distinguishing feature – tapered gibs and locking screws – allowed his bevel slides to be adjusted for wear. The possible use of this clever novelty was originally discussed in 1820 by a Dr A. Tilloch but promptly forgotten. It was, however, a natural corollary alongside Whitworth's scraped bedways which rekindled the idea – Victorian prudence if you like – to retain lifelong accuracy.

Though scant attention was ever given to matters affecting safety it was no doubt the potentially dangerous makeshift methods used in the railway workshops that compelled locomotive managers to persuade Whitworth to design special duplex gap lathes for machining loco wheel tyres and journals. The outcome was little short of wondrous. In the end his railway lathes were redesigned and given a double-gap construction which allowed even the biggest loco wheel-sets – including those eight feet diameter – to be supported between centres. Mounted on the bed slides back and front were duplex toolposts which allowed both journals and tyres to be machined simultaneously. The prodigious capacity of these machines was truly remarkable; the four pedestals, each of which had a compound swivelling toolpost, could be operated quite independently of each other; they also had auxiliary attachments for radiusing and plate-facing.

It is perhaps an indictment of British machine tool makers that beyond 1870 most modern variants of the lathe owe their origins to the post-Whitworth ingenuity of the American (New England) machine designers, Henry Stone, Frederick Howe, Christopher Spencer and Edward Parkhurst. All the later British versions of the bar lathe, the turrets, the capstans and the automatic lathes owe their universal popularity to the original work put in by these four innovative engineers. It was they who recognized the enormous potential offered by the additional lathe functions contributed by Whitworth twenty years earlier. For example, the inconspicuous collet chuck, invented by Whitworth, turned out to be the one key component which made feasible so many lathe variations. It was developed from his tapered shell bearings, the work it was called upon to do making it much easier to trace the sequence of his ideas. He started by modifying one of his lathes to machine 'endless' line-shafts. He required to feed the shaft through the tailstock and out through the headstock – an operation which required not just a plain revolving tunnel in the headstock but one which would, by movement of a simple lever, grip the workpiece tight: hence the tapered collet-chuck and the birth of the bar-lathe.

Prominent at the 1862 South Kensington Exhibition another of these special Whitworth lathes couldn't help but attract fresh American interest, it was so unusual. This particular lathe provided all the elementary clues from which the New England engineers hatched their second brilliant manifestation – the turret-cum-capstan lathe. Ostensibly Whitworth exhibited his machine as an updated 'duplex' lathe but he embellished it with a number of significant auxiliary pieces, not least of which was an entirely redesigned version of his twenty-year-old self-centring chuck. Most public attention, however, focused on its reversible tailstock. Again it was Whitworth's originality which quadrupled the lathe's productive scope when he provided the tailstock with a sliding poppet-barrel and handwheel feed – the poppet could take a drill at one end – perhaps a threading tap at the other end. The arrangement was unique because the tailstock was spigoted, therefore reversible. The whole thing was mounted on a conventional saddle and was moved along the bedway by rack and pinion, a capstan handwheel providing the leverage. This construction turned out to be the rudimentary forerunner of the capstan lathe; a machine which nowadays has become an extremely sophisticated piece of machinery. Though its elemental beginning was down to Whitworth, there can be little doubt that once his exported machines were received in New England 1863 or '64, the genius of Frederick Howe and the others quickly persuaded their draughtsmen to replace their own (horizontal-axis) turret-lathes with the British (vertical-axis) turret-cum-tailstock, thus providing the world with what is now known as the capstan-lathe.

Historically, the evolution of these special lathes was in reverse to the normal progression of machine tool developments. Unlike the usual scaling-up process, some models displayed at the 1862 Exhibition were the result of scaling down. In both function and basic design they were smaller editions (adapted from general machine shop work) of the big specialist machines Whitworth built to facilitate over-sized crankshafts, some with 20-in diameter journals requiring a 5 or 6 ft throw; all weighed an enormous tonnage yet he designed his machines to carry these heavy components between centres. Imagine the size of the lathes required to machine piston rods for marine steam engines of this power. To their eternal credit much of this original design work was done by Whitworth's early team, William Muir and Henry Goss though his later duo, William Hulse and Francis Wise, were entitled to claim responsibility for the final drawings, from 1843 onwards. In 1867, the magazine *Engineering* described these big lathes as being personally engineered by William Hulse, though later on the work was freely acknowledged by Hulse to have been overseen by Whitworth. As the magazine said, they were 'beautifully constructed, precise giants', as indeed they were.

One lathe particularly received great attention in the trade press, especially in the *Engineering Review* (10/2/1883). Using their cousin's well-known patterns they had his agreement to cast their work at Whitworth's Chorlton Street foundry. The first of these special lathes was 60 ft long and 80 tons in weight. The Hulse brothers adapted James Fox's 1820 traversing arrangement because of the lathe's inordinate length: the lead-screw remained stationary while a revolving traversing nut travelled the length of the machine. The power shaft was square in section along which a sliding bevel-gear fed the cross-slide. The lathe had three disengagement levers to enable the operator to stop the saddle. They were well spaced: they had to be on a lathe requiring a twenty-second walk from one end to the other!

Lathes of this size posed exceptional lubrication problems. Animal and vegetable grease lacked load bearing qualities. Fortunately help was on its way. In 1849 a chemist named Young, from Alfreton in Derbyshire, discovered how to extract paraffin from coal. By 1855 he had successfully researched methods for producing a comparatively good mineral lubricating oil, the same year an American named Gesner produced his own paraffin oil which he named Kerosene. By 1860, he too had researched the making of a viscous lubricating oil together with a thick petroleum jelly suitable for lubricating machinery. Young's work was a stroke of good fortune for machine tool builders, his thick lubricating oil coming at a time when their increased speeds and feeds required a far greater viscosity than vegetable oil.

During his appearance at the House of Commons to give evidence to the 1854 Select Committee, Whitworth said America was wrongly using rape oil for bearings and gears. In his opinion they should have been using whale oil particularly for bronze thrust bearings; moreover, in the case of hardened shell bearings he didn't think they would service at all well without whale oil. The only solidified grease available at that time was a mixture of animal fats called tallow. White lead was used for lathe centres and steadies and other places where a 'load-bearing' lubricant was required. Interestingly immediately a viscous mineral oil became available machine designers in both Britain and America set about incorporating oil baths to assist every moving part of their machinery. And though neither country had knowledge of the other's work, machine builders in both countries designed their lubrication baths in exactly the same way, using loose oil rings to dispense the oil.

The Origin of the Hydraulic Forging Press

Towards the end of 1844 Whitworth again extended his factory premises specifically to provide more assembly space for his giant lathes. He also enlarged his drawing office. He anticipated starting work on new fledged gearing and power transmissions. His modified duplex lathes would entail a great deal of new design work. Locomotive production in Britain was expected to double during the following three years and he wanted to be ready with his special-purpose machines when the boom came.

Joe recognized that his workforce would need to be increased to something like two hundred men including, probably, a design team of eight or nine draughtsmen; the difficulty being, now more acute than ever, finding not just suitably trained men but the kind of outstanding design engineers he required. His dependency upon a good team was increasingly apparent now that he was away from the works more often. These days he more willingly agreed to the many requests he received to join in committee work. Engineers after all had a lot to offer Manchester's cultural societies; he, Whitworth, wanted his engineering gospel understood. As more railway track was laid so he travelled greater distances, being away from home days on end. Railways, he discovered, were not time savers but time *creators*.

Whitworth felt rewarded by all this additional activity. He enjoyed getting out and about; he treasured the camaraderie. In some ways it had taken him unawares; it was unfamiliar but warm; a little disconcerting perhaps, for a loner; to enjoy a sense of kinship based on professional relationships was for him a fresh experience. Now turned forty, his professional talents instinctively steered him towards Manchester's other leading engineers, William Fairbairn, Richard Ormerod and Edward T. Bellhouse. They all became close friends, their mutual professionalism and expertise making a success of Whitworth's Chorlton Street new extension.

On one occasion the four of them attended the September (1844) British Association at York. They travelled back together in their specially reserved railway coach using the newly opened Leeds–Liverpool railway. Imagine them, as jubilant as schoolboys, passing across the cast-iron viaducts which they themselves had designed and built to carry the line in and out of the yet unbuilt Manchester Victoria Station. As the train cut across the centre of the town it spanned both roads and canals sometimes at a height of 50 ft. They were entitled to their merriment now that it was finished.

On a much smaller scale Whitworth asked Fairbairn to design and build his new lathe gallery supported as it was on cast-iron columns with a new drawing office on top of that. It also included a most prestigious piece of entirely new engineering – an hydraulic lift. It became a central attraction for all visitors. Jointly designed and installed by Edward Bellhouse and Richard Ormerod[17] it enabled Whitworth to lift ten tons of castings one floor up – only its limited size meant lifting his long-bed lathes in sections before manoeuvring them along the new gallery for machining and assembly. Whitworth's hydraulic lift – ten years ahead of E.G. Otis in the United States – was the first of its kind in Britain.

Richard Ormerod was arguably the most knowledgeable of the four on the subject of hydraulics. He probably contributed the bulk of the theoretical work which made the Whitworth lift possible. Not surprisingly, he and his father were devotees of Bramah, specializing in pumps and hydraulic systems since 1840. By late 1849, both young Ormerod and his up-and-coming friend, Bellhouse, had commenced manufacturing simple hydraulic presses mainly for use as baling presses for raw cotton and wool. In appearance they were upright box-shapes, dominated by four guide-pillars, the centre of gravity low down inside a substantially thick-walled cast-iron pedestal. The hydraulic ram was built inside the base forcing upwards a lower bolster thus exerting its considerable squeeze against a fixed top bolster. Exact positioning during each stroke was ensured by four vertical pillars.

Immediately prior to the 1851 Great Exhibition Bellhouse introduced a second genre; he adapted his baling press to make it suitable for metal presswork. By far it was the most imaginative idea yet – that of using hydraulics instead of screw-presses for sheet metal work. Bellhouse offered both these types of press for sale having first displayed them at the 1851 Exhibition. Richard Ormerod restricted himself to selling baling presses only. But sharing the same pavilion, Whitworth himself exhibited two mechanical presses, a fly-press and a punching and shearing machine which could be operated manually or be power-driven; there being no indication at that time that Whitworth had in any sense coveted the hydrostatics developed by his friend Bellhouse.

Edward Bellhouse was one of a number of gifted prodigies encouraged by William Fairbairn and had in fact completed a two-year stint as a trainee manager with Fairbairn at his Millwall shipyard. He then returned to Manchester to inherit from his father the Eagle Foundry in Hunt Street (now renamed Whitworth Street, Manchester). Richard Ormerod did precisely the same thing taking over from his father the St George's Foundry, Minshull Street, Manchester, an excellent foundry and workshop which literally backed on to Whitworth's own premises.

Curiously, now that Bellhouse had converted his hydraulic baling press for the production of sheet metal (presstool work) components and small die-forging, his tooling techniques became quite advanced even beyond those of Ormerod. But it was a commercial advantage he soon forfeited once Ormerod recruited a chief draughtsman named Ryder, an expert in hydraulic presswork. It was an inspired move, albeit a temporary one, later borne out when Ryder was persuaded to cross the road and join the Whitworth stable. Edward Bellhouse retaliated by moving into the business of prefabricated iron buildings, using the advantage of tooling up the sheet metal parts with a small hydraulic press.

The idea of press-tool work was not new; simple bench-presses had been used for a century by clockmakers and silversmiths. The earliest brass stampings and pierced decorative work – mostly from Central Europe – still remain collectors pieces. Bellhouses's fame arises from the fact that he lifted the whole business of presswork into a new era; he made the hydraulic press a machine tool. If we ignore the giant forging presses yet to come – they were of a different ilk entirely – and confine ourselves to the question who actually built the first commercial hydraulic sheet metal press, the answer must be Edward Bellhouse. Unquestionably he was the father of modern hydraulic presswork.

However, probably of much greater importance, the big, heavy duty forging press evolved in quite different circumstances. Knowing what they could do with thinner-gauge sheet metal press-work, engineers had long expressed their frustration by asking themselves the obvious question – why not scale up the same methods for blanking and shaping heavy boilerplate? By 1848 one or two leading mechanical engineers had begun to realize that it could be done by using a much more powerful hydraulic press. But who would design and build such a press? Ormerod perhaps? Maybe Whitworth or one of the new generation steelmen?

The answer began to blossom about the year 1850, prior to which James Nasmyth and Charles Fox vied with each other as to who first suggested the idea. The evidence supports Nasmyth. The story is fascinating, involving as it does both Fairbairn and Whitworth. Towards the end of 1847, the Earl of Auckland, First Lord of the Admiralty, set up an Admiralty special (expert) committee named the 'Iron Armour Committee'. Its purpose was to consider the iron plating of ships and the methods by which it could be done. Both Nasmyth and Fairbairn were asked to submit to the committee their expert opinions in pursuit of which they each constructed experimental hydraulic press rigs.

The all-important questions concerned the blanking and bending of heavy-gauge wrought-iron plate. Though neither engineer was aware of the other's work, their conclusions proved remarkably alike. Despite the crude improvisation of their work the committee were grateful for the positiveness of their reports but the Earl of Auckland, who had already seen Nasmyth's steam hammer 'work miracles with iron-plate' at Devonport Dockyard, failed to enthuse the Royal Navy with the idea of using a hydraulic press. Iron-plate was not yet on their agenda: it was not until 1861 that Parliament accepted the then First Sea Lord's recommendation and approved an order for five *iron* frigates.

To summarize Nasmyth's claim that it was he, in 1848, who first gave Charles Fox the idea of using an hydraulic press for the operation of piercing and bending thick plate, Nasmyth recalled his work for the Admiralty. Michael Faraday had asked him if he could suggest 'a striking example of the power of machinery' for a lecture he (Faraday) was giving to the 1848 annual Royal Institute. 'Yes', said Nasmyth, 'what about using the crude hydraulic press which I myself contrived to punch holes through iron? The punch went through a five inch thick iron plate like a piece of Stilton cheese'.[18]

Having despatched his suggestion to Michael Faraday, Nasmyth then sent a copy to Charles Fox. He knew that Fox was searching for ideas as to how best he could produce quickly and cheaply elongated plate chains made from flat wrought-iron bar. Fox also hit upon the idea of punching from solid, much thicker oval chain links which he could interspace every other one with conventionally forged links. Nasmyth apparently repeated the same advice to Fox as he had put to the committee, that the work should first be blanked and pierced then drop-forged while the material remained red-heat. This work and the annealing procedure was considered crucial by Nasmyth as he knew it was the intention of Fox to use his plate chains as suspension bridge supports.

Sir Charles Fox – as he later became – had amassed a long list of the nation's most prestigious clients. Robert Stephenson, for example, had appointed him senior engineering consultant to oversee the London–Birmingham railway. The Admiralty also called him in to investigate the advice it was receiving about armour plate; almost certainly he would be familiar with the experimental work undertaken by both Nasmyth and Fairbairn.

Fox knew that Whitworth had already developed 4 and 5-in diameter punch and die sets using Fairbairn's experimental hydraulic rigs. Also important for our purpose here (because of his work for the British government and the advice he gave engineering companies concerning work in India) we know that Fox came into contact with Messrs Benjamin Hick of Bolton, Lancashire.

With hindsight it now seems certain that once Fox had agreed that Hicks of Bolton should manufacture his plate chains the inauguration of the world's first powerful hydraulic stamping-cum-forging-press was well within sight. Probably Fox had written into the Hicks contract a clause giving him the right to specify how the work should be done. Hicks themselves also contemplated doing similar work for themselves which by common consent seemed unsuitable for the existing methods using a Nasmyth steam hammer.

It was fortuitous circumstances such as these (in addition to the recommendations compiled by Nasmyth and Fairbairn for the Admiralty) which probably explained why Charles Fox advised Hicks to approach Whitworth and Ormerod in the hope that the two engineers would agree to build and install a new hydraulic stamping press at Benjamin Hicks when the design work was finally tested and ready for making. That a very big press was subsequently installed is agreed; whether by Whitworth and Ormerod exclusively is open to conjecture; that it was at least in the 1000-ton category is suggested by the work it was designed to do. Fox named it axiomatically the 'Bramah' press in much the same way as oil became known as 'diesel'. One perplexity remains, however. If Whitworth and Ormerod did construct the 'Bramah' press it is strange neither they (nor anyone else) built another one for at least seven years.

The Times and certain of the trade magazines have made passing references to the Hicks press as a 'giant' but have given few details. Immediately following the engineers' lock-out, however, in February 1852, trade union members employed by Richard Ormerod and Co. informed the Manchester District Committee of the Amalgamated Society of Engineers that they intended to continue working over two weekends to finish 'urgent parts for the Bramah press at Hicks, Bolton'.[19] Whether it was a combined mechanical-hydraulic press or a straightforward hydraulic stamping press is not known; what is clear is that it was of such size and construction as to be a forerunner of the hydraulic forging-press Whitworth built in 1861 for his own use.

Ralph Hart-Tweddell, a highly respected engineering consultant from Newcastle upon Tyne, and an acknowledged expert on most matters concerning hydraulic presswork, presented to the Institution of Civil Engineers a paper entitled 'Forging by Hydraulic Pressure'.[20] In doing so he set out the historic record as he understood it, but he prefaced his remarks with an extremely apposite homily. 'Ever since the year 1846', he wrote, 'when Sir Charles Fox proposed the attachment of different (press) tools for the working of hot or cold iron by the Bramah press, many suggestions for its use as a forging-press have been made. But while many people can make such suggestions, the carrying out of them is left to the few'.

The point is a valid one, especially in the matter of hydraulics. The conversion of pure theory into hard practicalities is what 'applied' engineering is all about yet since the days when Matthew Murray, in 1814, patented what is claimed to be the first hydraulic press even the best of Britain's mechanical engineers delivered few new ideas prior to Ormerod and Bellhouse in the 1840s. The major reason presumably why the introduction of the forging-press was delayed till 1861 was the unsuitability of the 'wrought-iron' available. The quality of metal was poor, inconsistent, sometimes very brittle; its lack of essential ductility made forging virtually impossible.

The ironmasters present at a meeting of the Iron and Steel Institute (13 August 1856) recognized the significance of the occasion when James Nasmyth spoke up following the presentation by Henry Bessemer of his now famous paper. Holding up a small fragment of Bessemer's wholly decarburized iron, Nasmyth said 'Gentlemen, this is a true British nugget . . . I am not going to claim priority of thought . . . Mr Bessemer has gone miles beyond my own patent . . . I am going from this meeting and tear up my now useless patent'. Nasmyth resumed his seat amid a storm of cheers. The ironmasters then knew they were themselves shortly to become *forge-masters* – within a week, Nasmyth prophesied the development of the hydraulic forging-press far in advance of the experimental work he and Fairbairn had started way back in 1848. Bessemer had given British engineers – particularly Whitworth – the real opening they so desperately wanted – mild steel.[21]

'In the field of metal working', writes Ian McNeil, one of today's leading authorities on hydraulics, 'Fox's cropping, punching and shearing press was followed in 1860 by the first forging-press, made by Whitworth. A 1250 ton machine was built by the Kirkstall Forge Co. in 1863.'[22] How much this succinct opinion depends on Ralph H. Tweddell is difficult to say. McNeil is known to have researched the matter in great depth, his access to a variety of authoritative sources taken as read. He must have been perfectly satisfied that Joseph Whitworth was in fact first in the field though it is a claim subsequently disputed by some analysts. Historians writing the history of Vickers and the ESC have always claimed the first hydraulic forging-press was designed by John Haswell, locomotive engineer to the Austrian State Railways, and that it was built by the Kirkstall Forge Co. It was driven by a system of combined steam and hydraulic power and installed at the Sheffield Cyclops works of Charles Cammell and Co. in 1863. Locomotive and marine engineers, however, were not impressed, preferring the older method of hammer forging thus restricting the Haswell press to the bending of armour plate.

It is difficult to reconcile the detailed evidence which places this particular press as the first to be built. First, the date of its installation was 1863, leaving in limbo the hydraulic work Whitworth is known to have done between the years 1859 and 1862: that is to say, his experimental forging and his 'liquid-compression' treatment which could only have been accomplished on an adapted hydraulic forging-press. Second, starting in 1853 when Nasmyth worked on his patent 'Machinery to Facilitate the Forging of Iron', Whitworth also set his drawing office to work thinking through ways to manipulate the forging of huge marine shafts – as Tweddell says, 'some of these 35 ton monsters were 42 ft in length'. Whitworth also envisaged handling forgings of 100 to 120 tons in weight. As it turned out, hydraulic handling machinery became Whitworth's great forté in the forging business. Sir Edward Carbutt, an ally of Whitworth's, confirmed Joe's superb expertise when it came to the mechanized manipulation of these great forged shafts. He, Carbutt, had himself engineered heavy handling equipment but when, several years later, he saw Whitworth's arrangements, he admitted their infinite superiority.[23]

Sometime around 1858, Whitworth's rapidly expanding War Office interests caused him to reorganize his works management. His own design involvement was now stretched to the extent that he required expert assistance. First, he himself became Chairman of his own company inviting William Hulse to become a partner. For the first time he appointed a managing director, Manny Gledhill, an engineer experienced in hydraulics and handling equipment rather than machine tools, presumably leaving this side of the business to Billy Hulse.

As to the wisdom in recruiting John Manassah Gledhill, Ralph Tweddell had no doubts whatsoever. Turning aside the risk of offending the prima donnas among his audience he told the Civil Engineers: 'The introduction of the hydraulic forging-press is due to Mr M. [Manny] Gledhill, managing director of [Sir] Joseph Whitworth and Co. I have taken some trouble to ascertain to whom the credit of so distinct an advance in constructive machinery is due. I wrote asking the opinion of Colonel Dyer.' Considering it was less than fifteen years since Whitworth and Sir William Armstrong (Dyer's employer) had engaged in the most acrimonious row concerning the forging of guns, Tweddell's enquiry could hardly be described as timorous. Certainly Dyer was the right man to ask; ex-Woolwich Arsenal, currently works manager in charge of the forge at Elswick works (Armstrong's gun factory) and no particular friend of Whitworth. He replied to Tweddell's letter with equally unnerving innocence:

> The introduction of hydraulic forging is undoubtedly due to Mr M. Gledhill, who for many years has been the managing director of the well known works of Sir Joseph Whitworth of Manchester. He introduced the system and perfected all the details; if you apply to him he will supply you with the whole history of hydraulic forging. *Everything which has been done as regards hydraulic forging both in England and abroad is an imitation of the system which Mr Gledhill perfected.*[24]

It is unusual for engineers to be so adulatory but perhaps it was both Colonel Dyer's and Ralph Tweddell's style. Tweddell then went on to nourish his eulogy of Whitworth and Gledhill by referring to the designer of the Kirkstall Forge press. 'I also had some interesting correspondence with the late Mr Haswell about twenty years ago (i.e. 1873) and there can be no doubt but that to him is largely due the present use of hydraulic pressure for forging and working metals. He did much to popularize the hydraulic system and to set other minds at work.'[25]

During the discussion which followed Tweddell's lecture at least one leading forgemaster from Yorkshire visibly gulped at the fulsome treatment of Whitworth and his managing director, Manny Gledhill. 'Vickers of Sheffield and the late Benjamin Walker were working on the same lines', claimed the latter's son, Mr Tannett Walker of Leeds, 'but where Sir Joseph had contributed so much to the improvements achieved was in showing the way in which forgings could be manipulated'.

The story of hydraulic forging and the search for better quality steel occupied Whitworth for some twenty years of his life. Professor F.C. Lea explained why, in his opinion, Whitworth invested both time and a lot of money perfecting his 'fluid compression system' trying hard to improve the quality of steel. 'As is well known' Lea wrote, 'considerable opposition developed against the use of Bessemer and Siemens-Martin steels . . . largely because of the less pure materials used . . . but given equally good materials [Whitworth thought] ingots from these processes should produce ingots equal in strength and ductility to those of crucible steel'. These were the two qualities which Whitworth suggested determined the suitability of a steel for guns and other details. Professor Lea continued: 'An examination of the voluminous literature shows that heterogeneity of cast ingots still exists. In addition to the large cavity which is found at the upper part of the ingot there are discontinuities, or lack of uniform solidity, in the mass of the ingot, and in certain conditions cracking during the cooling may occur.' Quoting the *Engineer* magazine, Lea concluded: 'Some ingots were split longitudinally by Whitworth and revealed that the interior of the ingot was unsound from the pressure of air cells'.[26]

The answer to these problems, Whitworth thought, was to cast ingots for guns under pressure. He therefore devised a system of using a hydraulic press to 'squeeze' the molten metal so as to produce a uniformity throughout the mass. While certain critical steelmasters considered his method improvident for little, if any, improvement in the quality of the material there were numerous engineers and gunmakers – including Admiralty engineers – who wholeheartedly supported Whitworth.

It was during the early 1860s that Joe began his encounter with Sir William Armstrong, not only because Whitworth wanted to abolish the use of cast-iron for making gun barrels, but because he primarily wanted to introduce his own breech-loading guns made from solid 'fluid-compressed' mild steel. But more of this in due course; suffice it to say for the moment that Whitworth considered the quality of the steel he was using crucial to his purpose. His pioneering work however, good as it was, didn't survive much beyond 1875. New and improved Bessemer and Siemens-Martin methods quickly outdated the need for Joe's 'fluid-compression' steel.[27]

Though his metallurgy enlisted a number of expert devotees, his methods, at any one time, were never really in vogue. Engineering reactions were curiously mixed. The only positive encouragement he received from the government occurred when Lord Herbert, Secretary of State for War in Palmerston's Cabinet, set up yet another Special Committee in 1861 to again study the armour plating of iron warships and the manufacture of big guns. Fortunately, by the careful scrutiny of these reports it is possible to glean further insight into state-of-the-art engineering at the time of Nasmyth's experimental presswork. The fact that he 'blanked-out' a 5-in *thick* disc to make at least a 7½-in diameter hole (any less diameter would have caused the punch to seize up 'solid') of necessity meant that his improvised hydraulic press exerted at least 2,832 tons before it would have gone through the steel. Even more thought-provoking, his press almost certainly required a secondary 'stripper-action' of at least 500 to 600 tons to free the punch. These really were phenomenal results. They also provided additional reasons why Nasmyth (five years after he had prematurely retired to Kent at the age of forty-eight) was right to accept Lord Herbert's appeal for him to serve again on War Office and Admiralty expert committees.[28]

Across the town at Fairbairn's works, Canal Street – though not a member of either expert committee – Whitworth was doing similar work to Nasmyth. The fact that these two engineers were able to carry out such experiments verified the remarkable level of mechanical engineering possible in Manchester at that time. Fortunately, the result of their work was carefully minuted by the Special Armour Plating Committee and filed away in sufficient detail to refute the sceptics who had largely doubted whether Gledhill or Whitworth could ever deliver what they promised.

Whitworth's immense versatility, which now included almost all types of mechanical engineering from the most delicate precision instruments to the heaviest industrial plant, found its way into various government reports and was filed away. But what he would have prized more than anything would have been recognition by the War Office for his liquid-compression technique and an acknowledgement that it produced the best ever mild steel for guns; he did not get this, but gratifyingly it was an opinion advanced by the most influential writers of the day.[29]

Central to these new developments of course was Whitworth's hydraulic forging press. Endorsement that the original concept was Whitworth's is not really in doubt. What is perhaps questionable – and engineering historians should seek to establish the facts more clearly – is that his company actually built the first press. Much of what followed largely depends on this testimony. Sadly, his own 1858 works notebooks and drawings cannot now be found. But there does exist sufficient 'probable or possible' evidence to convince most historians he was the first in the field, or to put it the other way round, that the known limitations of his competitors suggests that they were second.

Again, the mother of invention, necessity, comes into it. Guns, heavy prop-shafts and railway forgings all required new techniques. But again, was it left to Whitworth? Intrinsically the answer must be yes although the search for intellectual truth concerning the wider issues remains worryingly fitful.

One failure was that of engineers to armour-plate ships' hulls satisfactorily end-to-end when the government first sought their help. For over a decade leading engineers, including Whitworth, procrastinated endlessly without ever admitting they could not – at that time – forge thick armour-plate to the sophisticated shapes required.[30]

Ignoring a very thinly plated iron frigate built for Mexico in 1849, both Sir Isaac Watts and John Scott Russell admitted much later that when the time came to launch the frigate *Warrior* in 1861, covering both its bow and stern with 4-in thick armour-plate, it had not then been possible. Indeed, of the first seven iron frigates built in British yards, only the last two were protected with armour at either end.

In 1859, Whitworth's ideas on forging were still in their infancy. Nor did the shipbuilding know-how exist which would have simplified the task of subjugating 4-in plate to the beautiful 'wave-line' shapes drawn by John Scott Russell. We do know however that the problem of fastening his big prop-shaft bearings to the steeply contoured stern plates was not satisfactorily solved until 1868 or even later. The reason was that Admiral Sir Edward Reed MP, the best of the British iron frigate constructors, had never been sufficiently confident to give the Iron Armour Committee the go-ahead before 1865 or '66. His first priorities were speed and gun power; he didn't want to overload his ships so that they lay too deep in the water. Not that he ever suffered the antipathy towards iron ships expressed by the American naval commander, Admiral Farragut, in April 1862 when he declared 'I will never go to hell in a tea kettle'.

Why then did these contradictions exist? If Whitworth had working in 1861 a giant hydraulic forging-press, why didn't the frigate constructors use a similar press – or better still, a more powerful version? The answers it would seem were more Treasury orientated than Admiralty conceived. Whitworth did have ideas for a bigger press but it was more to do with paying for the tremendous tooling costs rather than whether the First Sea Lord wanted extra defence by providing extra knots and gun power or giving his ships extra protection by providing cumbrous heavily-armoured hulls. The cost either way would still have been astronomical.

Not for the first time in Whitworth's dealing with Whitehall and Pall Mall did he insist that the Treasury fund the work from the beginning. Why should it be that he, a private company, should first have to prove that the work could be done before the Ministry would decide how much they would pay? William Gladstone, the Chancellor of the Exchequer, true to form, discouraged the whole business. It was in fact 1872 when Robert Lowe (Viscount Sherbrooke) became Chancellor, he authorized the Admiralty Budget, which included the laying down of HMS *Dreadnought* (10,866 tons) which carried 3,690 tons of armour in 4-in thick plate – for its time, a magnificently engineered ship. By then, it was too late for Whitworth.[31]

Sadly, Treasury anfractuous meanness had, for some twenty years, hindered a very important piece of engineering development. Maybe the fault for our not knowing the guilty ones lies heavily with those Manchester Victorians who failed to make a record of their own work. If only they had followed a more cavalier style set by their non-engineering brethren, engineers would have enjoyed historic scholarship equal to, say, English literature or perhaps even British politics. Far lesser mortals preserved every insignificant scrap of paper in their successful bid for posthumous grandeur.

Not in any way wishing to minimize the seriousness of these century-old weaknesses, in terms of lost documents there are other comparatively recent catastrophes to lament. Of particular regret were the floods during the 1930s which swept through the drawing office stores at Craven Brothers (Manchester) Ltd, destroying many of Whitworth's early machine drawings. There was also the inexplicable loss of the remaining Whitworth archives in 1970 during their final distribution between various technical colleges.

The British Science Museum and the Victoria & Albert Museum too must share some responsibility for the loss from their own collection of drawings which would, had they been available, have explained a great deal about the interdependence of the hydraulic presswork of John Haswell, Ryder and Whitworth during the period 1860–66. Who knows – between the V & A, the Science Museum and Craven Brothers there may yet be revealed an absorbing account of Whitworth's hydraulics. The Treasury and the War Office however still remain the most fruitful source.

CHAPTER EIGHT

The Great Exhibition, 1851, and Workshop Conflicts

Their machines . . . let them beware of their false gods

Matthew Arnold, 1869

Along with the benefits they bring, today's machines pose problems which I don't discount. It is essential that we concern ourselves with solving them

Henry Ford II, 1964

The opening ceremony of the 1851 Great Exhibition was an extremely impressive occasion. Everything was in abundance. It was royalty at its most lavish. Even the foreign royals; they too wore their most sumptuous glitter. Hyde Park simply oozed with international personalities both inside and outside the Crystal Palace.[1] As for Whitworth himself, he was billed as 'the greatest mechanician in the world' and he savoured every memorable moment.

Queen Victoria visited the exhibition half a dozen times, taking each pavilion in turn. She came to know the leading exhibitors quite well, particularly Whitworth. Not because she, even fleetingly, became enthralled with Britain's new technology but because Prince Albert was determined to make his mark as the first royal patron of British science and engineering. He had 'imbued the Queen with a sympathetic feel' for such matters. Albert himself was genuinely keen. On more than one occasion he found his way alone down to Whitworth's 'hospitality room' for a chat. As Henry Cole enthused, surpassing by far his more than frequent obsequiousness, he afterwards said of Albert 'A prince of pre-eminent wisdom, of philosophic mind, sagacity, with power of generalship and great practical ability, placed himself at the head of the Enterprise, and led it to triumphant success'.

Whitworth found the exhibition a vast new political experience. Observing the inner circle so closely and doing so for the first time was a profound eye-opener. Nevertheless he didn't neglect his primary purpose which was to grasp the many excellent engineering opportunities that came.[2] He didn't miss a single chance of pushing his campaign for *precise measurement*, in fact he organized things quite well. Adjacent to his main exhibition stand he had commandeered a place to serve as a hospitality room, not merely to entertain royals, politicians and military brasshats but to demonstrate a whole galaxy of toolroom gauging equipment plus his 'millionth' measuring machine. Of the twenty-four weeks the exhibition was open, he himself was on hand for seven or eight weeks to personally explain to his guests the wonders of his 'new era' methods. His various exhibits had received a good press; he personally had been given the principal star billing. Not surprisingly, he was considered a very interesting character and experienced no difficulty attracting the highest in the land to visit his lair. Once inside his hospitality room of course, Joe got to work pushing his ideas with all the hard-sell zeal of a crusader. Hopefully the majority of his guests went away convinced. But was it all helpful? Did he satisfy the Board of Trade and the Cabinet sufficiently that they were at last willing to adopt his Whitworth *inch* as the British standard?

Manifestly, the answer must be no: it was many years before the government finally recognized his work. But other compensations ensued. He got to know the royal family; he developed immensely his own political evolution and in a curious way he also gained a great deal of personal pleasure seeing the sheer wonderment his 'millionth' measuring machine gave his guests; they marvelled over it for years afterwards and that delighted him (see fig. 8). Probably, however, the most satisfying thing to have blossomed from his hospitality suite was the many lasting friendships it created, John Bright MP being the best example. Pre-exhibition he was just a friendly acquaintance, afterwards he became a firm and close friend. Sir James Graham MP was another. Indeed, typical of Whitworth's open-door hospitality, John Bright mentioned in his diary that he went back to the exhibition on 24 May for one of his numerous meetings with the engineer and again met Whitworth, James Graham and Charles Dickens along with other parliamentarians, all fortuitously caught together in the special room. Graham was a staunch Peelite and free-trader. Interestingly along with Cobden and Bright he at first opposed parliamentary intervention in matters like the limitations of factory hours and the laying down of standards – the very things Whitworth wanted – yet some time later Graham changed sides and thereafter supported the Ten-hour Bill and Whitworth's metrology. Perhaps Joe wasn't such a bad persuader after all.

Demonstrating his gauges and persuading his friends of the necessity of parliamentary action were not the only skills he required; making conversation (he who was supposed to lack word play) was important. His guests, when together, didn't pussyfoot around. For example in front of Whitworth they indulged in a kind of blunt political jousting, its very pugnaciousness set by the Queen herself. Specifically whenever she and her husband, Albert, wished to ridicule the Prime Minister, Lord John Russell, they referred to him as 'Johnny'; in this particular instance they were demanding he sack the Foreign Secretary, Palmerston. The 'Johnny' epithet had already entered the Cabinet vocabulary and within six months Palmerston was out! It was all part of the mutual loathing which, to some extent, robbed Whitworth's pleasant 'back-of-the-stand' exhibition gatherings of their lobbying potential. It must have been a salutary

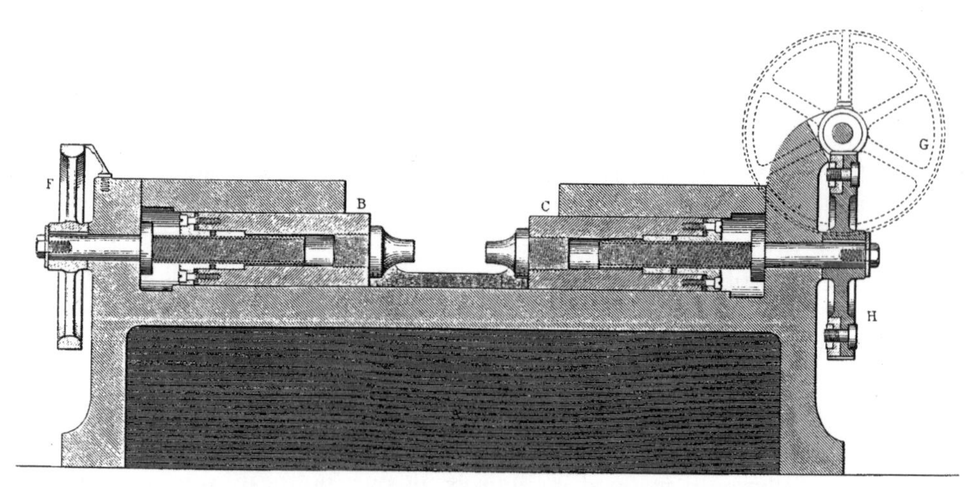

Fig. 8 Longitudinal section of Whitworth's 'millionth' measuring machine. At the 1851 Great Exhibition it was claimed to be sensitive to one microinch – a somewhat dubious assertion.

lesson – some would say a privilege – hearing at first hand the kind of royal machinations which finally toppled from office the shakiest Cabinet ever.

One contributive element which gave vent to this unbridled royal pressure concerned the visit to London of the Hungarian, Louis Kossuth. First the Queen, then the Prime Minister, asked Palmerston – the Foreign Secretary – not to receive Kossuth. He declined their advice, replying tersely that he did not intend to be told whom he might or might not invite into his own home, adding for the benefit of his Cabinet colleagues that 'he would use his own discretion as no doubt the Prime Minister would exercise his when it comes to remaking his next Cabinet'. The Kossuth question thus became a loyalty litmus, and if bracketed with earlier support for Louis-Napoleon, inevitably meant political suicide. Needless to say, come Christmas 1851, out went Palmerston. And though Whitworth himself had long recognized political controversy not being helpful to his cause, he never once hesitated to support his friends Cobden and Bright, he himself having already invited Louis Kossuth to his Manchester works on 11 December 1851. To offer personal invitations to foreign dignitaries was never a politically safe thing to do. Joe knew that. Nonetheless he must have been just as apprehensive as when he had welcomed Louis-Napoleon to his works. On this much later occasion, however, he and the others were pleasantly surprised by the exuberant public welcome Kossuth received on arrival at Manchester. The crowd cheered all the way from the station to the town hall.

Though he was well established and enjoyed a somewhat minor celebrity status prior to the Great Exhibition, it was Whitworth's machine tool (1851) collection – seen for the first time at the Crystal Palace – which won for him the indisputable international reputation he came to savour so much particularly when the going got tough. Essentially it was his machine design much more than his metrology which drew from both jurors and journalists such eulogies as 'these machines are of first-rate excellence' and 'Whitworth sets standards against which all other exhibitors must be judged'. These attributes, plus the medals, were lavished on Whitworth with genuine entitlement but being a very down-to-earth man he realized more than most that for every ounce of praise a pound of acridity lay in wait.

It was this latter fate which particularly concerned both Whitworth and William Fairbairn. Following the opening of the exhibition, a great deal of recrimination seemed to penetrate the Society of Arts. Men like Fairbairn, Henry Cole and John Scott Russell persuaded Prince Albert not only to lead the exhibition committee but to recruit Richard Cobden to give the whole concept political purpose and balance. This Albert had done, perhaps innocently, because Cobden was anti-military weapons. His involvement actually scattered a few seeds which were later to embarrass those Cobden supporters who had envisaged either military or naval engineering contracts coming their way as a future part of their own industrial manufacturing.

When he was initially invited, in January 1851, to join the exhibition committee, Cobden tentatively agreed only on condition that 'no instruments of war be exhibited'. More than anything he wanted it to be 'a dazzling demonstration of international peace and foreign trade'. He and Scott Russell even persuaded both the Queen and the Prince Consort actually to dedicate the exhibition to the 'gospel of peace – particularly between France and Germany – and the unity of mankind'. But when the exhibition opened and the Queen drew back the military stand curtains, there revealed from France, Germany and America were all the arms and military contrivances Cobden had asked to be banned. Even worse, they became an irresistable centre of interest, not just for army generals and the Prince Consort himself, but for politicians generally, thus their preoccupying interest quickly centred on Whitworth. It was the most natural thing to have happened. They all wanted to ask the man billed as Britain's 'best mechanician' the most logical question: 'Given your beautiful machinery, why can't Britain make guns better than anyone else in the world?'

Whitworth wasn't sure of the answer. Nor was he then to know that he himself was to research the matter five long years in pursuit of dream answers – at times the very extravagance of the work near-swamping his Chorlton Street drawing office.

Long after the exhibition closed, this one intriguing question concerning the mass production of military weapons still permeated ministerial minds from Louis-Napoleon's council of state to the Zollverein and on to St Petersburg. Though he didn't show it, Cobden was thoroughly disheartened by it all. When the Queen had opened the exhibition both he and Bright had refused to attend the ceremony, ostensibly because they refused to wear court dress. Whitworth himself probably suspected it was because of the rifles and other weapons which were on show. Later on Cobden also refused a knighthood for his work as an exhibition commissioner. Scott Russell, a devotee of Cobden and the only commissioner to be excluded from the honours list, seemed to resent Cobden's self-denial, quietly suppressing his own pique at himself being omitted, yet Cobden, conscious of these feelings, still refrained from any public petulance and referred to 'Albert's magnificent project' before going on to praise the exhibition and to reiterate his admiration for British mechanical engineering. Mid-flow he declared:

> Not a bale of merchandise leaves our shores, but it bears the seeds of intelligence and fruitful thought to the members of some less enlightened community; not a merchant visits our seats of manufacturing industry, but he returns to his own country the missionary of freedom, peace and good government – while our steamboats, that now visit every port of Europe, and our miraculous railroads that are the talk of all nations, are the advertisements and vouchers for the value of our enlightened institutions.[3]

As predicted, far more political tetchiness persisted well beyond the closure of the exhibition than was ever admitted. For those manufacturers leaving London to return home, they were glad to be free of the antagonisms seething away inside the 'learned' London circle. No doubt some of Cobden's views were at the forefront of this querulousness but even more unsettling for the 'insiders' were reports coming in from the British Ambassador in Paris concerning a possible Napoleonic coup. The news infuriated Queen Victoria and seemed to sever all normal relationships between her and the Manchester 'school', but not quite. One week before the exhibition closed on 15 October 1851, she and Albert, accompanied by her entourage plus the Dukes of Wellington, Norfolk and Derby, all travelled north for a two-day visit to Manchester and Salford. Could it be that Albert's mind still lingered covetously over the so-called mass-produced rifles exhibited in the American pavilion at the Crystal Palace? Whatever the incentive, Albert's part of the entourage included within its itinerary of town halls and monument unveilings a hurried tour through the Fairbairn and Whitworth factories: an indication perhaps that the Manchester engineers were witnessing the first signs that the Prince Consort – and Horseguards – had recently acquired a military interest in the Manchester toolmakers.

The international press coverage given to the exhibition had brought into the open further disquiet concerning the environmental consequences which most people believed must follow in the wake of the steam engine. Shining like beacons, however, Cobden and Bright stood head and shoulders above those who considered they held a more caring radical opinion. Significantly, the two Manchester MPs both supported the engineers and generally believed the 'new machine age' launched by the exhibition heralded new hope and would lift ordinary working people from the morass. Unlike many of their 'middle-class' conservationist friends, they argued in favour of Whitworth's industrial mass-production and that its economic benefits outweighed the environmental aftermath. But what they deemed as unacceptable was Whitworth's demand that engineering be given certain legal rights in return for a legally enforced environmental control of the industry and its machinery.

John Ruskin, for example, wanted none of it. Echoing *Punch*, the satirical magazine, he was scathing. *Punch*, it will be remembered, actually gave a name to the exhibition building: they named it the Crystal Palace (it caught on) while Ruskin called it the 'biggest greenhouse (some misunderstood him to say madhouse) ever built'. His main criticism, however, was reserved for the machinery it housed – and the belching chimneys the machinery created – 'the smoke having rendered the light of the sun unserviceable . . . no acre of English ground shall be without its shaft and its engine'. He even named Charles Dickens 'a pure modernist – a leader of the *steam whistle* party par excellence'. Samuel Smiles too seemed to do little more than apologize for engineers – that was his way of dealing with the problem – though most engineers, looking for encouragement, instinctively turned towards writers like him the more they felt clamped between Thackeray's polemics and Thomas Carlyle's prophesies. Others observed that 'the decade of the Great Exhibition marks the end of hope in the blessings of the machine'.

John Stuart Mill, more in his rôle as a philosopher than an economist, complained of being less than happy with the smoke-ridden debasement of society and what he feared would be a machine-led social depravity. Nevertheless, he eventually sided with engineering as a necessary stage leading away from mass poverty and barbarism. Though Joseph Whitworth was almost alone among engineers publicly arguing the case for mass-production and quality control, he did enjoy sporadic support from certain leading politicians. Richard Cobden, forever a friend but also forever *laissez-faire*, stood by his praise of Crystal Palace and its machinery when he forcibly argued 'Britain can defend its trade with cheapness', implying his endorsement of machine repetitive-manufacture but when it came to Whitworth's metrology he conveniently skimmed across the labyrinthine reasoning which recognized the necessity for parliamentary legislation before any real engineering progress could be made.

Sadly, Thomas Carlyle dubbed these demands 'a box of pills' when he referred to those advocates who thought 'there was a cure for everything' by pushing through parliamentary legislation. From his point of view it was an effective simile for it reassured and strengthened those doubting engineers standing on the periphery, engineers who themselves failed to grasp the necessity for legislation. In the end, Whitworth himself was left virtually alone to get on with arguing the benefits of the mass-production machine, the environmental issues now being voiced much more forcibly than ever they were prior to the exhibition.

Understandably, the non-initiated had gone along to the exhibition and seen for the first time some wondrous machinery and thought – wishfully perhaps – that the millenium was close at hand. It wasn't, and when people realized this they became disillusioned. The environmentalist lobby gathered tremendous support. The anti-engineering campaign – Britain's first serious 'green lobby' – persevered for close on two decades, in the end leaving it to William Morris to encapsulate their exemplary strategy with these lines from his memorable verse 'Earthly Paradise':

> Forget six counties overhung with smoke,
> Forget the snorting steam and piston stroke,
> Forget the spreading of the hideous town,
> Think rather of the pack-horse on the down,
> And dream of London, small, and white, and clean.

But hidden beneath these somewhat pleasant homilies lurked a much more vociferous argument beginning to make its way into the press. No doubt 'Earthly Paradise' had already reverberated around the lecture theatre and political corridors but now it was being augmented by some other recognizable stands – the pacifist argument against armament manufacture, for instance; the machine replacing skills and taking away jobs and employers resenting the possibility of higher wages which they cleverly linked to the widespread fear that smoke pollution could be more lethal than cholera: all in all, it was a formidable case. Fortunately, from Whitworth's point of view the combined argument was ahead of any visible stress and therefore considerably weakened. In regard to the exhibition, however, Cobden was proved right to criticize the presence of the rifles and other equipment. Though they represented only five per cent of the exhibits the international press particularly gave greater credence to improved gun manufacture than to any other of the exhibits. It was thus axiomatic that the Whitworth stand – much to his friend's irritation – was going to be at the forefront of the show, mainly because of its military potential.

Leaving to one side both the wages question and the military aspects, the environmentalist prophets were insistent that the smoke problem was going to get far worse. For townships especially, they argued, it would ultimately assume a pestilent hideousness. How right they were! But instead of acknowledging that the problem existed – and offering to fund at least a partial remedy (as was then possible) – engineering employers and industrialists made a telling error of judgement: they tended to dismiss the matter out of hand. It was a bad mistake – the forerunner of many other self-inflicted wounds earmarked to debilitate the industry. It is an identical attitude which these days jeopardizes the admiration and support nuclear engineers are today entitled to expect. During the 1850s and '60s, however, William Fairbairn, almost alone among leading engineers, emphasized his willingness to 'scientifically' research a possible 'pollution' remedy. But even he was not long realizing that without enforcement by law, smoke abatement would remain a myth.

Largely because of these questionable issues the immense welter of engineering prestige brought about by the Great Exhibition began slowly to erode. Middle-class opinion – and it was that which mattered most – remained passive. People simply concluded that atmospheric pollution was an inescapable price which had to be paid in return for engineering progress. The Victorian 'green' movement was no match for the better-represented *laissez-faire* enthusiasts. While the steam engine was destined to be the saviour of society both sides of the argument no doubt realized that in the absence of legislation, smoke from its chimneys would continue to inflict harm. And so it did – unclean air soon matched the sullied rivers yet the no-restriction-at-any-price lobby were able to lightly cast aside such fears: they would concede nothing. Of the two conflicting Lancashire expressions 'where there's muck there's brass' and the more apposite 'clean air is heavenly' it is a salutary lesson that a further eighty years passed by before any government had sufficient courage to enforce the second maxim commending clean air. As to whether the Victorians were passionate campaigners – hardly, on this score.

Who knows, maybe the exhibition had not after all lifted British opinion much beyond Thomas Carlyle's ageless cry, when, in 1850, he wrote 'Hudson's Statue':

> I do not want cheaper cotton, swifter railways;
> I want what Novalis calls God, Freedom,
> Immortality: will swift railways and sacrifices
> to Hudson help me towards that?

Seven years later the point was answered by William Fairbairn when he temporarily restored and elevated the status of mechanical engineering: he was called upon on 26 June 1857, by resolution of the city council, to unveil a statue (in Piccadilly, Manchester) to James Watt, probably the most significant figure in the history of mechanical engineering. To quote the engineering historian, L.T.C. Rolt, the bronze likeness undraped by Fairbairn was dedicated to one of Britain's greatest innovators. 'He (Watt) found mechanical engineering an *empirical craft* and left it an *applied science*'. Fairbairn too was equally unstinting in praise of his fellow Scot, closing his remarks as he began: his words rang out across Piccadilly and on down through the ages: a wonderful tribute to engineering.

> The steam-engine is the pioneer and promoter of civilization. By its agency the weak become strong and time and distance become short.

We can all say amen to that!

THE 1852 ENGINEERS LOCK-OUT

No sooner had the euphoria died, the exhibition doors closed, than the General Secretary of the newly formed engineering trade union, the Amalgamated Society of Engineers (ASE), circulated the Lancashire engineering employers (24 November 1851) explaining why the union wanted to end piecework and systematic overtime as from 31 December 1851. Indeed, the tail-end of their circular left little doubt as to the resolute character of the union's ultimatum: 'The Executive Council have decided to advise [their members] to discontinue the practices of systematic overtime and piecework after the 31st December 1851'.

The employers were outraged. The threat was rawboned and they saw it as a deliberate declaration of open warfare. The Manchester group in particular reacted strongly. With evil intent would be too much of an exaggeration but certainly their malevolent purpose clouded their judgement. Meeting first at the Clarence Hotel, Manchester, on 9 December 1851, the Association of Engineering Employers resolved to close down all their establishments. They decreed to 'lock out the whole' of their workforce – in effect to sack the lot – agreeing not to restart anyone until each man had signed a personal statement renouncing for life his trade union membership. At their next meeting they went further. Should any man be found to have retained his allegiance to the ASE, having signed the declaration, he would be dismissed instantly. And as a token of solidarity, each employer was levied ten shillings for every manual worker employed (Whitworth paid £140). Should any company fail to enforce these anti-union disciplines they would immediately forfeit their deposits. It was indeed a double-edged, simultaneous declaration of war with a vengeance.[4]

Two weeks later, a delegation of employers was sent from Manchester to a meeting in London. It was held at the London Coffee-House, Ludgate Hill, on Christmas Eve, 1851. The seriousness of their intent was verified by the fact that almost every leading employer attended. Significantly Fairbairn himself did not attend but sent his son Thomas while Whitworth had other 'urgent' business. Some employers even attended on Christmas Day to finalize their strategy. It was an historic occasion arising from which the Central Association of Employers and Operative Engineers was formed. It was led by men like George Rennie, John Scott Russell and Thomas Maudslay who persuaded those present to endow an elected executive with sufficient power to coordinate employers throughout the country – a remarkable step forward in the light of their own resolution to oppose *combination* of any kind, particularly criticizing the trade union (ASE) for setting up a national organization. It was in fact the setting up of this masters' federation which persuaded both Disraeli and Gladstone *against* the strengthening of the Combination Act of 1824.

The engineering masters finally closed their factories and locked their gates on 10 January 1852. They did so with such frightening unanimity that trade union leaders were taken aback. As each succeeding statement came out so tempers shortened and the gap widened. The ASE retaliated by deciding to pay their members fifteen shillings per week strike money, convinced the dispute would end quickly. They completely misjudged the mood. When George Rennie spoke on behalf of the employers he emphasized that the employers would deliberately support non-trade unionists:

I am proud on this public occasion to acknowledge the virtues and value of

> the artisans of this country. It should not be forgotten, however, that the men (i.e. the unions) had taken the initiative in this act of aggression, and that self-respect as well as prudence required that the masters should defend *themselves and peaceable hands* from a dictation which was ruinous to both.[5]

The words *peaceable hands* became the employers' official code language for craftsmen who were not members of a trade union. From then on the most important issue was made abundantly clear: they wanted no truck with any organization which threatened to interfere with their sole managerial rights or came between them and an absolutely unfettered free-bargaining arrangement between foremen, piece-masters and men. For them, the lock-out was now a *cause célèbre.* Ruefully the trade union leadership had from the beginning underestimated just how provocative their bargaining stance had become. Having survived the Combination Acts they now faced the employers' own 'legislation'.

No doubt largely the result of press comment, invigorated by this new belligerency, Whitworth's own attitude towards the trade unions was considerably sharpened. By the time he went to the United States his views were quite clear: it was for the master to decide who was skilled irrespective of the machine the man operated or the job he did. It was for the master to decide how much the man would be paid and the hours he worked: it was not a matter for the trade union. In Whitworth's view, anything short of this complete freedom would seriously impede progress inside the workshop. To some extent he himself could afford to play the dictator without offending his workforce; his rates of pay were that much higher and the trade unions themselves excluded him from criticism. In July 1861 – exactly a decade after the lock-out – the ASE questioned all their branches nationally in regard to trade conditions. One answer, returned from a Manchester branch – composed mostly of Whitworth's men – modified their general criticism of the industry's employers by adding five simple words: 'except Whitworth's and best others'. He would have loved that![6]

Not all the Lancashire engineering employers joined the Federation. Interestingly divisions began to appear. Reflecting the pressures piling in from the Unitarian church and other community groups, Whitworth tended to sit 'firmly astride the fence'. He closed down his own machine tool production but kept open significant sections within his main factory. Of his closest Manchester friends only Richard Ormerod and William Muir kept their factories open, fully working. Fairbairns, Sharp Roberts, Bellhouse and James Nasmyth closed down completely. Edward Bellhouse, like William Fairbairn, also shared a warm friendship with Whitworth and would, at times unashamedly, echo his opinions. Whether or not, as on this occasion, Bellhouse was repeating the 'maestro' is unclear, nevertheless his opinions seemed to fit the extraordinary views at the time held by all four of the Manchester engineers. On becoming president of the newly formed Association of Foremen and Draughtsmen, Bellhouse said he believed that the purpose of unions was to provide services such as sickness and death benefit only and that (the union) was not a tool through which workmen should try to increase their wages. When reminded by his own workmen that the lock-out was not about wages, he rightly replied that a shorter working week for the same rate of pay was tantamount to a rise in pay. Just so.

In regard to Whitworth, one or two Manchester employers were irritated by what they understood to be the way Whitworth's management intended to proceed during the dispute. Joe reacted truculently and on hearing further criticism wrote a defiant letter to his namesake, *Henry* Whitworth, the Masters' Federation Secretary, informing him that he intended to keep his factory open for the sole purpose of providing his apprentices and labourers with work from nine until four daily. Edward Bellhouse followed suit, conscious of the dire poverty among those families not in receipt of strike pay.

Inside Whitworth's own factory his employees had enjoyed conditions vastly different from most other engineering establishments. For months either side of the 1851 Great Exhibition they had worked regular weekend overtime but being machine tool men they worked little or no piece-work. The unusually precise nature of the work ensured that the men's individual skills had always been well rewarded, but now that his own factory was under constant scrutiny the press quite scandalously singled out the much higher wages he paid and wrote that the engineering industry *as a whole* was overpaid, shamefully greedy and now strike-ridden. Granted, Whitworth's tool and gauge room was well paid: according to ASE District Reports he paid (consolidated) wage rates from 38 shillings to 49 shillings per week – which included a supplementary bonus in lieu of piece-work – as against a combined district average of 39 shillings and fourpence per sixty hour week.[7] Considering that the majority of Whitworth's toolmakers worked seven days a week – take-home pay around 64 shillings – sufficient for their wives to employ a housemaid, the figure implied a somewhat breathtaking fringe benefit when compared with today's poor situation.

Though the press stories were a grotesque misrepresentation of the more general trade, the conduct of the strike was made to sound much worse by the fact that Joseph Whitworth shared the same surname with the secretary of the Employers Federation, whose name was Henry. Granted, when the press mid-last century used the name *Whitworth* without an initial it must have been confusing even for his engineering contemporaries.

It was in fact *Joseph* Whitworth who first put to the Federation the plight of the unorganized non-skilled. He himself had gone ahead and made available financial help. This he combined with the argument that employers generally must prioritize their protection and support for their non-unionized craftsmen – a policy the Masters' Federation were later happy to endorse. But not being wholly altruistic, Whitworth's policy did two things; first, it prevented the lowest paid – now largely the unpaid – becoming the most savagely treated victims of the lock-out and secondly, it gave himself a loophole through which he continued to employ his most prized (and in his case largely non-union) highly paid toolmakers.

Whitworth was also aware that some of his men were planning to emigrate to Australia. The ASE members among them were not prepared, secretly or otherwise, to sign away their rights nor their lifelong integrity. They would leave the country first. He later learned from Tom Hughes QC that some thirty toolmakers did in fact leave Britain in 1852 and established the first ASE overseas branch in Sydney, Australia.[8] Each man had borrowed £1,000 to ensure that he and his family got there. Moreover the lawyer's story ended happily; the whole of the money borrowed was repaid with interest! As for Whitworth himself, he too escaped what could have been a calamity. By following the advice long since offered him by his friend, Edward Tootal, 'Never give your men cause to look over the hedge', and by making a great many *surreptitious* man-to-man 'arrangements', he had been able to keep together the majority of his best machine builders alongside his tool and gauge people. It was little wonder the more puritanical members of the Federation soured somewhat in their relationship with Whitworth once they could see what was happening and that he personally would probably survive the lock-out without too much bruising.

To appreciate the intense anger on both sides it is necessary to recall the vacuous handling of the dispute by the press. In the most freakish fashion they offended the union by their dishonest invention while the employers believed what they read and became deeply incensed. The simplest demands at the outset became vexed, non-negotiable issues converted by a press ostensibly claiming to be helpful. Take first the highly localized demand made against Hibbert and Platt of Oldham. The men (the press alleged) wanted all 'unskilled' operators working on Whitworth's planing machines to be replaced by time-served ASE men. But the union nationally disowned this local demand; the President, William Newton, clearly stating that the union would make two demands only; the abolition of the piecework system and secondly, the ending of systematic overtime.[9]

The *Manchester Guardian* remained unconvinced, unimpressed even by the clarity of the union's executive statement. They followed instead the President of the Manchester employers when he said 'we are defending our right to manage our affairs without dictation from these *missionaries of agitation* and that we will do 'till the end'.

Later on, the *Manchester Guardian* editorial dated 21 January 1852 returned to the attack reiterating the now extinct 'Oldham demand': 'The few guilty ones – and it is a guilt of no small degree – paid delegates and *missionaries of agitation* – take care to secure their (own) liberal payment, while the hard-working thousands whom they delude and cajole, are the severe sufferers with their wives and little ones'. Then, as if to reactivate the threats and start up the war of words all over again, the newspaper reiterated that in its opinion the union still demanded 'that the "unskilled" workmen, employed as machinemen and labourers, should be discharged and their places filled with union (ASE) men'.

Other newspapers together with the trade press gave much prominence to this latter point; one suspects because they themselves had seen the birth of a twin, another 'craft' *print* union in the making, as they, the press, gazed into their own crystal ball. The 'cap' was a very close fit and few newspaper employers, if any, wanted their workmen 'classified by trade unions as skilled or otherwise'. The ASE Executive Council immediately recognized how damaging this accusation could be and made strenuous efforts to deny its authenticity. Once again, the President of the union, angered by the way the image of the new craft union was being shaped, not by themselves but by the 'enemy' (the press), again repudiated the whole idea. 'This union', he declared, 'will not support the removal of unskilled workmen from self-acting (Whitworth) machines'.

The question still niggled and wouldn't go away. The pressures, however, came not from the shop floor but the boardroom. Leading employers sensed history was being made. Some were convinced that if they falsely accused the unions of demanding equalized pay (the rate for the job argument) and the sacking of non-union men, the more powerfully the union would refute these claims and the less likely it would be that such policies would ever materialize. But did the ruse work?

One such believer in this subterfuge was William Fairbairn's eldest son, Thomas. He conducted a long correspondence in the columns of *The Times* newspaper under the pseudonym 'Amicus'. First, he went over the old ground about the unions demanding the replacement of semi-trained labourers operating self-acting machines, then he accused the engineering union of 'just waiting' to launch their campaign for the equalization of wage-rates. Thomas Hughes QC, retained by the Association for Social Science to inquire into the 'facts behind the lock-out', said:

> Anything more untrue could scarcely have been invented. This body of the highest paid workmen in England were as notoriously opposed to equalization, in the sense used here, as they were to the reduction of wages . . . they had not had fair play from the press and blame for this reckless dishonesty must be laid to the account of this anonymous writer, Amicus.[10]

Though this back-and-forth rally was widely reported it made little impact. Thomas Fairbairn still insisted – and still under the cover of his *nom-de-plume*, Amicus – that it was the future policy of the ASE to insist on the sole employment of time-served union men and that they should be paid a minimum union rate of wages irrespective of the man's skill. The issue eventually engulfed everyone in the trade; it being quite beyond the comprehension of the Employers Federation why anyone should fail to grasp its significance; why the railway companies, for example, were so complacent in the face of what could become catastrophic dictation by the trade unions. A railway director, Mr Samuel Fielden, in a letter to *The Times,* 18 Februrary 1852, wrote:

> The fact is, this [Amicus theory] is an invention contrived to injure the cause

> of the men. It was only the other day that a deputation of the masters reported it to a meeting of railway directors, of whom I was one . . . 'that these aims were the intention of the union'. Upon being taxed with the falsehood, however, they were obliged to withdraw their statement.

The controversial method of paying variable wage rates in engineering has remained a perennial source of resentment for over a century. Much of it exacerbated by the traditional highly personalized self-esteem of the toolmaker, the system has long bred an angry but tolerated malice between what should be toolroom equals. Great secrecy about how much each man was paid in addition to feeding an individual's conceit has long proved to be the master's technique. Every Saturday night wages and bonuses would be paid through a tiny window. The queue would form immediately the bell rang and as each man reached the window, he would stoop to give his name through the slit provided; a sharp-eyed wage clerk would then ritualistically identify him and slide the man's packet under the window. Thus favoured, the recipient would carefully secrete the packet inside his clothing to wait for a moment of absolute privacy before counting the contents. Keeping the master's trust mattered – toolmakers really were aristocrats!

For those employed in the less distinguished payment-by-results machine shops the Saturday pay routine remained the same but the need for secrecy served to support a much weaker morality; a new and more competitive tyrant called piece-work. For some ten years or so, Whitworth had enthused the Mechanics' Institute and other groups with the necessity of adopting an equitable method for paying wages based on production but he never spelled out the detail. He envisaged a simple, straightforward system as being of equal benefit to both master and man. He envisaged mutual agreements between price-fixers (the piece-master) and the workman, both agreeing a price before the work commenced; the workman then going ahead, he thought, to earn a comfortable bonus while the management would welcome the increased production. It was a civilized view but if Whitworth thought a fair system would fall into position without legislation it was crass naïvety. In the event the post lock-out conflict became increasingly brutal. The piece-masters insisted on the cheapest price irrespective of mutuality; the quickening pace brought awesome changes. The workmen, skilled and unskilled alike, strove to avoid debt; they loathed the system believing it to be rotten through and through.

Looking back over the period it is inconceivable that when Whitworth first talked about the mass-production of standardized parts and the consequential need for men to be paid by the piece, he never suspected the fearful hardships the new system would entail, particularly if the system failed to be handled compassionately. Given his acute understanding of workshop psychology, it seems suspicious, for example, why Whitworth failed to emphasize the necessity for a mutuality agreement when he talked of men sharing the benefits. His omission excludes the one crucial factor that could make the system fair and operable. When listing the benefits of his new wage system he talked of the 'equality of rights', yet it remained a meaningless slogan in the absence of mutuality and the right of the operator to opt out of working to a fixed price. Two Parliamentary Select Committees inquiring into the relationship between masters and men concluded that it was the absence of mutuality – the employers' one-sided reduction of job times, naturally the most explosive issue – which had directly caused a thousand major strikes in ten years and laced every one of them with a suicidal bitterness.[11]

During the mid-Victorian years the piece-work system became the subject of many inquiries. It was (and still is) a central part of our industrial culture. But it was a race the operative seldom won. Before mutuality, the employer held both stick and carrot. As the 'donkey' galloped faster so the piece-master reduced the price: thus he kept the carrot the same distance in front. The system divided the 'shop floor' because favouritism made it corrupt. It was demeaning, workmen accused other workmen of 'horsing' (*doing* too much) or of being a 'sheeny' (*earning* too much). Although it was only after Whitworth developed his Sackville Street site in 1857 for the manufacture of rifles, that he himself introduced piece-work into his own works. He regularly talked of the benefits and though he was uniquely placed to do so, he never actually cautioned about the dangers. For a man with such towering influence during these particular years, his silence must have been a calculated discipline best described by his critics as a cowardly escape.[12]

Surely it was the duty of engineers – particularly men like Whitworth – to both caution and to advise the more learned of Victorian societies of the complex human problems he and other engineers anticipated in the wake of their revolutionary steam power and machine tools. The fact that they failed to do so underscored a strange indifference. Other equally radical new methods of manufacture, like chemicals, also required a fundamental restructuring of industrial society. Again, the failure to do so did in fact go on to prove just how precarious the gap was between commercial success and environmental disaster. Certainly there was a glaring need throughout all the professions, including mechanical engineering, for strict environmental regulation. For engineers never to have gone into any of this deserved the caption bequeathed by environmentalists that it was 'an age of mindless deception'.

Ironically, it was probably the likes of Whitworth's chief draughtsmen who got nearest to predicting trouble. They themselves drafted the literature which the Whitworth company distributed to potential purchasers of machine tools advising them how to cut the costs of production by cutting piece-work prices in line with the new machine technology.[13] They also advised how masters could gain further advantage by going for semi-skilled operatives doing straightforward repetitive work. But only rarely was there any reference to these matters in the trade press; a much deeper analysis naturally being provided by trade union journals and the political weekly, *Beehive*. Companies like Whitworth's no doubt argued it was not a question of morality but one of commercial good sense. Sadly, it was precisely this kind of cultural stealth which garnered for engineers a second-class reputation.

Equally so, the campaigning of the trade unions was barely tenable – in retrospect it was more ritualistic than thoughtfully considered – indeed they were to spend sixty profitless years striving to establish special recognition for those men who had served an apprenticeship and that it should be used as the only yardstick to determine who should receive a 'skilled' rate of pay. In the event, the trade union criteria *aided* rather than arrested the employers' obsession with the payment of low wages. When carefully compared with the American, less rigid merit orientated system, the results generally confirmed historically why American toolmakers now enjoy a far higher living standard than their British counterparts. To that extent, the monumentality of the craft unions' mistake remains self-evident.[14]

Maybe it is far too easy an option criticizing Whitworth (as some did) for not following his engineering friends, Joseph Locke and Daniel Gooch, into Parliamentary politics. Though the precedents in this case were not the best – Gooch never actually addressed the House of Commons during his whole membership, although he was active in committee – while Locke, the engineer most responsible for laying down the French railway track, could possibly have persuaded the House (had he tried) to avoid including in Britain's early railway legislation the silly conditions from which the system still suffers. Had Whitworth followed his example little purpose would have been served but had he pursued a similar course to that taken years later by another of Manchester's engineers, Sir William Mather MP (thirty-three years younger than Whitworth), he would have made an invaluable contribution on behalf of mechanical engineering. It was William Mather, incidentally, who corrected many of the myths regularly quoted in Parliamentary debate about the 'love' men had for working long hours. His own works, Mather and Platt of Manchester, became the first factory in Britain to introduce a forty-eight hour week. Nevertheless, it still remains a strange phenomenon; that of Whitworth's six engineering contemporaries to enter Parliament, all of whom were responsible in their own way for the most profound changes in society, none of them – apart possibly from William Mather – contributed politically anything like the historic profundity equal to their engineering.

There was, of course, a positive side to all this. Had Whitworth entered Parliament the world would have been denied half his engineering accomplishment; a focal point no doubt in any disputation as to whether political enactment or engineering invention has effected greater epochal change in society. The evidence so far suggests that engineering wins easily.

Sadly, much political effort has been dissipated over past decades, arguing fatuously whether industry should be state owned; the real question, as Whitworth recognized, was, and still is, what kind of enforceable regulation is required to free entrepreneurial invention while preventing the damaging misuse of society by kowtowing to a bogus *laissez-faire* system. Whitworth just about got it right when he argued for the state regulation of mensuration and against the state manufacture of guns. Similarly, had Joseph Locke MP and Daniel Gooch MP argued in Parliament (as they did as engineers and in boardrooms) for the ruthless state planning of railways, world transport would today be far superior. (The French side of today's tunnel is a good example.)

By 20 March 1852 the end of the employers' lock-out was well within sight. The ASE had reduced its strike pay from fifteen shillings down to ten shillings per week having virtually given up the contest. The union General Secretary, William Allan, then made it known within the privacy of the branches that those members still locked out should now return to work. They should comply with their employers' condition that they sign a declaration denouncing their trade union membership but they should keep a sharp look out 'for the masters informants' who may suspect they had signed the document though continuing their membership of the union. William Allan warned that if they were found out not only would they be sacked, but they would be blacklisted for life. In regard to their wage rate they would have to settle for the best they could get knowing it would be less than the union rate for the job.

The three-month dispute had been a wretched experience. An aching poverty, an organizational weakness on the part of the union and a pitiless disillusionment all combined to push the men into accepting their employers' 'no compromise' return to work. As we now know, as soon as the employers had locked their gates on 10 January 1852, they had put up notices confirming their non-negotiable terms. The returning workers would have to face the same piece-masters, accept the same wretched piece-rates and work overtime in just the same way as the same foremen had previously demanded. It was a dreadfully humiliating experience.

The General Secretary's warning to all union members about the danger of informants sank fear deep into the minds of the ASE membership. Absolute loyalty was the only protection members had against the risk of blackmail, against the threat of piece-masters demanding a weekly 'subscription'. Instant dismissal and with it a lifelong blacklisting was again a regular dread following a union branch meeting. No matter how dark the night or how secretively members left the branch meeting – the historic reason why union branch meetings are held in public houses was in fact to deceive anyone taking names – nevertheless sackings continued to take place and bitterness rampaged.

Stories appeared in the press listing the most brutal acts committed against members suspected of *informing* on other members. As a preventative the most intimidatory and bizarre procedures were thought up for the initiation of new members. On taking the oath each novice was made to kneel before the branch. Blindfold, each man was told to take the Bible in one hand while raising the other in affirmation of his loyalty. To be doubly sure that the gravity of the occasion was thoroughly understood, the Chairman of the branch held a gun against the new member's head as he repeated the union's oath of allegiance. Whether or not this macabre business worked is not known, but in answer to the employers' stratagem to kill off the trade union, ASE total membership revived from an initial drop of 2,000 (during the dispute) to climb back and reach a record number of 17,000 within a decade.

The history of the 1850s was an abnormal mixture of political and industrial highs and lows: extensive boy labour – absurdly called apprentices – and the deliberate contraction of skills were recurrent scandals throughout the period. James Nasmyth revealed all when he was asked in 1868 by the Chairman of a Parliamentary Select Committee how much impact self-acting machine tools had on skills. Referring to the period 1852–3 and the planing machine in particular, he recalled:

> my machines worked with such precision and rapidity . . . that all that class of men who depended upon mere dexterity were set aside altogether, and I was able to move on with these (young) lads. Instead of having the old proportion of one boy to four mechanics, I had four boys to one mechanic nearly. There were an immense number of labourers in the neighbourhood . . . and I got them into my employment, and in a short time they were as good workmen as could be desired.

This numerical relationship between unskilled men and boys quoted by Nasmyth was extraordinary in every sense. The Masters Federation had allowed employers to bring in apprentices and labourers during the lock-out and on this evidence it would seem that Nasmyth, angry and frenetic, scoured the district for upwards of four hundred young boys. It was an incredible thing to have done and totally out of keeping with his character. To have deliberately reduced the level of skill inside his own factory to that of untrained boys could never have been sensible. It was so thespian, it wasn't Nasmyth. To some extent it also happened elsewhere but on nothing like the same scale. Charles Beyer, of Beyer Peacock, was later to reflect on this astonishing preponderance of so-called apprentices, left as they were to perform repetitive operations with neither education nor skill training, and called upon his trade associates to reconsider their reckless myopia. Fortunately, they took seriously what he had said and within a few years a much more rational approach was adopted.

In regard to Joseph Whitworth's own attitude towards the trade unions, he was neither pro nor anti; he just ignored their existence. He didn't see the trade unions playing any part whatsoever in any aspect of industrial management nor did he encourage them to do so. Inside his own factory he was the sole governor, the sole arbiter: he was the final decision-maker.[15] As with so many self-made paternalists he looked upon his workforce not as a team in the conventional sense but as a collection of separate individuals. Being in concert was for him a straight mutuality between himself and one other. Under no circumstances did he recognize the right of outsiders to intervene, even less to consult; whether it was a matter of payment for work done or the conditions under which the work was performed. It was, however, a sheltered arrangement within which the trade unions were happy to work; their shop-floor membership was never actually challenged by Whitworth. The ASE branches reported quarterly that he paid his men higher wages than any in the district and that seemed an adequate arrangement.[16]

Though Lancashire and Yorkshire engineers had acquired a reputation for being grasping personalities it was perhaps a wholly unjustified image gained possibly by their plain speaking. Years later, in answer to questions posed by Parliamentary Select Committees on Employment, Whitworth and his colleagues proved themselves considerate, more rounded, more erudite creatures than the majority of Victorian employers. Nonetheless, they remained essentially individualists. Like his two friends, Edward Bellhouse and Richard Ormerod, he was opposed to the trade unions becoming anything other than glorified welfare, provident societies. Sick pay and provision for a 'rainy day' was very much a private matter – occasionally topped up perhaps by a genuine kindness on the employer's part. It was a strategic philanthropy, mixed as it was with his dignified paternalism; it began and ended inside the workshop.

VISIT TO AMERICA

Following Britain's outstanding success with its 1851 Great Exhibition it was not surprising that the United States quickly copied London and went ahead with its own Industrial Exhibition in New York. Referred to as the New York Crystal Palace (it was in fact very similar in appearance) it was scheduled to open on 1 May 1853 but due to many delays on the part of the building contractors it eventually opened on 10 July 1853.

The British Government were keen to see for themselves how Britain and America compared industrially, in particular to compare side by side the military weapons of the two countries. It had been said at the London Crystal Palace two years previously that the United States was far in advance of Britain and Europe: a fact in itself sufficient to goad Lord Aberdeen's Cabinet into action. Predictably, as soon as Aberdeen appointed Lord Clarendon Foreign Secretary, in February 1853, he requested the Foreign Office to urgently consider the selection of a Royal Commission 'to attend the Exhibition of Industry in the City of New York'. On 26 April, *The Times* reported 'we understand that HM Government are about to appoint the Earl of Ellesmere, Sir Charles Lyall MP and Mr Wentworth Dilke MP *and three others* as Commissioners to attend the American exhibition at New York and to report upon it'. But why the mystery? The Foreign Office quickly obliged by announcing the names later that afternoon. They were Joseph Whitworth, George Wallis and Professor John Wilson; a trilogy as interesting and as revealing as the Foreign Office was tight-lipped.

Commenting upon the selection of the Royal Commission the next day, 27 April 1853, *The Times* said ' . . . the most valuable member is Joseph Whitworth', but before going on to refer to his prowess as an engineer they failed to reveal the key mystery man scheduled to accompany him. His name was George Wallis,

Headmaster of the School of Art, Birmingham, but more to the point he was also the head of the only school of rifle design in Britain. He was an acknowledged expert in the matter of small arms. It was interesting that he should be listed as a member of the Commission who was famous in the decorative arts. The truth is that he and Whitworth – both of whom were briefed by the Foreign Office and Horseguards before leaving London – were chosen as the perfect 'undercover' experts to visit the US armouries and private gun trade without attracting too much attention. Whitworth was considered the world's most knowledgeable tool engineer – if anyone could tool-up guns it was he – while Wallis would undoubtedly know what he was looking at while innocently wandering around the 'occasional' armoury. It was this rather special combination which pleased the War Minister – and the Foreign Secretary too – for they had both requested Cabinet to acquire a reputable engineering opinion as to the state of the American gun trade.

While they were crossing the Atlantic the two Commissioners were a little apprehensive about prying beyond the normal interest of gun customers, but they need not have worried. The US was anxious to sell to Britain, and other than the most elementary commercial safeguards no further restrictions applied. In the event, Whitworth was made especially welcome by America's leading gun and machine tool manufacturers together with various government ministers. Only once, towards the end of the visitors' tour, did the US query any aspect of Whitworth's and Wallis's presence. *The Times* New York correspondent cabled his London office on 21 June as the British Embassy reassured the Americans: 'It was never intended by the British Government', he wrote, 'to limit the Commission to the Exhibition alone. They have a far wider interest. Lord Ellesmere was not leader. The delegation had no leader as such. Each one has received his commission direct from Lord Clarendon and for a specific purpose.' It was a case of the Embassy avoiding an untruth by telling only half the story.

The Commissioners had left the Thames on 10 May 1853, aboard the steam sloop, *The Basilisk,* and were accompanied across the Atlantic by the frigate, *Leander.* The kind of crossing they endured is not reported though they landed at New York two days late which suggests some pretty awful squalls. It was probably similar to the description of a bad crossing written by Charles Dickens who crossed to Boston in January 1842: 'The noise, the smell, the closeness was intolerable; the sea was stupendous – wet and rolling decks'.[17] He stayed in the Ladies cabin with his wife Catherine and her maid, playing whist. He had to put the tricks in his pocket because of the ship's rolling; the three of them were repeatedly flung from their seats and picked up by the stewards – the *SS Britannia* was an unforgettable experience he didn't repeat for twenty-five years. But of his second crossing in 1867 he wrote 'I wasn't sick for a moment. I made plenty of after-dinner speeches and thoroughly enjoyed the whole thing'.[18]

The Dickens experience is worth recalling because it probably explains the absence of leading British engineers at a time when Anglo-American exchange visits were to be expected. Both Whitworth and Wallis made one trip; they both had good business reasons to return but like their Manchester contemporaries, Fairbairn, Nasmyth and Beyer, none of them proffered a greater marine faith beyond crossing the English Channel. John Bright MP was the same. Even though he greatly valued a personal invitation from the President of the US, he never actually set foot in America. On one other occasion both he and Whitworth received a special invitation to join Edward Collins, a New York packet operator, aboard one of his Collins Line Atlantic steamships. Neither took it up; they preferred to enjoy their friendship with Collins on dry land. All three were anxious to develop still further their ideas for telegraphic links between London and New York. Their American friends joked that sending a message was far less sickening than crossing by boat – either by Collins or Cunard.

On the occasion of the Royal Commission's May 1853 crossing, however, one can be assured that whatever comforts were requested, the ship's officers and crew would have made every effort to provide. For Whitworth personally, he seems to have enjoyed the dry-land experience, gaining much confidence for the views which previously he only tentatively expressed. On returning from America it is significant that his opinions about mass production and technical education and the necessity for a free press became unhesitant and powerful. His report,[19] much of which he had written during the voyage home (its tone and content possibly influenced by George Wallis and Professor Wilson) confirms how impressed he was with American ambition and the managerial flexibility which the new Englanders cultivated as a means towards their ambitious targets. And as if by comparison, his one observation concerning emigrants from Britain directly followed a visit he had made to the steel mills at Pittsburgh. 'Workmen were obtained from Sheffield', he wrote, 'but they were intractable and failed to give satisfaction to their employers'. Presumably his remarks echoed the complaints about 'stubborn craft-dignity' about which British steelmasters had so often quibbled, later becoming noticeably sour when Henry Bessemer introduced his new steelmaking.

The SS *Basilisk* docked at New York on 26 May. Whitworth and the Commissioners quickly 'found their land legs' before boarding a train for Washington DC. The itinerary suited both Whitworth and Wallis as arrangements had been made for them to visit factories on their way, stopping off at both Philadelphia and Baltimore before going on to Washington. Lord Egerton, the senior of the Royal Commissioners, had agreed to act as their spokesman during the formalities on Capitol Hill – after that each Commissioner making his own way, as in Whitworth's case, to look into the state of American general engineering and then jointly with George Wallis, to examine American methods for the mass production of military small arms.

At first, Whitworth was surprised by the size and generality of the engineering establishments, particularly the marine and engine works in New York and New Jersey. In his Special US Report (published February 1854) he specifically alluded to the mixture as though it differed from England. 'The practice which prevails', he wrote, 'combines the manufacture of gearing, engine tools, spinning and other machinery. In others, marine engines, hydraulic presses, forge hammers and large cannon were all being made in the same establishments.' He then went on to comment on American machine tools (engine tools as he called them), saying:

> they were generally similar to those used in England some years previously, being much less accurate in their construction than those now in use (that is in Britain 1853) and turning out less work in consequence.

He then made an unusual observation, contrary in fact to our general understanding, saying that American technology and ideas leading towards repetitive production were much in advance of Britain yet the quality of American toolmaking was poor in comparison, say, to Manchester standards. 'The proportion of slide to hand lathes is greater than in the generality of English workshops'. Significantly, he considered, American workshops possessed far more lathes using power-driven cross-slides and attachments (copies probably of imported Whitworth lathes) than would be found in Britain.

Retracing the history of this technology it will be remembered that Whitworth was the first to equip his centre lathes with coordinated cross-slides and a quick-release power drive. He did so as early as 1835. Four years later, he exported copies of these machines to Francis Lowell, the largest textile manufacturer in America. This example was quickly followed by a number of firms throughout Massachusetts and Connecticut to whom Whitworth had also agreed to sell his machinery. It was a strange experience no doubt for the man himself to now see, ten years on, the American delineations of his own original ideas – the progenitural offspring in fact of Whitworth's lathes and 'quick-return' worm-driven planing machines.

Both types of machine – they were mostly American-built – were in common use throughout the factories he visited but surprisingly there were comparatively few horizontal shapers or vertical slotting machines. This shortcoming, Whitworth observed, undoubtedly caused a considerable amount of unnecessary hand labour and though his report didn't mention the design of these seldom seen machines, we now know that American machine designers shared Whitworth's dislike of rack and pinion mechanisms. Unlike their Manchester counter-parts, however, they went on to develop the most sophisticated transmission systems themselves and in consequence, by 1870, had left the remainder of the field far behind. Whitworth was absolutely right when he predicted: 'American manufacturers will want machine tools of a better description than those in use; and before long there will, no doubt, be great improvement in this respect'. He was convinced that the great American vision balancing mass production with mass consumption of itself demanded world class machine tools and that such a need would be fulfilled. The one self-satisfying conclusion he could hardly resist – that nothing he saw in America during his 1853 visit equalled his own design skills or factory organization. He was ready to admit, however, '(American) foundries are, for the most part, large and well arranged and are furnished with good powerful cranes'. It was this one solitary concession alongside his other truisms which made his report even more prophetic.

Of his report generally, two particular statements attract attention. Both are indicative of skill shortages which the Americans were determined to overcome. First, in Whitworth's opinion, the factories he visited from Pittsburgh to New Hampshire lacked machines of toolroom quality. Not just in his view, but an opinion shared by American engineers themselves, the machines lacked bed-flatness, spindle and face-plate accuracy plus a certain bearing crudity. These weaknesses clearly refuted the European belief that American workshops in 1853 were capable of machining interchangeable parts. The machine tools Whitworth observed would not have had sufficient precision to allow the separate manufacture of parts prior to their assembly in one central place bringing together randomly selected pieces. The marvellous idea that different factories could specialize and be tooled-up accordingly was a premature dream still at least a decade away.

The second point he made was that American machine tools were generally much more powerfully built than their European equivalents. They proved themselves capable of far heavier duty, built in fact to take cuts three times the average speeds and feeds used in Britain. His report emphasized

> The iron castings in some of the establishments were very good, and cylinders from 8 to 14 feet in diameter were well bored, with a finishing feed of cut of about three-eighths of an inch per revolution, which is at a width of cut at least three times as great as that ordinarily given in English works.[20]

Though Whitworth himself seldom allowed pessimism to colour his views – he was much too confident in his own engineering ability – nonetheless from a British point of view he was apprehensive as to how soon the Americans would overhaul the lead he himself had given Britain. That the US would ultimately win he had no doubt. He was sure that the engineers he was then meeting in the US would inevitably gallop ahead of the world. As a realist he recognized the incentives. Everything he wrote about America revealed an innermost admiration yet curiously, much of what he practised in Britain proved the opposite. He applauded the American style of management, for instance. He liked their open-door approach and its democratic subtleties although he kept himself to himself in his own factory. He liked the idea of delegating authority within the team but until his later years he kept a tight hold of the reins. It was all so contradictory.

In little over seven years after the publication of his 1854 report, both Whitworth and Manchester were deeply embroiled in the American Civil War, more than any other British city. Within three years of the war ending, however (1868), the American machine tool industry started to gain the ground predicted by Whitworth. Some of their machinery was brilliantly conceived, matching exactly American policy of equating mass production with mass consumption. It reminded Whitworth of the advice he had given the Board of Trade during earlier years but which the Government consistently ignored. At the time Joe mistrusted their anti-Americanism but much worse was to come.

William Gladstone, on becoming Prime Minister in 1868, inexplicably appointed the Rt Hon. Robert Lowe MP as Chancellor of the Exchequer. Lowe (later to become Viscount Sherbrooke) was caustically anti-American in all he said and did; he even accused John Bright MP of wanting to Americanize Britain. He attacked the likes of Whitworth and his ideas in wanting to pay workers sufficient wages to enable them purchase mass-produced articles. He reduced taxation, admittedly, but workers didn't normally pay tax. Robert Lowe was brilliantly lucid; an Oxford intellect, he filled the House of Commons whenever he spoke, he attacked reform, he was a vociferous anti-democrat. '. . . Give workers power,' he said, 'the idle, the drunks . . . give them power and down will go the nation.' He was equally anti-technical education; he opposed Manchester when it applied for university status on the grounds that its university would become science orientated. Above all, he was anti-engineering, virtually anti-every thing Whitworth advocated, except free-trade. Shamefully, Joseph Whitworth ducked every time he had the chance to rebuke the Chancellor. In 1868, he was a Vice-President of the Society of Arts, being the fifth recipient – following Michael Faraday and Louis-Napoleon – to receive the Albert Gold Medal. It was a glorious platform for him to 'take on' the Treasury oracle, but his courage failed him. Perhaps after all Whitworth should have 'searched' for a seat in the House but the record suggests that he would have behaved no differently than his friend, Daniel Gooch MP; he would have 'failed to rise' and said nothing.

Once his US report was published in 1854, the trade press only fleetingly referred to the three main issues he raised. On the first, an assessment of American machine tools and their economic potential, editors naturally followed his comments but the second issue, a comparison between American and British workers, they largely ignored. The third question, which impressed Whitworth immensely, was the absence from American society of any snobbishness, of any restriction or artificial reservations between groups of people. These were probably more of his contradictions but he deeply envied their universal press, combined as it was with a liberal system of education. It was these progressive institutions, he believed, which created the relationships and attributes he much admired. In his report he powerfully observed:

> It rarely happens that a workman who possesses peculiar skill in his craft is disqualified to take the responsible position of superintendent, by the want of education and general knowledge, as is frequently the case in this country. In every State in the Union, and particularly in the north, education is, by means of the common schools, placed within the reach of each individual, and all classes avail themselves of the opportunities afforded. The desire of knowledge

> so early implanted is greatly increased, while the facilities for diffusing it are amply provided through the instrumentality of an almost universal press. No taxation of any kind has been suffered to interfere with the free development of this powerful agent for promoting the intelligence of the people, and the consequence is, that where the humblest of labourer can indulge in the luxury of his daily paper, everybody reads, and thought and intelligence penetrate through the lowest grades of society. The benefits which thus result from a liberal system of education and a cheap press to the working classes of the United States can hardly be over-estimated in a national point of view; but it is to the cooperation of both that they must undoubtedly be ascribed. For if, selecting a proof from among the European States, the condition of Prussia be considered, it will be found that the people of that country, as a body, have not made that progress which, from the great attention paid to the education of all classes, might have been anticipated; and this must certainly be ascribed to the restrictions laid upon the press, which have so materially impeded the general advancement of the people. Wherever education and an unrestricted press are allowed a full scope to exercise their united influence, progress and improvement are the certain results, and among the many benefits which arise from their joint cooperation may be ranked most prominently the value which they teach men to place upon intelligent contrivance; the readiness with which they cause new improvements to be received, and the impulse which they thus unavoidably give to that inventive spirit which is gradually emancipating man from the rude forms of labour, and making what were regarded as the luxuries of one age to be looked upon in the next as the ordinary and necessary conditions of human existence.

In regard to the operators called upon to work the new machinery installed from Washington to the Great Lakes, Whitworth makes the point that unlike British workers, the Americans positively welcomed its introduction. Most workers in New England, he thought, looked upon the new technology as a means of raising their living standards while British trade unionists – here he was referring not to the engineering unions but to textiles, carpets and joinery – resisted mechanical invention because they saw it as a threat. This further extract from his report gives vent to these irritants which so annoyed him in Britain. Referring wholly to the United States he wrote:

> The details which I have collected in this report show, by numerous examples, that they leave no means untried to effect what they think it is possible to accomplish, and they have been signally successful in combining large practical results with great economy in the methods by which these results are secured.
>
> The labouring classes are comparatively few in number, but this is counter-balanced by, and indeed many be regarded as one of the chief causes of, the eagerness with which they call in the aid of machinery in almost every

department of industry. Wherever it can be introduced as a substitute for manual labour, it is universally and willingly resorted to . . .

It is this condition of the labour market, and this eager resort to machinery wherever it can be applied, to which, under the guidance of superior education and intelligence, the remarkable prosperity of the United States is mainly due.

The results which have been obtained in the United States, by the application of machinery wherever it has been practicable to manufacturers, are rendered still more remarkable by the fact, that combinations to resist its introduction there are unheard of. The workmen hail with satisfaction all mechanical improvements, the importance and value of which, as releasing them from the drudgery of unskilled labour, they are enabled by education to understand and appreciate. With the comparatively superabundant supply of hands in England, and therefore a proportionate difficulty in obtaining remunerative employment, the working classes have less sympathy with the progressive invention. Their condition is a less favourable one than that of their American brethren for forming a just and unprejudiced estimate of the influence which the introduction of machinery is calculated to exercise on their state and prospects. I cannot resist the conclusion, however, that the different views taken by our operatives and those of the United States upon this subject are determined by other and powerful causes, besides those dependent on the supply of labour in the two countries. The principles which ought to regulate the relations between the employer and the employed seem to be thoroughly understood and appreciated in the United States, and while the law of limited liability affords the most ample facilities for the investment of capital in business, the intelligent and educated artizan is left equally free to earn all that he can, by making the best use of his hands, without let or hindrance by his fellows.

It may be that the working classes exhibit an unusual independence of manner, but the same feeling insures the due performance of what they consider to be their duty with less supervision than is required where dependence is to be placed upon uneducated hands.[21]

'An artizan', he reported, 'should be free to earn all he can, by making the best use of his hands, without let or hindrance by his fellows.' Quite so. But by leaving the argument so abruptly he failed to do his own efforts justice, for it was he himself who reasoned with the *Masters* Federation not two years earlier – that the Federation was wrong to advise employers to limit piece-work earnings to 'time and one third'. It was always the 'piece-master' who reduced the price. It was this brazen embezzlement which so appalled the trade unions – and presumably it equally dismayed Whitworth. The ASE tried hard to convince the press that they welcomed new machinery, especially so because they believed machines would create more leisure time, increase production and in consequence raise wages. Karl Marx was even more cogent than the trade unions:

> the maximum substitution of machines for men would bring the 'whole man' into being and enable him to unfold the full range of his potential abilities.[22]

Two or more decades later – when things didn't materialize – Marx became more critical – not particularly of the machines, but more of the employers.[23]

There are a number of other colourful stories which attempt to explain the origin of Britain's low productivity – part of the so-called British disease – by blaming the trade unions. Two of the most interesting also concern Whitworth and are properly dealt with here. The first relates to Colonel Colt's factory at Pimlico, London and the second, the Small Arms factory at Enfield. Tom Rolt's book *Tools for the Job* reiterates the popular theory that Colt's factory was prematurely closed because 'the British workmen of the day would not tolerate the "*American*" system'. It was nothing of the kind. Sam Colt opened his factory in 1853, Whitworth having supplied his toolroom machinery. The factory lasted no more than four years before it was taken over by the War Office in 1858 and transferred to the RSAF repair department at Enfield. The reason why it was taken over was not because workmen refused to operate the '*American*' system – they loved his higher pay and his modern wash-rooms – but because Colt was caught 'red-handed' supplying revolvers to the Russians (Britain was at war!), in addition to which the War Office didn't like the way Colt duplicated his invoices.

The second story concerning the RSAF at Enfield personifies an even stronger rebuttal of similar myths. As a result of their US tour Whitworth and Wallis recommended the installation at Enfield of American machines. A subsequent delegation led by Sir John Anderson visited Massachusetts to purchase the famous Blanchard woodworking machines in addition to some special purpose machine tools. Far from objecting, the ASE workmen were very impressed and in response to a Ministry letter dated 8 May 1856, asking how things were going, John Anderson included the following statement in his report:

> The American machinery is so different to our own, and so rich in suggestions, that when fully organized it should be thrown open to the study of the machine makers of the kingdom, for it is a positive addition to the manufacturing resources of the nation, and shall enable us to keep up with our transatlantic competitors.
>
> A few hours at Enfield will show that we shall soon have to contend with no mean competitors in the Americans, who display an originality and common sense in most of their arrangements which are not to be despised, but on the contrary are either to be copied or improved upon.[24]

The fact that the ASE Enfield Lock Branch is one of the oldest in the country helps repudiate this 'blaming the unions' fantasy. The Branch was founded in 1855 and first met at the Red Lion pub, Enfield Highway. The landlord at that time, a Mr John Foot, kindly allowed the Branch to keep its box and minute books in the attic. When the Branch moved, in May 1870, the box was forgotten and left in the attic. Almost a century later, in June 1969, the current landlord found the box, papers and books untouched, including reports which had been requested by the ASE executive council in regard to the completion by William Fairbairn in March 1859 of the new rifle factory at Enfield and the installation of the new American machines. The total workforce had, by 1860, escalated to an impressive 2,000 men producing an average of 1,744 rifles per week compared with the American Springfield armoury where 13,000 workers produced 1,970 rifles per week. The Branch also reported that skilled wage rates at Enfield were among the highest in the country: both men and machines doing well, it would seem.[25]

Whitworth himself was thus an advocate of what became the *American* system long before the Americans. His visit to the United States merely strengthened his resolve to persuade Britain to *think* mass production: to welcome new and better (i.e. faster) machine tools. Ostensibly, the purpose of the 1853 Royal Commission was to visit the New York Exhibition but the fact that it failed to open until after the Commission had returned to Britain didn't seem to detract from their success. On arrival in London, the Foreign Secretary regretted that his Commission had not been able to see the Exhibition but promised to study carefully what they had reported. Privately of course both the Foreign Office and the War Office had closely questioned Wallis and Whitworth on what they had learned from their tour of American armouries. They both confirmed they had been given enough freedom to assess whether the Americans were competent gun manufacturers – they thought they were. The War Office need not have worried; as Whitworth left New York, Jefferson Davis, the US Secretary for War, reassured the British Government that the US Ordnance Department would provide all the help needed should London require to buy either guns or machinery.

For the record, Whitworth's American tour lasted five weeks and covered well over two thousand miles. He had an extensive itinerary and must have been tired; nevertheless he resumed his work immediately on landing back in Britain. On leaving Pittsburgh he had travelled via Buffalo and on to Boston, touring machine tool factories and Government armouries in Massachusetts and Connecticut, spending most of the time at the Springfield armoury before returning to New York. He personally benefited a great deal; winning new friends, gaining political and professional confidence the whole time. At the age of fifty he was a more radical, unabridged man as a result.

Practical Politics

What has sometimes been dubbed the railway decade was, for Whitworth, the busiest, most dominant ten years of his life. His career really came of age amidst the kudos and celebration of the 1851 Great Exhibition. But like all engineers he suffered a setback the following year: he felt trampled on by the engineers' lock-out but even then he survived undiminished, happily to be appointed a member of the 1853 Royal Commission to visit the United States.

The post-exhibition ballyhoo was working. He returned from America to full order books for his latest machine tools. The work necessitated considerable expansion for his company, but by this time many other interests were beginning to nudge their way into his life. Though every single one warranted priority none more so than the government's own deep anxiety as to the poor quality of its military weapons. By mid-1854 the War Office and its ministers were pressing Whitworth desperately hard to consider seriously their gun problems. Little did he then realize that his part acceptance signalled the start of what was to become a mercurial – at times upsetting and disordered – twenty years' relationship with both government and politics.

It was sometimes said of Whitworth that he was the most assiduous industrialist of his generation but one suspects that neither he nor his friends needed much insight to understand why he was in such great demand. It wasn't just the War Office, but also the railways and a myriad other manufacturers who felt that by using Whitworth's machinery they were within easy reach of immense success; however, they just didn't quite grasp how to harmonize their men, their machines and their new products. For them, where lay the Whitworth rubicon? The truth of the matter lay hidden in his campaigning for mass-production and the use of up-to-the-minute machine tools *plus* essential skill training. There was no magic formula – just flair and hard work – but the simple questions asked of Whitworth persisted: 'tell us, how can it be done?'

The first of these requests came from locomotive builders. Only in size did their production queries differ from the dairy equipment and the agricultural machine-makers; all of whom asked Whitworth for advice. His response was sharp and immediate: it was to his everlasting credit that he willingly found time to investigate their difficulties. His reports were mostly not to their liking for usually he recommended better quality control and more thorough skill training for their workmen; neither of these themes was popular with employers because they always feared having to pay higher wages. Their dilemma was universal; the machinery was generally good but finishing each work-piece to within the limits recommended by Whitworth was beyond the operatives. The employers no doubt hoped that the problems could have been overcome by adding some extra piece of mechanical self-acting wizardry but they were sadly disappointed. Contrary to common belief, since the Great Exhibition, practical skill instruction was more costly and slower.

Some of these problems were incredibly difficult to conquer yet by modern standards it is almost impossible to comprehend that they were ever serious quandaries. The time was still early 1854. Steam boilers, for instance, suffered a whole series of disasters. William Fairbairn worried incessantly, as did John Ramsbottom, the locomotive engineer, as to how they could overcome these serious setbacks. The number of deaths – usually by scalding and other equally horrifying injuries – was grimly increasing and Fairbairn invited Whitworth together with Henry Houldsworth to meet him urgently to study the question of safety. Along with a John Hetherington,[26] Fairbairn had invented the Lancashire boiler and to some extent felt responsible for its safety. The group studied the problem from every angle. Finally, they convened a special meeting at the Manchester Town Hall, on 19 September 1854, to launch the formation of the Manchester Steam Users Association, a group of employers set up specifically to try and prevent boiler explosions. Fairbairn was made President and Whitworth Vice-President. Their research papers were freely circulated, much appreciated overseas, but seldom, if ever, acknowledged at home as being wholly funded by the original Manchester engineers. One other obstacle they had to surmount; having decided on certain operational precautions, they had to convince their *laissez-faire* political friends that safety legislation was absolutely necessary. A difficult task indeed.

This safety work undertaken by Fairbairn and Ramsbottom was all-important. They both concentrated on new safety valves, Ramsbottom especially, getting accepted within three or four years his famous 'safety valve' and 'double regulator valve'. It was a different kind of development, however, which overcame the problem known to cause most explosions – the sudden drop in the water level. Ramsbottom designed an elbow pipe fitted with fusible plugs which melted-out immediately the water level dropped and the temperature soared upwards. Fairbairn too worked on similar ideas but it was while he concentrated on the problems of locomotives that he hit upon the idea of the tank engine. As for Whitworth's contribution, his drawing office got to work and tooled-up many of these valve developments especially their spring components. The lethal weaknesses of boilers, however, were by no means over. The shocking death-rate continued until July 1858, when a huge explosion shattered the main boiler at Sharps Atlas works, Manchester. Seven men were killed outright and many were seriously injured. Its closeness to home immediately recruited the best engineering expertise and convinced the Board of Trade of the necessity for regulatory powers. At last remedial design changes were a matter for urgent attention.

Much of what Whitworth had preached in regard to improved workmanship and systematic organization was slowly being accepted by leading employers. The London North West Railway Company was so concerned about the poor quality of its engineering they invited Whitworth to investigate the matter. Mr Hadfield, the Chairman of the company, wrote to Whitworth in December 1855, explaining his dissatisfaction. By the end of January, back came the report.[27] 'There are some parts of your engines', wrote Whitworth, 'which are continually being worn out; the manufacture of these should be constantly in progress . . . a stock kept . . . used both for the new and the repair of old engines'. He then asked rhetorically 'whether it would be more politic for the company to manufacture its own engines rather than to purchase them outside?' It was a provocative question, bearing in mind his friend Ramsbottom was chief superintendent at Longsight – shortly to take over the whole LNWR at Crewe – while Fairbairn and Beyer were themselves private manufacturers of locomotives. Unbelievably, Whitworth then revealed a vacillating side to his character not seen before. 'It would be advantageous to do both to some extent', he choked, no doubt desperately anxious to avoid offence to any of his friends.

The Engineer magazine was a little more forthright. The questions posed by the editor reverberate to this day. 'It is quite sufficient for a railway company to repair', he stated, referring to the alarming rate at which locomotives were breaking down, 'but whether the company should build its own engines is questionable. We would have, *as a rule*, all engines built out of, and only repaired in, the company's workshops.' Whitworth was right to call for the standardization of parts, said the editorial, 'but not to have an absolute uniformity in the construction of an engine. For all railway companies to select one class of engine . . . is out of the question.'[28]

The Engineer continued its critique of Whitworth's recommendations, based as they were on the division of labour. 'Men become skilled hands by constant practice, by repetition of work'. In that sense, Whitworth was right to advocate that the companies go in for group production; but although this would mean repetitive work on no account would it ever amass the benefits of mass-production. The numbers were much too small. Even if a single company built every locomotive Britain required for a generation, the savings would never justify the dubious advantages of such draconian monopolism. Whitworth was wrong to suggest otherwise. On the other hand, conceded *The Engineer*, 'all must agree that cylinders, pistons, connecting-rods, axles, wheels, the threads of screwbolts; all these, and many other parts, present themselves at once as capable of being brought under one law of uniformity'.

It is frequently thought that the Railway Regulation Act 1846 put an end to the debate about gauge width and other railway production issues. No so. Indeed, it was virtually the start. It was argued that the narrow gauge held back British locos but most foreign railways kept to the same narrow width and by 1865 had overtaken the British. William Fairbairn illustrates the point. Ten years earlier he was nominated by the French to act as Chairman of Jurors (Mechanical Section) for their 1855 Paris Exhibition. When he got back to London in 1855 he reported to the President of the Board of Trade, Lord Stanley, 'I am of the opinion', he said, 'that the locomotive engines of Great Britain are superior to *most* others; and although they may not have the same amount of polish, there is nevertheless a simplicity of form and a soundness of workmanship which gives character and stability to these important constructions'.[29]

Intriguingly, seven years later, he occupied a similar position at the 1862 South Kensington Exhibition and because of his visits to France and Germany was then in a position to make valuable comparisons.

> The French and German engineers are in advance of us in theoretical knowledge. Not only have they overtaken some of our best efforts in mechanical science, it would now appear the Germans have excelled in the quality of their steel and mechanical workmanship.[30]

How Whitworth himself reacted to this is difficult to evaluate but we do know that his personal adviser, John Aston, pointed to expert internationalists attending the Kensington Exhibition and quoted, 'the Whitworth machines equal – if not better – anything in the world'. 'Yes', Professor Wheatstone confirmed, 'in my opinion, that is so'.

Whitworth's most pressing task at this time was undoubtedly sorting out what kind of facilities he would require were he to accept the War Office challenge and research a whole new gun system. He had so many other preoccupations that by spring 1856 his own theory 'division of labour' was the best advice he could practise. Needless to say he ignored any need for selectivity and quite tenaciously stepped up his activities all round. He had already been elected, in December 1855, a council member of the Civil Engineers; now he was elected for two years, President of the Institution of Mechanical Engineers, taking the chair for the first time on 17 September 1856 at their meeting in Bath Street, Glasgow.

Normally, the President's address would simply be a straightforward reading: this time it was different. Whitworth presented an enlivened miscellany, part politics, part engineering. Gladstone would have been proud. 'I propose to address you shortly', said Whitworth, 'on a few topics more or less connected with our profession of mechanical engineering'. 'A Scotch mechanic', he joked, 'once south, never crossed the Tweed a second time'. And with that, treading some familiar water, he was off in favour of *income* tax as against the indirect taxation favoured by the Treasury moguls. He then predicted huge agricultural benefits to be gained by engineers mechanizing the land. Chemists would provide fertilizers. For example, his own agricultural machinery, patented in 1853, was just a start but it signified that a land revolution was not too distant. 'That great and good man, Sir Robert Peel, has given us hope', proclaimed Joe, applauding his great hero. 'He also forecast the coming wealth of a nation', provided, as it undoubtedly would be, 'by our talented mechanical engineers'.

Whitworth's politics were based on the simple belief that everyone should pay tax according to their income. He was opposed to having a duty to pay on any aspect of trade. He almost subscribed to the 'Manchester School', except he *beseeched* the government to intervene and lay down standards throughout industry. The taxation aspect, of course, was one of his main planks: he honestly believed that people would buy if the price (without tax) was affordable; hence his creed – mass production – became his culture. 'As you know', he again repeated, 'the very soul of manufacture is repetition'. It was Whitworth's constant recital. If only industrialists would listen. 'Reduce the number of sizes', he pleaded. Marine engines, locomotives, carriages, windows, doors, even bricks. The list was endless: architects and builders could help. 'Our friends across the Atlantic manage matters in connection with their buildings much better than at present we do', he said. Just before William Fairbairn rose to move a vote of thanks to the President, he heard Whitworth conclude his address by saying 'when the industry of this country has been systematized upon sound principles . . . and carried nearer to those standards which, in the case of mechanics, I have endeavoured to indicate, we shall have less reason than at present to doubt the stability of our manufacturing pre-eminence'.

At the adjourned session of the Institution's annual meeting with Whitworth as President in the chair, the level of expectancy was quite different. The Engineers' Council this time had suggested that he present a paper on the decimalization of fractional measurement after which the members present would be asked to adopt an approving resolution moved from the chair by Whitworth. The motion read: 'That this meeting pledge themselves to the adoption of the decimal scale, the inch being divided into one thousand parts.'

If the resolution went through unamended, he felt confident the government would follow and that Britain would then change over to the new decimal system. The date was Thursday 25 June 1857, a red-letter day indeed, both for Whitworth personally and the industry generally. He had waited two and a half years.

Opening the debate, the President said: 'To state the case broadly, instead of our engineers and machinists thinking in eighths, sixteenths, and thirty-secondths of an inch, it is desirable that they should think and speak in tenths, hundredths and thousandths.' Egging the pudding with as much egg as his conscience would allow, he quietly bragged: 'In the manufacture of my standard gauges of size, the workmen measure to the one twenty-thousandth of an inch and these measures are as familiar and appreciable as those of any larger dimensions. My argument is shortly this; if we had a better system of notation for our measures . . . the importance of minute and accurate measurements would become more familiar, more appreciated, and more generally applied.'[31]

His arguments were convincing. He handed round copies of his proposed decimal scales including his Standard Table of Limits. As in the past, William Fairbairn opened the debate: 'Mr Whitworth's paper was one of very great importance . . . the country was much indebted to him . . . the sooner a start was made the better.'

Similar sentiments were echoed by all the speakers who followed; particular emphasis being given to the absolute need for Britain to retain the *inch* rather than convert to the metre. Henry Maudslay Jun. wanted the matter referred to a committee but Whitworth, from the Chair, considered 'any such proposal would simply result in doing nothing'. The resolution was then read out and carried and things at last looked as though they were on their way, although it was 1864 before the Palmerston coalition brought in an Act to legalize the use of decimals in Britain. It was appropriate, said the parliamentarians, that the original resolution should be styled the *Manchester decision* because it was there that decimalization was first practised long before the 1864 Act reached the statute book.

On the day following this extraordinary meeting, Whitworth invited to his estate at Fallowfield a number of the leading engineers who had that day supported his decimalization plans. But readers, understandably, will appreciate the detail of this noteworthy gathering during an account of his field artillery in the next chapter. Meanwhile, events from the beginning of 1857 moved on so rapidly that it is difficult to keep up. Joe's friend, John Bright MP, was the first shock. Bright lost his Manchester seat to Sir John Potter during the March general election. It was a bewildering defeat at a time when Whitworth needed some Parliamentary help, but it was even more bewildering when Bright, a pacifist, was returned unopposed four months later for Birmingham, the centre of the gun trade.

There were many more eventualities to come. Whitworth was elected a Fellow of the Royal Society in mid-April. His letter of acceptance probably crossed with the correspondence he exchanged at that time with Prince Albert and his secretary, Major-General Grey, on the question of both rifles and artillery. This kind of involvement with members of the Royal Family was obviously a much more relaxed arrangement than it is today. Just how relaxed it was is demonstrated by *The Times* editorial, 23 April 1857.

Headed 'A Story of the Palace' (taken from the *Manchester Examiner*) appears this incredulous account; that on the night of the 14 April, Queen Victoria was in labour. Albert, her husband, desperate to help, failed to awaken the Palace staff – everyone, that is, from the 'master of the horse' to equerries, even to 'old gold sticks'. The situation was getting ever more urgent, both doctor and midwife were needed immediately. The Prince Consort did no more than set off himself down the Mall and across Horse Guards Parade in search of a cabby, heart palpitating. One solitary cab and sullied horse glimmered between gas and moonlight. Off they went to High Holborn to collect the midwife – then back to the Palace. In the end, all was well, but what a story! As *The Times* said:

> We pay handsomely for the maintenance of a retinue of servants to wait on her on all occasions . . . regardless of expense . . . yet a host of lubberlip grooms were snoring in the Palace chambers.

This remarkable story of the Palace is repeated here because it helps overcome the natural disbelief that the Prince himself – or any other member of Victoria's household – could possibly be so diligent and caring as to be involved personally in lobbying the Cabinet. Both he and Queen Victoria were, in fact, active political lobbyists. Albert was determined to pump as much new technology into military matters as he possibly could and Whitworth's work impressed him very much. His relationship with leading industrialists was also quite informal. When he deputized for the Queen and opened the Art Treasures Exhibition at Manchester on 5 May 1857 he called on Whitworth privately. And as soon as the Queen resumed normal engagements after the birth of her child, she and Albert returned to Manchester on 30 June to spend another two days at the Exhibition. He again visited Whitworth. Thirteen days later Prince Louis-Napoleon also visited the City and he too visited the Whitworth factory.[32] An incredible number of dignitaries made their way to his

Chorlton Street works. Clearly his gun fame was the attraction but he also had very much wider interests. Since early 1856, for instance, he had been unusually engaged in building four of the latest American rotary printing presses: the first two for *The Times* newspaper. They were the latest 'ten-feeder' cylinder machines invented by a William Hoe of Philadelphia.

The first two prototypes of these machines were erected by Colonel Hoe himself in Paris for the daily paper *La Patrie.* The first machine Hoe built in London, however, was for *Lloyd's Weekly. The Times* went over to see it and ordered two but stipulated that the machines must be made by Joseph Whitworth. After some quibbling about design matters, Joe accepted the job and agreed to have them finished and erected in Playhouse Yard, August 1857. Whether he delivered on time is not clear; contemporary writers suggest that due to various difficulties, mostly down to the Whitworth company, Colonel Hoe wasn't satisfied and established his own factory in London, henceforth manufacturing his machines here in Britain. One thing is clear: if these machines were built to Whitworth standards *The Times* itself must have been satisfied. They ran for twelve years. In the end, *The Times* patented, manufactured and marketed its own rotary presses called the *Walter Press.* To do this, they built a workshop at Printing House Square and installed Whitworth machine tools and gauging equipment – testimony indeed that their faith in Whitworth remained undiminished.[33]

A wholly contrary view – at times perverse and hostile – challenging the very essence of Whitworth's prowess and factory organization, emanated from the pen of another American associate of Whitworth's, a Charles T. Porter.[34] If true, the evidence he offered is devastating. Some dissection is therefore necessary. Concerning the Hoe printing machines, Porter claimed that Whitworth's works superintendent, Mr Widdowson, had told him that the works experienced great difficulty making the Hoe machines. 'Every tape ran-off its pulley . . . not a spindle was parallel with any other. The works had no idea of method . . . after a few revolutions every spindle stuck fast in its bearings'. It was a strange story for a manager to tell against his own competence – if indeed it was ever told – but Porter seemed to insist it was true when he declared: 'Mr Whitworth was absorbed in his artillery and spending most of his time in London . . . he had no knowledge of how things were going (at Chorlton Street)'.

Whitworth had agreed to build for Porter, on an experimental basis, a Porter-Allen steam engine in addition to a number of 'alternative high speed governors' which Porter – if they were successful – intended to patent. He also wanted to exhibit them at the 1867 Paris Exhibition before marketing them worldwide. He had crossed the Atlantic especially and gone to Whitworth's because of the tremendous prestige and market clout Whitworth's reputation would bring the engine. In the event, the whole thing finally fell through because Whitworth insisted on the right to amend the design of any part of the engine if he didn't think it good enough. This, Porter refused to sign. 'Mr Whitworth was the most dangerous man possible to be entrusted with such power. His disposition was despotic', said Porter. 'After that . . . we got along on a *modus vivendi* plan, to get the engine through the Paris Exposition'.

In his book, Porter again 'quoted' Whitworth's work's superintendent, Mr Widdowson, as saying (in 1866): 'The intelligence does not exist in these works to make a steam engine. Nobody knows how to set about anything.' In fact, a new foreman was appointed to oversee Porter's work and in Porter's own words, 'everything seemed to go wrong. It is hardly to be believed. He could not get a rod turned round, or a hole bored round.' It was – as Mr Porter himself said – difficult to believe! The implication suggested that the Chorlton Street factory thrived on scrap!

The fact that Charles Porter was a reputable lawyer and engineering writer much published in the American trade press strengthens the opinion that his writing should be considered properly, no matter how improbable it all seemed. He also had an American reputation for much of his own Porter-Allen steam engine but it is difficult to be serious when he advanced such criticisms of the Whitworth's factory as: gearwheels cut eccentrically with irregular teeth; bored holes like ploughed fields; that most circular work was beyond Whitworth's lathe operatives; lathe spindles had an eighth of an inch 'wobble' in their bearings; all these and many more such dubious examples were given by Porter as evidence that the Whitworth factory was run-down and devoid of work due to Joseph Whitworth's personal neglect. He asserted he had observed all this during the period 1863–66. Astonishingly, it was the very period when Whitworth deliberately made a point of inviting groups of leading IMechE engineers and Government ministers to inspect his works and study his methods: something he would hardly do if things were as bad as Porter alleged.[35]

Also, in 1866, Whitworth was again President of the 'Mechanicals' and was especially proud of the machine developments he had encouraged his draughtsmen to elaborate since the 1862 South Kensington Exhibition. Visiting engineers were shown his latest design work in hydraulic presses; an aspect highlighted in the technical press which emphasized particularly the fine quality workmanship to be seen throughout the factory. Unusually, one or two photographs were published illustrating the genius of the Whitworth organization; moreover, at the 1867 Paris Exhibition, about which Porter was so keen, Whitworth actually received one of only five gold awards issued, which seemed to confirm the excellence of his engineering. Twelve months later he was admitted by Louis-Napoleon to the Legion of Honour.

Charles Porter came to England in 1861, and stayed for seven years: in between, he was at the Whitworth factory for about two years, 1865–67. One would have thought he would have known the factory well but his description of the drawing office suggests the opposite. Porter describes the place illogically. 'They had a pretty large drawing office – empty', he wrote. 'I was told that until a short time before my coming they had kept one draughtsman employed, but no one paid any attention to his drawings'.[36] The point is ludicrous, but when criticism reaches absurdity due to a crazed phobia – as Porter had about Whitworth – there sometimes appears just a grain of truth. And so it is here.

Although Whitworth himself was a brilliant visualizer and an innovative engineering designer, for the past twenty years he had clearly failed to fully exploit his own talents by not employing sufficient draughtsmen to follow through in detail his outline ideas. In the early days not only was this Whitworth's blind-side but like so many of his engineering contemporaries, even in later times, he just could not bring himself to delegate to others the job of processing his bright ideas. Brunel was the same – Fairbairn too – and even some of the great locomotive designers had to do it themselves, hence they became workaholics. Indeed they were less than they could have been due entirely to their unbelievably short-sighted view that drawing offices were largely unnecessary overheads and therefore to be kept to the absolute minimum. In Whitworth's own case, that is to say, around 1856 onwards, he patently required the help of professional gun people – specialists in explosives and cartridge design – and he could well afford them, yet he chose not to do so. Indeed he could not afford to be without them yet it took him a long time and much unnecessary aggravation to learn his lesson and reverse his ways.

He also desperately needed specialist gun draughtsmen – his old friend George Wallis for one could have helped – but he kept his design problems to himself and he occasionally missed the boat as a result. Good engineering draughtsmen have always recognized that additional expert eyes pin-point solutions more quickly but also that extra draughtsmen undoubtedly strengthen the collective design qualities of an office. The rule certainly applied in Whitworth's day. There is also one other reason for extra draughtsmen. It was inevitable then, as it is now, that production crises would arise throughout any day and compel draughtsmen to break their concentration in order to attend to an immediate situation. It is perhaps less than a harsh judgement to say that the apparent inadequacy of his drawing office was something other than petty frugality. Bad judgement possibly, frugality no. In fairness, a possible factor leading to Whitworth's inability to employ more specialist gun designers during his early gun period was an indecisiveness which understandably arose because of his doubt as to whether he really should get involved in the manufacture of military weapons at all.

Certainly, the truth of the matter lay a long way from the assumptions made by Charles Porter. Nor was Porter remotely correct to suggest an empty drawing office during the early sixties. When Whitworth's chief draughtsman, the thirty-three-year-old Tom Pemberton, left him to go to the United States, in late 1856, Whitworth agreed with Tom's successor, George Andrews, that he would employ more draughtsmen to deal with any military work. Both Pemberton and Andrews were Unitarian lay preachers and anti-war, neither willing to design guns, but naturally, as chief draughtsmen, they would have to supervise the staff involved. Not surprisingly, Andrews followed Tom Pemberton across the Atlantic in 1861; not that he was to know that the American Civil War would engulf most engineering work in the New York and Boston areas. For some four years or so the sheer irony of the situation must have dismayed poor George Andrews; unlike his friend he had to accept whatever work was going.

By the time Charles Porter was ready to leave the United States as the Civil War threatened, Tom Pemberton was fairly well established and had already published in the United States one or two magazine features on Whitworth.[37] It is a reasonable assumption therefore that Porter was attracted by them and that he made contact with Tom, learning as much as he could about Whitworth, his factory and Manchester. It is also a fairly safe supposition that none of the manic anti-Whitworthism later included in Porter's autobiographical writing originated with Pemberton.

Interestingly, a brief explanation here of Tom Pemberton's personality is a justifiable digression. It probably tells us a great deal more about Whitworth's character than a whole mountain of direct quotations. It also tells us just how closely knit the Manchester engineering fraternity really were. Tom Pemberton was born in Leeds around 1822 being some eighteen years younger than Whitworth. His father, who was a principal chainmaker in Liverpool, was also a Congregational lay preacher and like Joe's father, worked as a pastor in both Leeds and Liverpool. And naturally, because of their church work, they knew each other personally. In his early days Tom, somewhat strangely, wanted to be a Church of England rather than a Congregational Minister but his father had other ideas. 'Tom' he said, 'I can give you something better than money – and that something is a trade. You had much better be a good mechanic than a poor parson'. And so he paid £100 to have his son indentured as an apprentice without wages with Peter Fairbairn and Company of Wellington Foundry fame, Leeds.

It was a good start for he was allowed to work on the drawing board in the afternoons and to be tutored by the talented Thomas Greenwood. Once out of his time, however, he quickly moved to Sharp Roberts and Company in Manchester and secured a job as a draughtsman under the skilled eye of that great locomotive designer, Charles F. Beyer. The drawing office there must have been the doyen of all drawing offices at that time and name-dropping among the staff was legendary. The morning Tom Pemberton started, one of the most distinguished of all locomotive engineers, John Ramsbottom, was leaving to take charge of the LNWR railway at Longsight. As for Tom Pemberton, he remained with Charles Beyer until 1848 before signing on as a sea-going engineer, working his way up to become chief engineer before he was thirty years of age. It was then that he decided to return to the drawing board and went back to Manchester to secure a senior job with Joseph Whitworth. In the event, he started with Whitworth immediately following the 1852 Engineers' lock-out; not a stone's throw from his old office. Then, some eighteen months later, in 1853, he was promoted chief draughtsman. Whitworth, it will be recalled, had by then been to the United States with the 1853 Royal Commission and it was on his return to the Chorlton Street works that he promoted Tom Pemberton to be his chief designer.

All this, of course, is by way of explaining that Joe had a gift for spotting talented designers and was not averse to giving younger men the top job. In the case of Tom Pemberton it was significant that he had appointed a man much in support of the trade unions and also a strong advocate of training and the employment of good draughtsmen: views, it must be noted, that were very much minority opinions among employers at the time. Furthermore the half-dozen or so men – who later became well-known engineers – employed by Whitworth over the years, indicated not so much that Joe Whitworth was difficult to work with, or that he didn't pay sufficient salary, but rather was it a sign that his top people used their Whitworth pedigree as a passport to the best management jobs in engineering. It was very much as John Ramsbottom had done when he worked across the road at Sharp Roberts – and all the others as well – so it was not entirely Whitworth's blunt unforebearing attitude (as some writers have suggested) which irritated his staff. But it was noticeable that as the years rolled on Joe relaxed more and spent longer periods in London. Porter was right of course, about that.

Obviously he was beginning to delegate design authority and again contrary to Charles Porter his drawing office grew bigger; similarly his design staff matured with long service. Admittedly in Tom Pemberton's case it was slightly different. He soon found responsible design work in New York but he also took to writing. He wrote feature articles on technology for the newspapers; he became associate editor of the magazine *The Technologist* and wrote two or three books on draughtsmanship and the ethos of the workshop. He published, for his American readership, all Whitworth's lectures delivered to the Institution of Mechanical Engineers and he never turned down an opportunity to praise Whitworth's qualities both as an engineer and his fine work as an educationalist. Undoubtedly, both he and George Andrews were genuine admirers of the man: a man, it must be said, who must have appeared to his chief designers to have ditched his professed belief in rationalism and opted for the dubious profits of the gun trade thus making it impossible for them to continue working together. If that is in fact a true explanation of events, it is a remarkable tribute to Whitworth's image coming as it did from two very intelligent men, both of whom were willing to sacrifice their own employment rather than swap principle for gold.

The Machinist magazine once quoted Pemberton as saying, 'Whitworth was never *contumacious*'. A word, perhaps, which today sounds somewhat heavy but it was a view also put at one time by John Pender MP when he refuted his House of Commons Select Committee colleagues by answering those who considered Whitworth stubborn with the words 'a stickler for accuracy yes; but never obdurate'. Like Whitworth, however, Tom Pemberton never ceased to preach the dignity of manual skill. 'There is no necessary connection', he wrote 'between manual labour and degradation; neither is there a law of nature which separates good manners, high morals and elegant accomplishments from the active duties of a mechanic'. That, in precise terms, was Joe Whitworth's view.

Once Charles Porter resumed his activities as Vice-President of the Southwark Foundry and Machine Company, Philadelphia, and became an occasional correspondent both of the *Power* magazine and the *American Machinist* he was then near enough a fellow journalist of Tom Pemberton; by then editor of the New York magazine, *The Technologist.* But when writing about Whitworth the two revealed remarkable differences: they surely were not writing about the same man. As we have already seen, Pemberton tended to eulogize his subject while Porter, though he recognized certain of Whitworth's outstanding talents, generally laced his opinions with sarcasm. He had felt cheated by Whitworth and although his judgements were condensed, his antagonism came through. Writing in the *American Machinist,* Porter said:

> [Whitworth] was in all respects a phenomenal man. He was not only the most original engineering genius that ever lived. He was also a monumental *egotist.* His fundamental idea was always prominent; that he had taught the world not only all that it knew mechanically, but all it ever could know. He closed his long and wonderful career by giving to the world the hollow engine shaft and the system of hydraulic forging.[38]

But the exact opposite to these impressions regularly flickered through the many jottings contributed by journalists throughout Whitworth's life. The *Manchester Examiner and Times* happily collected them together using a few of them for their obituary column. Of Whitworth the paper noted:

> He was amiable, unaffected, readily accessible, and as *modest* in the assertion of his views as was consistent with the necessity of advancing them. He was not a handsome man, but he had a marked physiognomy, and a figure which, if not stalwart, was erect and sufficiently the reverse of insignificant. His manner was remarkably quiet.

The last three years of the decade, 1857–60, were momentous years which celebrated a whole series of radical changes for Whitworth personally. Indeed, engineering itself was undergoing a fundamental change, much of it down to Whitworth himself. In terms of his own company, however, now with something like 730 employees, he reshaped the whole management structure by bringing in, for the first time, a managing director, Manny Gledhill, together with a company secretary, William J. Hoyle. He also started a new chief draughtsman, Charles Richards, a Manchester engineer from Sharps but someone who had recent experience of heavy artillery – the most significant feature of his newly appointed staff.

CHAPTER NINE

The Whitworth Gun is Born

> He ended by producing the very best weapon ever invented
>
> Mr James A. Turner MP, 25 June 1861

> Mr Whitworth should proceed to apply to heavy ordnance the *same* system of rifling which he has proved so singularly successful in small arms
>
> General George Hay to Field Marshal Lord Hardinge, 16 March 1856

When Whitworth finally left the 1851 Exhibition to return home to Manchester, he was lauded to the skies. Festooned with awards, loftily crowned Britain's greatest ever mechanician; yet within ten years he was humiliated. By 1862 he was dubbed by some the world's greatest gunmaker; by others a self-seeking publicist and a humbug. Why was this: why the extremes?

The simple answer can only be that once the accurate shooting of Whitworth's guns defeated the inferior weapons the army had earlier chosen, the generals responsible reacted by angrily denigrating Whitworth personally. It was ever thus. But the post-Crimean challenge had created a new era in military and naval engineering and Whitworth had come up with an hexagonally-bored weapon revolutionary in concept. The more he perfected his system, the more contests he won; the louder his disparagers ridiculed him.

By 1857, having completed almost two years of experimental trial and error, Whitworth then went on to manufacture guns which easily out-performed all the rest. His pay-off however was not the Cabinet's blessing but an acrid savaging by the War Department and by at least half Britain's gun manufacturers. Inextricably, Whitworth thus found himself entangled in the lewd acrimony of military politics. In the first real post-Crimean weapons debate in the House of Commons, on 25 June 1861, the motion to be debated called for a Select Committee to examine why the British Army had not been supplied with a more efficient weapon than the French-designed Enfield-Minié rifle. Mr Hussey Vivian MP (Glamorgan) asked, 'Why has the Whitworth rifle been rejected?' He went on: 'Mr Whitworth's (rifles) beat the best rifles in the French army by two and three to one.' He then recalled that Whitworth had received the congratulations of Louis-Napoleon, Emperor of France, thus capping an English season which included: 'The Queen's Prize at Wimbledon; the Prince Consort's and the Duke of Wellington's prize; all these contests were all won with breech-loading rifles made by Mr Westley Richards under licence from Mr Whitworth.'

Speaking in the same debate, Lord Elcho MP said: 'Mr Whitworth, it should be remembered, was not a gunmaker, he was what might be called the prince of toolmakers. He had applied to rifle-making the best mechanical science. The results were won hollow in favour of Mr Whitworth's rifle.' Mr James Turner, MP for Manchester, then joined the debate in support of his constituent:

> It had not been Mr Whitworth's wish to enter upon the manufacture of these rifles; but, having been applied to by the Government, he gave his skill and energy, and devoted thousands of his money to carry on experiments which were first originated at the insistence of the Government. Mr Whitworth had no desire to make a fortune by the manufacture of rifles.

Most pro-Whitworth speakers both in this debate and an earlier debate in the House of Lords quoted *The Times* newspaper. The gist of their remarks emphasized that from the first day Whitworth commenced his experimental gun work at Fallowfield, March 1855, to the day he and his assistants arrived at the Government School of Musketry, Hythe, Kent, in April 1857 (equipped with six experimental rifles) Whitworth's work represented the most fruitful two years in the history of gunmaking. The improvements between the older Minié-Enfield rifle and the new Whitworth hexagonal bores were awe-inspiring but to get a full savouring of Whitworth's historic work let *The Times* newspaper, dated 23 April 1857, report the story:

> For the last few days a very interesting and important series of experiments have been in progress at the School of Musketry, Hythe. The trial, which was of the most searching and impartial character, was conducted by Colonel Hay, the able head of the School, and has terminated in *establishing beyond all doubt* the great and decided superiority of Mr Whitworth's invention. (*The Enfield rifle* which was considered so much better than any other as to justify the formation of a vast new Government establishment for its special manufacture has been completely beaten [by the Whitworth]. At 1400 yards, the Enfield failed to reach the target).

The Times editorial continued:

> These are great results to have achieved, and amply justify the forethought of the late Lord Hardinge in securing the services of so eminent a mechanic as Mr Whitworth for the improvement of the rifle. Until he took the subject in hand the proper principles for guidance in the construction of the weapon had not been accurately determined.[1]

After the Crimean War ended, Parliamentary opinion reacted strongly to the statements put before MPs by the Roebuck Committee investigating the Crimean carnage. They rightly condemned the pathetic inadequacy of the weapons carried by the troops and described their plight as 'systematic homicide'. British and French soldiers had paid a dreadful price for their out-of-date weapons. Of the first detachments going out with Lord Raglan many thousands of British troops were slaughtered during the early battles simply because the enemy fire power out-distanced the British guns, yet regardless of all this, not only did the old musket remain the arm carried by some infantry regiments well into the war, it was still considered worthwhile and put into reserve storage long afterwards. The Roebuck Committee were absolutely right; the guns were no good.

The *Edinburgh Review* on more than one occasion got very close to the 'morality' of the issue when it compared the more expensive guns used for culling animals with the cheaper weapons used when communities culled each other. The *Review* declared: 'Money and skill were bestowed without stint on a rifle to bring down a deer; or on a fowling piece with which a pheasant was to be shot; but any weapon, however clumsy, was thought sufficiently good when the issue of a battle or the fate of an empire was in the balance.'[2]

A different kind of contrasting morality effectively challenging the death-dealing efficiency of Britain's mid-century arsenal was put by two of Whitworth's leading supporters. Sir J. Emerson Tennent LLD FRS, criticised the British Army's use of the 'clumsy and capricious Brown Bess at the Battle of Salamanca, west of Madrid, when only 8,000 men were put 'hors de combat' although 3.5 million cartridges were fired together with 6,000 cannon balls, so that only one rifle-shot in 437 took effect'. A similar, equally graphic point was put during the course of a lecture delivered at the United Service Institution, London, November 1859, by a Colonel Wilford who stated that during the Caffre War, Cape Province, 80,000 cartridges were fired in a single engagement in which only 25 of the enemy fell. These figures are even more astonishing when it is realized that the hit-to-kill range of these weapons was no more than eighty yards.[3]

This sort of criticism, in addition to the humiliation brought on by the Crimean experience, eventually changed the Foreign Office attitude. From 1856 onwards, British Foreign Secretaries acknowledged that international power and influence depended on military power. The Foreign Office handbook was rewritten: there could be no going back to aristocratic adventurism. Put crudely, no longer was it permissible for diplomats to sever relations without first assessing the comparative strength of each other's armed forces. Some historians actually believed that the Palmerston-Derby period of government was impervious to public criticism. It wasn't. Such was the venom aimed at ministers during the 1850s both the War and Foreign Offices bowed before the bruising onslaught mounted by MPs like Roebuck and Bright. The upshot being that though both Whigs and Tories settled for Roebuck's better guns rather than Bright's pacifism; the essential point being that both political wings adopted very different military strategies. By 1855, the Treasury could no longer resist including in the Estimates money for the tooling-up of an entirely new and enlarged Enfield armoury and provision for a new generation of field artillery. The Admiralty also argued for a new iron-clad navy and won! Of course, the chance had long gone of repairing the Crimean damage but the Cabinet, at last, was determined to break new ground and move towards a new era of military weapons.

A universal race for better weapons soon became a desperate search for good engineers with, need it be said, innovative ideas and an absence of nationalistic prejudices. Louis-Napoleon virtually sent out canvassers. In Britain, while not exactly canvassing, a whole generation of prime ministers-in-waiting, Russell, Derby, Aberdeen and Palmerston, let it be known that Britain was urgently head-hunting an engineer who could deliver modern, world-class guns. Indeed, four months after Whitworth returned from the United States, in October 1853, the War Office had approached him offering almost patron saint status if he was willing to mastermind the mass production of the new gun from France, the new Minié rifle. It didn't work out quite like that – not because the War Office went off Whitworth, or he them (that particular contretemps came later) – but because Joe himself never believed the suggested 0.577-in diameter bore Minié muzzle-loader was worthy of mass production.

Whitworth honestly believed that if he was going to get involved in rifle manufacture then he himself should look into the whole business of gun design, particularly those aspects which were so unsatisfactory, namely the ammunition question and the inaccuracy of the barrels themselves. And once having proved by actual performance the best possible system, then – and only then – should either he himself or some other equally reputable engineer get on and tool-up its manufacture. It seemed to Whitworth ludicrous that he should tool-up a rifle which, at 300 yards, couldn't hit the 'proverbial barn door', yet that is exactly what the War Office wanted him to do – and no more. 'The quality of the gun is not his business', said the War Department. 'Presumably not', replied Whitworth, but clearly he made the *quality* of the gun a pre-condition for his tooling-up the weapon.

To understand this strange and impassioned twenty-year encounter between Whitworth and the War Ministry it is necessary to follow the turbulent interplay between his imaginative genius and the blocking resilience of the government. That which follows is such a parable. It explains much about the safe orthodoxy of governments and why they were unable (even when proved wrong) to scrap what existed and to start again.

THE STORY OF THE WHITWORTH RIFLE

By summer 1853, the War Office was convinced that a powerful Small Arms Committee made up of Britain's foremost engineering brains would be the best way to fathom out the supply of improved weapons for the army. The Cabinet, led by the Earl of Aberdeen, agreed with this and gave experimental gun work top priority but the Treasury, much in keeping with the philosophy of the Gladstone-Disraeli 'turn-about' Chancellorships, failed to match with money these important decisions. The pro-free-market economists advanced the fear that if the state manufactured its own weapons, the Enfield state armoury would become far too big and that the Birmingham gun trade would disintegrate.

As for Whitworth himself, he was never an enthusiast about committees, unless possibly, it was a committee of one. He supported the classic House of Commons witticism . . . that because of its ludicrous shape, a camel must really be a horse designed by a committee! His more serious objections, however, turned out to be well informed and profoundly perceptive. His reluctance in this instance to accept the chairmanship of the Enfield factory committee was part engineering, part political. His friends would say he mocked his own ambitions by refusing to lead the manufacture of a new breed of weapons but Whitworth knew what he was doing. Of course, the serious reservations he expressed about the committee idea inevitably delayed the start of its work but when the Crimean War was over he personally was never name-called as a scapegoat: the rationale of his opinion was recognized, though never accepted.

In regard to the Enfield armoury itself, it was Whitworth's view that manufactories run by the state *should be subject to free market competition for the purpose of comparison and discipline.* This precise point was put to Whitworth at a hearing of the 1854 Parliamentary Select Committee on small arms:

> Would you recommend the Government to undertake at once to manufacture entirely for themselves, on a scale equal to producing 500 muskets a day?

Whitworth replied very firmly and, as always, pointed the way forward:

> I would not. But I would recommend the Government to have an establishment as perfect as could be made, to produce a limited number, and to set an example to other [private] gun-makers.[4]

It was a very interesting answer, considering that he was within a month or so of his agreement with the War Department to take on the challenge of re-tooling the Enfield armoury. It also clarified another important remark Whitworth had made elsewhere to the effect that the government should fund the most advanced research thus allowing private industry under licence to compete against the very best and not be 'crippled by the heavy cost of experimentation'.

Lord Hardinge first approached Whitworth in October 1853, to inquire if he would undertake the design and building of an entirely new rifle manufacturing plant. Joe evaded a direct answer but explained the reasons why he didn't want to commit himself then and there, promising that if Hardinge so instructed his new Master General of Ordnance, Lord Raglan, he, Whitworth, would carefully consider how best he could assist the government once he received their draft proposals. In the event, Raglan did write to him, on 7 November 1853, proposing that Whitworth become the Chairman of the new expert committee responsible for small arms manufacture. To those unaware of the bitter feuding inside the War Office, it seemed a marvellous idea: that of bringing together the world's best machine tool professionals to build and tool-up a whole new government plant capable of mass-producing interchangeable rifles and bayonets in the quantities required. Only one snag clouded the minds of the ex-Wellington zealots: if someone like Whitworth was appointed Chairman and given 'his head' the military hierarchy feared they would lose control.

The very thought of Whitworth becoming Chairman was sufficient to counsel caution. The fact that the weapons' directorate at Horseguards became so tetchy explains a great deal as to why the committee was repeatedly put off. Nevertheless, the military threat posed by Tsar Nicholas, plus the upheaval throughout Central Europe, very quickly spurred on Lord Hardinge; he right away demanded a concerted effort to get the rifle question moving. His first action was to enquire of Lord Raglan whether or not Whitworth had responded to the tentative overtures put to him on 7 November 1853 about the Chairmanship. 'Not yet he hasn't', replied Raglan before going on to assure the Chief of Staff that he would continue to press the matter. 'And if Whitworth remained unwilling to accept the Chair', he, Raglan, would not hesitate to call on James Nasmyth, another machine-tool maker from Manchester – and in Raglan's opinion (a view not shared by Hardinge) a better prospect than Whitworth who would work with the War Office much more easily.

Soon after Whitworth received Raglan's invitation to become Chairman he replied on 15 November 1853 saying that he would first like to consult his friends and business advisers, meaning probably that he would like to consult his lawyers and the Birmingham gun trade before deciding anything. He very much appreciated the kudos to be earned as Chairman – it naturally fed his ego – but he was no romantic.

Considering the many parts which make up a rifle, Joe was confident he could mass-produce rifle locks and the other small pieces without too many problems. To machine accurate and reliable rifle barrels, however, was another and more difficult matter entirely. All the silly talk in the past about so-called self-acting machine tools had given the parliamentary laymen an unwarranted dream that iron bars could be fed in at one end of the Enfield factory and tumbling out the other end, untouched by humans, would be beautifully finished rifle muskets.

In reality the situation was very different and Whitworth was right to be cautious: the age of automation had nowhere near arrived. Not only that, he knew it was going to be his own drawing office and factory which would have to design and build the machinery. Yet if he was Chairman of the Committee it would hardly be right for him to both allocate the contracts and fix the price.

Whitworth also understood that as the Crown regulations stood, he would not be allowed to patent his own designs, nor could he prevent other private gun makers, either at home or abroad, exploiting his ingenuity. This restriction applied to all work undertaken on behalf of the Crown. Under these circumstances he felt unable to accept the Chairmanship and informed Lord Raglan by special messenger on 17 November 1853 that it wasn't possible at that stage to accept his invitation. What he did concede, however, was a willingness to assist Nasmyth and the Committee in the best way he could. Moreover, should the War Office change its mind about the Minié musket he would personally research an entirely new weapon and organize its manufacture.[5]

Thus relieved of pursuing what he considered to be the 'tiresome Whitworth enigma', Raglan quickly turned to James Nasmyth who had earlier confirmed he would be delighted to accept the Chairmanship. It was an astonishing piece of decisive action. It was all over within days, including the personal endorsement of the appointment on 12 December 1853 by the Secretary of State, the Duke of Newcastle.

> Thus (wrote Nasmyth in his autobiography), I was appointed a member (Chairman) of the Small Arms Factory Committee for the purpose of re-modelling and, in fact, re-establishing the Small Arms Factory at Enfield. The United States Government, though possessing only a very small standing army, had established at Springfield, Massachusetts, a small arms factory where, by the use of machine tools specially designed to execute with the most unerring precision all the details of muskets and rifles they were able to *dispense with mere manual dexterity* and to produce arms (by machine alone) to any amount.

Nasmyth wanted to do exactly the same at Enfield.

Regrettably the very idea was sheer fantasy. Indeed some years before he wrote the above statement in his autobiography he and Whitworth both gave evidence to the 1854 Select Committee and Nasymth then made the same point when he declared to the Committee: 'With properly contrived machinery you might reduce the employment of manual labour; I may say down to zero.' A member of the Select Committee, Colonel Lindsay MP, then turned to Whitworth and asked: 'You heard Mr Nasmyth's evidence; do you agree?' Whitworth replied without hesitation: 'I do not agree in that opinion.'[6]

Once the new Committee got working (without Whitworth) at its first meeting, January 1854, (Sir) John Anderson, Chief Superintendent ROF Woolwich, was nominated its senior technical adviser. They also decided to send a mission on behalf of the Committee to the United States, possibly to place contracts for the manufacturing of a British-modified Minié rifle and to purchase new American machinery for the Enfield factory.

Immediately the Birmingham gun trade learned of the Committee's decision to discontinue placing War Office gun contracts with private gunmakers in Britain they could hardly contain themselves. It had all happened before and Birmingham again sniffed corruption in high places. They were infuriated that a man called George Lovell, an American, had been brought over by Lord Raglan to supervise and inspect the work done by the private gun trade. Almost before he had landed, Birmingham labelled Lovell 'a perfidious villain'. It was crude stuff indeed. In the opinion of the trade, Lovell's wickedness later extended to his family – two sons and a brother – all employed by the Board of Ordnance. Indefensibly Raglan made one son 'Assistant Inspector' to Lovell himself while the other acted as his father's agent in Paris buying and selling various small arms.

George Lovell subsequently became the most criticized of the Raglan appointees. Originally he was a bedstead maker but once in Britain he became Inspector of Small Arms in addition to being the Master Furbisher, vis-à-vis the gun trade, and as such held a very powerful position. But none of the favouritism he bestowed upon his sons was half so devastating or nearly so costly in terms of human life as Lord Raglan's own outrageous nepotism when he appointed five of his nephews to be staff officers attached to his own regiment. So far as Whitworth was concerned, the Raglan-Lovell axis didn't trouble him until the Birmingham gun trade suspected that a Lovell edict introducing set dimensional limits for all gun work was Whitworth-inspired. It was quite laughable. Whitworth was about to visit Birmingham in search of gun experience when he learned that Lovell had enforced on all gun makers the Whitworth doctrine of precise gauging and the interchangeability of gun parts.

Quite righly of course, Lovell insisted that all gun suppliers must use Crown drilling and filing jigs for all rifle locks and gauges. Overall barrel sizes became compulsory. The standards specified were not impossibly tight – certainly nothing so good as Whitworth standards – nevertheless they profoundly upset the private trade especially when the Lovell-Enfield 'viewers' got to work and rejected whole batches of 'bought-in' rifles as not being of the quality required. The Birmingham reaction, although predictable, was as ridiculous as it was astonishing.

> The Enfield viewers (their report said) behave litigiously . . . insisting upon a vexatious nicety of gauging and finish. If the principle of exact jigging, gauging, moulding and other fantastic accuracies applies to our guns why shouldn't it also apply to the troops? Let's insist all men be exactly equal in stature, length of limb and shape; the absurdity would be little more in one instance than the other.[7]

This kind of silly in-fighting between the trade and the Enfield inspectorate went on for over a decade, though mercifully the Birmingham people did not enlarge upon the more serious of their bribery allegations published in an earlier gun trade pamphlet directed against Lovell and his superiors. The trade had argued – all of it in print – that the only reason Britain adopted the French Delvigné-Minié musket – thereafter known by its English nickname, *Minnie* – was that the French had bribed George Lovell and a number of British ordnance supply officers led by Lord Raglan, or Lord Fitzroy Somerset, as Raglan was known prior to October 1852. It was, in fact, following this date that Raglan took his seat in the House of Lords and became a Parliamentary Under-Secretary. Strangely, the allegations were never refuted. Indeed, early February 1855, they were repeated. During one of the bitterest Crimean debates prior to the collapse of the Aberdeen government, Hansard reported that for 'thirteen long years, a certain Captain Delvigné of the French army was in constant contact with George Lovell, the Inspector of Small Arms at Enfield'. How, or how much, the go-betweens were paid we do not know. What we do know is that Lovell had a house in France and his son lived in Paris making money as an arms dealer.

Despite the enormity of these accusations the gun trade persisted in venting what they believed to be their biggest problem: the increasing number of gun contracts being placed with the state armoury at Enfield. Whitworth held slightly different views but his more advanced ideas were well respected by the gunmakers. He personally supported – had done for a decade – the much-quoted judgement offered by a Colonel Maberly MP during the first ever Parliamentary debate on the public ownership of industry, April 1830, when the MP declared:

> . . . this is a question which involves a great principle, namely, whether the Government should be its own manufacturer knowing that government manufacturers *will always* lose money . . . MPs of principle must be for ever vigilant and oppose.

In addition to these particular aspects Whitworth honestly believed that all departments of government had a principled obligation to be far more generous towards those engineers who were being asked to contribute their innovative ideas for patriotic reasons rather than private gain. 'Engineers as a breed were not profligate by instinct', he insisted, 'and the Government should be less doubting'. He consistently believed that government establishments should be pace-setters doing the finest work at the highest level and that private companies should be able to benefit from their example. Whitworth's plea was that Ministers should have enough confidence in people like himself to get on with it without constant reference to the civil service pigeon-holers.[8]

But it was utterly frustrating that a person like Lord Raglan should be in charge of all military engineering throughout this, the most critical period. His Lordship was essentially army-trained and in no way competent to welcome the fundamental design changes which were then necessary if progress was to be made. However, some army engineers had the kind of perceptive creativity which, had they still been in leadership when Whitworth himself tried hard to change the army's ideas, would have been his powerful allies. But Raglan – a very brave soldier – was not a brave innovationist. As a young aide-de-camp to Wellington at Waterloo he lost an arm but, apart from two short spells as British

Ambassador in Paris, he remained in the army and was promoted to Field Marshal, in November 1854. Lamentably a further departmental weakness with which he was associated and which irritated Whitworth beyond belief was the string of misfits he appointed to take charge of Britain's weapon manufacture and procurement. But as bad as the outlook appeared, Joe never lost hope that the Cabinet, or at least Field Marshal Hardinge and William Gladstone, would soon be back seeking his help for a new rifle.

Within hours of Big Ben ringing in the 1854 New Year, the Small Arms Committee with Nasmyth in the chair decided to send a purchasing mission to the United States in the belief that both rifles and machinery could be purchased off the peg. James Nasmyth himself, due to other engagements, was prevented from accompanying the mission; presumably the idea of crossing the Atlantic in a 1,600 ton side-paddle didn't attract him; accordingly three only, John Anderson, Lt.-Col. Robert Burn and Capt. Picton Marlow of the Royal Artillery made up the team in addition to Thomas Greenwood. Intriguingly, there is no mention of Greenwood in the Official Report due, one suspects, to an embargo on the sending overseas of technical information and an equally idiotic ban preventing British engineers travelling abroad in case they passed on secret machine designs. Thomas Greenwood, chief draughtsman and a director of Sir Peter Fairbairn's company at Leeds, was credited at the time with being Britain's leading authority on woodworking machinery.

The mission left London for New York March 1854, six weeks after the special Whitworth (USA) Report was published. On landing, the four men made their way to the US armoury at Springfield and then on to other gun factories in New England and some machine tool factories further south. The mission was anxious to spend as much time as possible at the main Robbins and Lawrence armoury, but first they called at a new factory which the company was building at Hartford, Connecticut. There they saw the manufacture under licence of the Sharp's breech-loading carbine and rifle. Like the factory itself all the machinery was new and made by Robbins and Lawrence themselves. It was in fact this latter point which impressed John Anderson most and led the mission to recommend the placing of large contracts for the supply of rifles.

Back in London, news of the Robbins and Lawrence situation was received by the War Office with absolute jubilation. They immediately appointed Messrs Fox, Henderson and Company, the consulting engineers of Spring Garden, London, to act on their behalf. An order for 25,000 rifles was placed for the 1853 Minié-pattern Enfield rifle musket (0.577-in calibre bore) at a price of £4 each including a bayonet. Fox, Henderson insisted upon a penalty clause in the contract – that the guns must be completed within 12 months starting June 1855. The contract was signed on behalf of the company by the Chairman, Richard S. Lawrence, but when doing so he prophesied that unless the British Government gave them a further signed contract for another 300,000 guns as promised by Fox, Henderson, then his firm would soon go bust. The cost of tooling-up the first 25,000 was so prohibitive and irrespective of the penalty clause it was not possible for the firm to carry such a massive capital investment and survive. Lawrence in fact disliked signing the contract but finally conceded the point. 'I told Mr Robbins that the minute we signed the contract we would be floored – that we had better cut off our right hands'. Sadly his prophesy came true. The British War Office did not offer another contract and the uncertainty led to endless rows between Lawrence himself and his partner Mr Robbins. The firm split up in 1858 – Lawrence taking over the Sharps Rifle Works at Hartford and Robbins (primarily a sewing-machine manufacturer) transferred the rump of the original firm to England as the Enfield Gun Machinery Company. Richard Lawrence continued his overall interest in machine tools and together with the famous engineering designer, F.W. Howe, went on to have a tremendous impact on the American machine tool industry.

Ironically, shortly after the Robbins and Lawrence collapse, so too did Fox Henderson collapse and were declared bankrupt. Curiously this whole sad episode at the very beginning of America's engineering development, authenticated Whitworth's own one-time hesitancy over the size of the guarantees he would require from the British Government before he himself went into rifle manufacture. The first payment handed over to Robbins and Lawrence at the end of 1855 by Fox, Henderson was £80,000, but of the original contract only 5,600 rifles were delivered to Enfield. Astonishingly (*at today's prices*) the cost per rifle to the British Exchequer worked out at over £700 each!

Once the Robbins and Lawrence Company had gone a firm called The Union Arms Company took over but they were never able to continue production beyond June 1858 when the whole Robbins and Lawrence gun business folded. The real reason, however, why no further Fox, Henderson gun contracts were placed in America was the poor quality of American barrel-making. After all the bally-hoo, the level of expectancy was such that the War Office in London simply refused to sanction any further contracts until the Windsor-made rifle barrels equalled the Enfield barrels. The truth of the matter was that America, like France or Germany and Britain, could not at that time make rifle barrels anything like the standard the War Office had put to Whitworth.

Before they started work, Robbins and Lawrence asked London for sample rifles and gauges instead of drawings. Enfield responded and sent several rifles considered good enough to act as production models together with some *hard-wood* gauges – all of which, incredibly, turned out to be the wrong sizes, made useless even so by excessive dampness during the sea voyage. Compared with later workshop practice it is difficult to appreciate that the best of American engineering companies could not at that time work straight from the drawing. For one thing they had no accepted method of measurement based on international standard sizes thus preventing them working accurately to the limits specified. If the drawing had specified one inch, for example, on which one-inch were they to base their measurement – their own or Enfield's or Whitworth's? There could be a variation between all three.

Despite the latest and most beautifully finished American drop-forge dies and their improved revolving drift-files – used for cleaning out the barrel bore – the rifles received by Enfield were mostly outside the specified limits. Once they arrived at Enfield they were rejected by the inspection department. The Chief Inspector, James Gunner, proclaimed the barrels to have a 0.006-in variation in diameter and to be dog-legged to the extent of 0.050 inch or more. In practice they shot no better – nor any worse – than the identical Pattern 1853 Minié rifles made at Enfield which suggested that the home barrel production suffered the same degree of discrepancy as the Springfield product.[9]

In reality, had James Gunner, the inspector, been asked, hand on heart, to verify the truthfulness of his inspection reports he would have to admit that his own gauges and equipment were just not capable of such precise checking. The very problem of engineering such a small diameter hole with such precision throughout a whole metre in length and through such poor quality wrought iron was, at that time, well beyond engineering expertise anywhere in the world – hence the perceived ingenuity of Whitworth constantly occupied the minds of the military.

The Small Arms mission remained in the United States some eight months. Whitworth's American friends – Colonel Ripley and Colonel Mordecai, both Senior Commissioners of the US Ordnance Department – stayed with and looked after them throughout. At Springfield they demonstrated machinery for making their own new smaller-bore 'interchangeable' rifle which had first appeared at the Great Exhibition. The English party were mesmerized by the sheer cleverness of their multi-operation machines. They didn't hesitate to place contracts for their shipment to Enfield, England.

All the American woodworking machinery was 'brilliant', particularly the special Blanchard machines designed to shape and finish walnut gunstocks. These Blanchards were the nearest thing to self-acting machines yet designed; essentially they worked as profile milling machines; the revolving milling cutters were controlled by a 'follower' which hugged and copied a model gunstock. They were the first 'copying' machines imported into Britain and the world's most advanced at that time. But to get things in perspective Thomas Greenwood (who accompanied the Mission from England) gave an address to the Institution of Mechanical Engineers in 1862 specifically about gunstock machinery damping down the praise a little by suggesting that the original machines purchased were not a success.[10] Only those supplied to the London Armoury Company (which earlier had been known as the Adams and Deanes Company) and those resold to the Russian Government by Colonel Colt, worked as they were intended to. In fact that great battery of machines installed at Enfield took some three or four years to overcome their teething troubles despite the supervision of James Burton and the Ames Company men sent over from America. The machines cost more than £40,000 and were capable of turning out over 2,000 gun-stocks per week. James Nasmyth was well satisfied. Indeed, it is worth noting that some of these machines worked seventy years, until 1931, before one of them was offered to the Science Museum.

Whitworth himself was both technically well briefed and extremely interested in all types of Blanchard machinery. Indeed, contrary to popular belief he himself was a pioneer in the business of mechanized woodcarving. His credentials are nowhere better illustrated than in the retelling of his experience at the House of Commons.

The story began in 1847 during the rebuilding of the fire-damaged palace. The carved wood panelling was already behind schedule. A Mr Jordan, an internationally known architectural wood carver, working alongside craftsmen from the Frederick Sage Company of Tottenham, North London, called upon Whitworth's ingenuity to help speed up the work by mechanizing (if that was possible) the hardwood carving not only for the Chamber itself but also for the Committee Rooms and Lobbies. Joe responded willingly and built four experimental profilers powered by small independent steam engines. All the machines were delivered and working before the end of 1848 and according to handed-down folklore three of the four machines were pantograph copiers in principle and consisted of a universal milling head which was either integrally belt driven or on the end of a single flexible drive. Considering the beauty of the final carving, however, the main purpose of the machines would probably have been roughing-out, leaving the more delicate carving to be hand finished by the craftsmen themselves.[11]

When Whitworth himself appeared before the 1854 Select Committee he was asked by the Chairman about his little steam-driven profilers. 'Is such machinery applicable to the making of gunstocks?' he was asked. Joe hesitated a moment, no doubt admiring the carved oak verticals either side of the committee room fireplaces, then answered, 'It would be applicable, no doubt, for some parts of the stock but my machines were not so well adapted for a musket as the machinery which I saw in America'. The Chairman, no doubt feeling very proud that this was the first Select Committee to use the newly opened House of Commons committee room, persisted with his diversionary aside and put a further question.

'To what extent did your machinery cheapen the carving?' 'I am not aware,' replied Whitworth, 'but I know that Mr Jordan told me that in some cases the cost was not more than one-fourth, but what it was on average I am not aware.'[12]

The question of cost was really irrelevant: the thing that mattered was speeding up the job. The real success, however, according to Mr Jordan and the woodcarvers was that the Whitworth machines enabled the massive tonnage of hardwood sculpture and decorative panelling to be generally finished in time for the opening session of the new Commons in May 1850. All agreed that without the machines the official opening would have had to be delayed, probably till the year end.

Before leaving the subject however, a less than serious example as to the versatility of these mobile profilers, concerned the making of two rather special mahogany snuff-boxes; one for the House of Commons; the other, an anniversary gift Whitworth wished to present to his much beloved Scramble Club in Manchester. He got the idea during one of his visits to the Commons when he learned of the long-established tradition whereby the doorkeeper at the entrance to the debating chamber always kept handy a well-patronized snuff-box. Any MP desiring a 'pinch' before entering the chamber merely asked the doorkeeper for 'the box'. Unfortunately, the original box had been destroyed in the 1834 fire and Joe's woodcarving friend, Mr Jordan, had been requested by the House Committee to make a new one. Whitworth saw it and because he admired it so much he asked Mr Jordan if he would make another one, perhaps bigger and more elaborately carved, suitable for use by the Scramble Club. It turned out a beautiful piece of carving – somewhat different from the House of Commons version – stretching full length each side of the lid was an exquisitely carved recumbent nude. It made a memorable gift. Whitworth was delighted. Needless to say, when Mr Jordan visited the club's new headquarters at the Clarence Hotel, Manchester, to deliver the box, he was made an honorary member of the club. No doubt had Augustus Pugin seen it, the architectural designer of Parliament's woodcarving would have been as proud as Whitworth and Jordan of their 'mechanized' artistry.

So much for this lighthearted digression: the truth is the only exciting thing to come out of the American gun inquiries was the Blanchard machinery and the making of walnut gunstocks – confidence in either British or foreign ability to improve any other part of a rifle was non-existent. Most independent experts had written off the Birmingham gun trade. Enfield had various ideas for improving the Minié 0.577 bore but couldn't make a precision barrel. Their efforts had proved no better than America's. And though Nasmyth didn't expect his Small Arms mission to return from the United States much before November 1855 the evidence twenty-five months earlier suggested that neither he nor the War Office had any more faith in America than they had in Birmingham. Where then should they turn? Discomfiting it may have been, but uppermost in the minds of Lord Hardinge and most Cabinet ministers was Whitworth, waiting for his country to call.

The new experimental gas lights installed at the War Office, Pall Mall, flickered well into the night, as did the coal fires keeping Hardinge warm in Wellington's old office overlooking Horseguards. Lord Hardinge and his staff pondered their strategy. Unclear as to what they should do the Chief of Staff was mindful of the letter Raglan had sent Whitworth dated 11 February 1854 asking him to do no more than concentrate on the improvement of rifle barrels and their manufacture; but Hardinge knew only too well that Whitworth would never accept a cramped directive of that sort. He also knew that Whitworth had promised to reconsider the situation once he had completed his consultations with the Birmingham gunmakers. That was it: Hardinge was convinced Whitworth must be their man and that he himself must go all out to persuade the Manchester engineer to become a gunmaker.

WHAT THE GUN DEBATE WAS ABOUT

As a ballistics hypothesis Whitworth's system demands serious respect.

Major-General A.R. Valon MIMechE (February 1928)

He (Whitworth) was the founder not so much of the Whitworth rifle as of the greatest and most fruitful period of experimentation and development in the British gun trade

D.W. Bailey II (*Guns Review,* March 1969)

The development of the modern rifle happened in a most fragmented and disordered fashion. As early as 1835 the Prussians perfected a breech-loader. Then came an engineer from Switzerland called Wild who became the first experimentalist to prove that by using a rifled gun a bullet would remain on target nose first. In other words, *if* the bullet was breech-loaded to avoid ramming it down the barrel and *if* the barrel was perfectly straight and *if* it was rifled to impart spin, the bullet would fly straight as an arrow. But could these imperatives ever be engineered? How was it to be done? The manufacturing problems were still unresolved twenty years later, a Crimea-shattered 1855.

Joseph Whitworth was first made aware of these difficulties when William Greener, the Birmingham gunsmith, came to see him in September 1852 to ask his advice whether it was yet possible to accurately bore and rifle a barrel 39 inches long. Whitworth no doubt explained that the necessary drills and broaches together with the boring and rifling machines were not then invented. Nevertheless, it was remarkably fortuitous for Whitworth that the man who came to see him happened to be Greener since it was he who had invented both the *self-expansion* bullet and a *mechanical fit* bullet; thus he was able to explain to Whitworth in some detail the unresolved engineering problems which held back the two systems. Naturally, as an engineer Whitworth was appalled that the old muskets were still used; that the way troopers, when using muzzle-loaders, had to ram each bullet down the barrel of their musket. No bullet, abused in that way could possibly shoot straight; hence Whitworth readily saw the advantages of a breech-loader using a *mechanical fitting* bullet.[13]

Greener's alternative to his own *self-expansion* bullet, the '*mechanical fit system*' was based on what he called a '*winged bullet*'. That is to say, he designed a two-groove rifling system, the bullet having two male keys; one each side down the length of the bullet. The idea being that the 'keyed' bullet would be a '*mechanical fit*'; a nice sliding fit to take the deeply cut rifling track spiralling the length of the barrel. In this way tremendous spin would be imparted to the bullet as it left the barrel. So good did Greener consider the system he devoted a whole year's work to designing and making what became known as his 'Cape' rifle with its 'winged' bullet. Later, in association with a Mr Purdey, another famous gunsmith of London, he developed a number of other similar small-bore rifles by late 1856. Internationally, their 'Cape' gun became known as the 'Express' rifle. And although at one time it was considered good enough for big game hunting in South Africa – hence the title – its shot turned out to be wildly inconsistent and was, ironically, superseded some years later by a very powerful sporting rifle made by the Whitworth Rifle Company, equipped, it must be added, with a 'Cape' gunsight.

Two major weaknesses brought about the downfall of Greener's Cape rifle. Firstly, a *winged* bullet was not the best aerodynamic shape to produce an absolutely steady flight and secondly, the bullet was expensive to make. A suitable barrel, with its deep cut rifling was little more than a notional concept prior to 1860 hence Whitworth, as early as 1852, was probably then beginning to picture in his mind the possibility of adopting a hexagonal shape as the optimum method.

Joe kept faith with Greener; he was immensely indebted to the man. Not only did he learn from him a great deal about guns but he also began to understand much of the underhand dealing that was beginning to invade the gun business. Almost certainly a combination of Greener's engineering problems and the treatment he received at the hands of the Government, cradled Whitworth's own ideas. Five years on from these incipient foundations, late 1857, Whitworth had by then put in three years of exhaustive experiments and proved theoretically correct his own *mechanical fit* system. On that account alone the great beauty of making this historical analysis is that it offers a chance of tracing the genius of Whitworth's hexagonal rifling ideas back to all these unpromising and largely misinterpreted concepts.

As for Greener's other invention, the *self-expanding* bullet, that too was turned down by the British authorities because – or so they said – it was oval in shape and like his 'winged' bullet, aerodynamically *wrong*. It had a flat base perforated in the centre and under test conditions (which continued at Tynemouth until 1850) it too proved erratic in flight. Even so, oval or not, it raised considerably the accuracy and range of existing rifled muskets. The coming of the *self-expanding* bullet – the forerunner of modern ammunition – thus established an international landmark, the *expansion* concept – that is to say, the bullet, on being fired, expanded sufficiently to take the spirality of the bore, therefore spinning at great speed as it shot from the gun. That really was the principal attribute of his invention, not the comparative trivia around which the government allegedly rejected his idea.

Greener was profoundly disappointed and found the War Office reasoning hard to swallow. Sadly, there the matter rested until the Frenchman, Captain Minié, turned up in 1852 with a very similar 'invention'. Unbelievably, but true to historic form, he was awarded £20,000 by the British government following the bullet's almost overnight adoption by the British services. Naturally Greener was incensed that the Duke of Newcastle, the then Secretary of State for War, should credit Minié and not himself with having first conceived the idea of an 'expanding bullet' – on top of which, to award Monsieur Minié the money was as perverse as it was unjust.

The Greener Company pursued the injustice tenaciously and a Mr Schofield,

MP for Birmingham, raised the matter in the House. The Minister conceded the case and William Greener was belatedly awarded £1,000 in the 1857 Army Estimates. Of course justice was never fully restored but at least what had become known as the first-ever '*expanding bullet*' was now officially credited to Greener. Not that it was the end of the wretched affair. Gun trade accusations criss-crossed the country not only about the Minié bullet but also about the adoption of the French Minié rifle. Questions were asked in Parliament. Were there any bribes involved? Why was the private gun trade ignored? Serious questions indeed but met on all sides with absolute silence.[14]

It was little wonder after the unprecedented way the War Office had compensated Greener that widespread rumours soon pointed to George Lovell as having betrayed Greener. The suspicions were that a secret file on Greener's bullet must have been handed to Captain Minié for money long before *The Times* published the design details. Others attempting to exonerate Minié and his French associates from any dishonourable practice claimed that Greener himself in his own writing on the subject had earlier set out his ideas on bullets and the rifling of gun barrels. Whichever way it happened both Lord Raglan and the Secretary of State looked pretty sick having credited Minié with the invention and having paid out £20,000. The critics were right! The Government was throwing money at the wrong problem and at the wrong people. The point at issue had never been other than one of manufacture: whatever design of gun they had, the question always remained – how well could it be made?

Suddenly, Whitworth's life became a whirlwind of engagements. Billy Hulse, his cousin and factory manager, was anxious not to allow this new involvement in military weapons distract Joseph from the various machine tool changes wanted by his drawing office but now it looked as though the gun work was taking priority. Whitworth had said that he wanted to visit gunmakers in London and Birmingham and he was now determined to do just that. W.J. Hoyle, his company secretary, got down to the job of organizing his tour and arranged for him to go back to see Charles Lancaster and William Greener before going on to meet for the first time Westley Richards. The date fixed for meeting Richards was 12 March 1854 and a further meeting was arranged for the following day in Manchester. Both men had a mutual respect for the other's professional expertise and both agreed they would work together. It certainly suited Whitworth to have a reputable gunsmith alongside him, especially as he wished to convince the military people in London of the high standards he intended to set for his own experimental work.

Whitworth's next engagement was to give evidence to the Parliamentary Select Committee on Small Arms but before attending the House of Commons on 19 March he wanted a free day in London to consult his own constituency MP, John Bright, already a friend since their Crystal Palace Exhibition meetings. While Whitworth was never a political clone of Bright's, he was probably much nearer to him ideologically than most people thought and certainly he had the greatest respect for Bright as a parliamentary adviser, a service which Bright freely offered Joe, particularly in regard to his Select Committee appearances. In retrospect it was an astounding relationship; an anti-war campaigner and a gun manufacturer; a relationship made possible, it can only be assumed, by their rational intellect and an open frankness with each other. However, one particular faculty lacked by Joe was prophesy. Had he known just how seriously his decision to manufacture guns was about to change his whole life, he would no doubt have explored more thoroughly the time-consuming ramifications and very carefully reconsidered the 'don't-get-involved' advice given to him by John Bright when they met at Fentons Hotel, St James Street.

The following morning, 19 March, Whitworth went straight to the House of Commons. The three expert witnesses called to give evidence, George Wallis, tutor of gun draughtsmen, Charles Lancaster the gunsmith and Joseph Whitworth, all stood together in the committee corridor deeply anxious about the impending war and the future well-being of their industry. All three had arranged to attend a day early not only to discuss the situation but to enable Whitworth to hear the evidence given by the other two. Predictably, Whitworth had assumed he would be questioned about the actual making of guns rather than their performance and, unusually, had arranged for two of his men from the works in Manchester to bring down two or three cast-iron surface plates together with a whole series of ring, plug and screw gauges, square angle plates, diagrams and model workpieces. With a rare touch of piquancy all were trundled into the House of Commons committee room, hopefully to convince the Chairman and his Select Committee that Whitworth was entitled to his fantastic reputation. Seldom can the policeman at the door have seen anything like it.

'Are you an engineer?' asked the Chairman innocently. 'Yes, I am', replied Whitworth, settling down not only to demonstrate his surface plates and ring gauges but to answer a record 316 questions spread over the next four hours or so.[15] Not only was it a test of his stamina but also it was an endurance record for the Committee, indicative perhaps that the Select Committee and the House were intent to learn not just Whitworth's opinion about guns but whether he could design and build hundreds of self-acting machines capable of automatically turning out thousands upon thousands of deadly accurate weapons. The very idea at that time was preposterous but it didn't prevent either James Nasmyth or Whitworth from frequently alluding to 'self-acting' machines. As we know, Nasmyth actually referred to '*zero labour*' – a thrilling concept no doubt but at least forty years ahead of its time. When asked, Whitworth himself rightly thought it *not* possible.

Quite blatantly, however, in the way he answered the Chairman's next question, Whitworth confirmed that his overriding and sole purpose in attending the Committee was to propagate the idea of manufacturing all things by machine. He also wanted to put across the message that well-designed machines could mass-produce identical parts of anything far more quickly and far more accurately than the finest craftsmen. His enthusiasm, however, carried him away, at times bordering the absurd, especially when he repeatedly claimed that the cost of machining a perfectly finished flat surface from a rough casting to be one-penny per square foot, or less than five minutes in time taken. The Committee warmed to his theme. When he demonstrated his theory that precision engineering was a matter of flat surfaces, straight lines and perfect measurement, they positively gleamed.

The Chairman sympathetically set the tone of the questioning thus allowing Whitworth to develop his case. 'Is there much advantage in having machines *self-acting*?' he asked. 'Yes, generally more', Joe happily confirmed. 'Will you explain for what reason?' 'Yes – *not* requiring the attendance of a man, the work is often of a superior quality and more regular than it would be if moved by hand'. His reply was misleading, if not dishonest. He should have corrected the Chairman and said: 'You mean *power-fed*, not *self-acting*'. But he didn't. Not only did his machine require the attendance of a man but the degree of skill practised by the operator very much determined the quality of the work produced. The answer also contradicted Whitworth's own campaign for workshop education and skill training.

'Has your attention been called to the extent to which machinery is applied to the military gun trade?' 'Not particularly till this time', retorted Joe defensively. The Chairman paused incredulously – 'Has your attention been called to it lately?' 'Just recently', repeated Joe. Why on earth he wanted to feed the stories which magazines circulated regularly, suggesting he didn't know a muzzle from a breech, remains a mystery. For the past eighteen months he had given a great deal of thought to the matter. Perhaps he didn't want to admit that he didn't know how to overcome the still massive problems associated with barrel manufacture.

Clearly Whitworth had acquired a great deal of gun expertise in recent times and the impatient reaction of some Select Committee members indicated he was in danger of overdoing his 'innocence bit'. A quite different view was put by Professor John Tyndall, the distinguished scientist. He was generally supportive of Whitworth's ideas and gave his opinion of the engineer thus. 'He, Whitworth', he thought, 'was as ignorant of the rifle as Pasteur was of the microscope when he began his immortal research on spontaneous generation: but like the industrious Frenchman, he mastered his subject to an extent never previously reached'. On another occasion, Professor Tyndall referred to Whitworth's gun data by asserting sincerely: 'his genius brought scientific orderliness to what hitherto had been the most speculative experiments'.

Back in the Committee Room the Chairman of the Select Committee continued the marathon questioning of Whitworth. 'Are you acquainted with the manner in which gun barrels are made at Enfield and other places in this country?'

'Yes I am', answered Joe.

'Does that system of making barrels agree with your ideas of producing accurate gun barrels?' This time Whitworth considered his answer carefully. 'It is a very difficult matter to make a perfect barrel because of the light material.'

'Have you ever seen a barrel bored out of a solid?' It was a bull question – engineers throughout the world were desperate to do it – Whitworth for once replied unequivocally, '*Not a gun barrel*'. The Chairman – four years ahead of the time it was actually done – pushed Whitworth further. 'Could it be done?' he asked. 'No doubt it could; but whether it would be economical to do so I am not able to say'.

And so the questioning went on until the turn of Edward A. Seymour MP. He was an influential descendant of the famous Petworth family and an interesting questioner. An ex-Member of Russell's Cabinet, he was Minister of Works until 1852. Had he been less irritated by Whitworth he would have been of immeasurable help to him because originally he supported Whitworth and the concept of '*mechanical fit*' rifling. In August 1855 he inherited his father's title, Duke of Somerset, and went into the House of Lords.

So much for his pedigree. It was now his turn to question Whitworth pitching some sixty-odd questions including one or two about labour relations and strikes. His main concern was the machining of the new rifle and he wanted to know if the Americans were better at it than Britain. 'Unfortunately I did not see barrel making in America', replied Joe. 'I don't believe they have an improved system. I did not see it. But it is my opinion that with regard to an American musket, taking a number of the different parts of it, there is greater identity than there is in the rifles manufactured in this country, because over there . . . there is so much more attention paid to the machinery'. And then he added most emphatically, as if to make the point '. . . and also to the persons attending that machinery'. Whether or not this latter quip was intended to put right his earlier exaggeration about self-acting, manless machines is not clear but patently Whitworth was paying tribute to the Americans for their commitment to the education and skill of the operator.

Immediately after the hearing, Whitworth travelled back to Manchester. He knew from John Bright that Britain was about to declare war on Russia – within six days, in fact, 28 March 1854 – but first of all he wanted to send Lord Raglan his reply about Enfield and the Small Arms Committee. Events tumbled over themselves in quick succession. No sooner had he got his letter away when the Palace announced Raglan would be commander-in-chief, British Forces. The press greeted the news with absolute incredulity. Why Raglan? The mildest comment being one of extreme surprise; sentiments which were later passed off by Queen Victoria as 'boorishness'.

As Raglan left Downing Street and returned to his office, Whitworth's reply concerning the Enfield armoury landed on his desk. 'Yes', he read, Whitworth was ready to get on with the tooling-up of Enfield if agreement about the funding of his experimentation could be settled. Joyous news, one would have thought, especially for someone as harassed as Raglan. But no. The idea that Whitworth, Britain's 'most celebrated engineer', had volunteered to concentrate on weapon manufacture elevated his mind not one jot. In fact on receiving the reply – instead of sending it by hand either to Lord Hardinge or the War Minister – he did no more than send it straight to Colonel Chalmers, secretary of James Nasmyth's Committee on Small Arms. Under the circumstances it was an unbelievably insensitive thing to do but at least it confirmed Raglan's open hostility towards Whitworth and what Raglan described as Whitworth's idiotic ideas. Naturally neither Hardinge nor Whitworth knew anything about this astounding piece of behaviour until some time afterwards. As it turned out it was made even more provocative by the absence in the United States of John Anderson, Nasmyth's Woolwich adviser, leaving Colonel Chalmers, on receipt of the letter, no other choice but to consult direct with his committee chairman James Nasmyth.

Not surprisingly, Nasmyth, because he had never made secret his constant irritation with Whitworth, almost instantly approved the brief reply which Chalmers had drafted, totally rejecting Whitworth's offer. On second thoughts, he asked the secretary to amend the wording slightly but in principle Nasmyth's blunt rejection remained intact. It was a thoughtless dismissal of a very serious offer by Whitworth, animated no doubt by personal antagonism. Certainly the reply was not guided by principles of military engineering. In quite a different context it was also an act contrary to Nasmyth's character. In his autobiography, he claimed he was no rubber stamp either of the armed forces or of the civil service, yet here was an example of him behaving like the humble lackey of this inside rump partly because it satisfied his personal dislike of Joe. There was no necessity for it – Nasmyth was too big a person for that sort of thing.

The Small Arms Committee's reply to Whitworth's note, via Raglan's office, signed by Chalmers, was dated 15 April 1854 and read 'The Committee' – meaning of course the War Office anti-Hardinge rump plus Nasmyth the chairman – 'were of the opinion that it is not at present desirable to commence a series of expensive experiments such as you (Whitworth) have suggested'. The remainder of the letter followed the same negative response and probably reflected the desire of both Woolwich Arsenal and the Enfield people to be left alone. The notion that Nasmyth himself might have wanted to tackle Enfield never really rang true and was finally dispelled when he heartily approved of the American machinery shortly to be ordered by his own committee.

The ire of Nasmyth's venom was reserved for Parliamentary lobbyists. As Chairman of the Gun Committee he no doubt received many 'solicitations' from the same people who regularly paraded the 'fleshpots' under the noses of Ministers. Bribery to get War Office contracts via the Ministers Office was then the order of the day. Perhaps he associated Whitworth with this syndrome? If so, he would have been very wrong. In his autobiography Nasmyth made some acrid references to his experiences with contractors (at the Admiralty) and their lobbying of Parliament when he wrote:

> It is the schemers and the satellites who haunt the contractors that are the vermin of the dockyards. I gave them all a wide berth. But worst of all are the men who get their employment through parliamentary influence. They are a detestable set.

It was indeed a robust view and by its implications could include practically the whole of the mid-Victorian engineering leadership from Stephenson to Gooch, from Armstrong to Whitworth.

By the time Nasmyth's reply reached the War Office, Lord Raglan was already in Paris on his way to the Crimean battlefield. His office in his absence did no more than attach a 'compliment slip' and despatched the whole lot to Whitworth in Manchester. While there is no record of Joe's immediate reaction, the word livid is probably the most apt. Years later Joe confirmed how shocked he had been at the time to have received such an 'ill considered reply' and that he had immediately written in protest to his friend, the Earl of Ellesmere, ironically a neighbour and benefactor landlord of James Nasmyth.

Whitworth knew Ellesmere very well: he was the chairman of the 1853 Royal Commission with whom Joe had travelled to the United States and with whom he had since discussed engineering matters many times. Ellesmere promised that he would write Lord Hardinge, the Chief of Staff, and that he would deliver the letter personally on his return to London. Ellesmere was true to his word. Hardinge warmly thanked the Earl for doing as he did but was scarcely able to conceal his own anger at the way Raglan had behaved and said he would invite Whitworth to meet him in London. He wanted to hear first hand Whitworth's criticism of the present issue of military rifles and that once he became familiar with Whitworth's ideas he would raise the matter with Ministers.

The meeting with Hardinge was quickly arranged and proved to be an historic occasion. It was very much the turning point in Whitworth's life and took place at Horseguards on 2 May 1854. Hardinge wanted Whitworth to explain his ideas especially for the benefit of those of his own departmental staff present at the meeting. It was exactly the occasion Whitworth had waited for and he started off by explaining the deeply felt repugnance he experienced as an engineer when witnessing soldiers loading a rifle. First, they stuffed the flimsy paper-wrapped cartridge down the muzzle. It contained an iron cap, powder and a soft-lead bullet. The soldier then repeatedly hammered it home with a heavy ramrod. Admittedly cartridge design was getting better all the time; the latest partially protected both the bullet and the powder with a cardboard tube while some other varieties had grease-paper fastened to the bullet. The grease-paper development was done by ammunition girls manually lassoing the neck of the bullet with thread. But it was the repeated hammering with the ramrod which so offended Whitworth. In the end the soft bullet was so badly deformed by this brutality that he correctly concluded it would never maintain a steady flight when fired irrespective of the quality of the barrel. He then explained to his listeners that the most formidable engineering problem of all at that time was the making of a perfect barrel – be it a small rifle or a piece of heavy artillery.

Lord Hardinge and his War Office staff were fascinated, for they were listening to an engineer describe for the first time the problems associated with barrel manufacture. At that time the making of a rifle barrel for instance, wholly depended upon the skill of a blacksmith using a 5-pounder hammer swaging a tube from a white-hot iron skelp. And as Whitworth pointed out to his listeners, no drill when used as a reamer would do other than follow the irregular bore made by the blacksmith. Lord Hardinge and his staff were convinced that Whitworth's criticisms were absolutely right. The whole system had to be carefully reconsidered and then, and only then in the meeting's view, could the re-tooling of Enfield go ahead.

Lord Hardinge and his advisers indicated it all made good engineering sense and promised that they would muster what influential support they could. But first they wanted to know what were the essential decisions Whitworth required. His original letter to Raglan was handed round the meeting and, yes, there set out in the letter was the case explaining the need for an experimental shooting gallery under Whitworth's sole control. He himself would pay his own expenses and meet the cost of his assistants but he rightly expected the Government to pay for the building of the gallery. He explained the necessity for certain scientific experiments and that the gallery must be enclosed to minimize the influence of the weather and other disturbances.

Joe said he would commence a series of trials with the most accurate rifles he could make, and from those which shot the best he could then determine the precise form the barrel and the rifling system should take. Most importantly, he wanted to learn the theoretical reason why a particular system excelled where others failed. So far as it is known it was the first time anywhere in the world that an engineer or scientist had wanted to deal methodically with the kinematic phenomena associated with guns. Albeit in ignorance, Whitworth was then about to stumble upon a whole new world of dynamics and the hitherto mysterious behaviour of projectiles in flight. Certainly Hardinge and company were excited by Whitworth's presentation and as reports of the meeting were circulated so a more confident approach to weapon improvement was generated. But as in all things to do with the War Office it was much more realistic to recognize that any gun progress made by Louis-Napoleon's France or by the Prussian Zollverein would motivate Horseguards far more effectively than any analysis from Whitworth. The fact that Britain's European neighbours were urgently experimenting with alternative breech-loaders, pin-fire bullets and one-piece artillery barrels undoubtedly moved the brass-hats more quickly than anything else.

Some two weeks after the meeting, on 17 May 1854, Lord Hardinge sent to the Treasury his famous Memorandum. It was a fully comprehensive document setting out Whitworth's case in detail. The Commander-in-Chief strongly recommended that the whole plan be immediately agreed. The government, he wrote, 'urgently required a million rifled muskets' which Birmingham could not supply in less than twenty years. Nor could they guarantee that the rifles would be anything like identical. Some would be good, some bad. No one had yet discovered the secret as to why one shot was on target while the next flew wild. To make them identical by using machinery seemed the only answer, but, said Hardinge, 'the most celebrated mechanician of his country, Mr Whitworth, had declined the responsibility of producing the machinery until he had first, by the most careful experiments, ascertained the true principle for constructing and rifling the barrel. So essential did he consider this precaution that Mr Whitworth would rather defray the attendant expenses himself than proceed without preliminary investigation. Mr Whitworth is very confident he can discover the secret of the perfect gun and copy it'. Lord Hardinge concluded somewhat darkly: 'If this necessary demand of Mr Whitworth's be denied there would be an end of the plan of making rifle barrels by machinery'. In other words, as far as Lord Hardinge had assessed the situation, he knew of no other engineers in Europe or America who had even tried to replace the blacksmith with a machine in the making of more accurate rifle barrels.

The Treasury received the Hardinge Memorandum with a lamentable scepticism. It was a novel approach and the vast majority in the House of Commons doubted whether the Birmingham gun trade or Whitworth himself could in fact improve the situation before the war in the Crimea ended. Very few anticipated it would last two years anyway. Nor did they think for one moment that the French and British armies were going to die in their thousands. Even the mounting accusations of lethal incompetence levelled against the military leadership failed to stir the Cabinet. In fact the case for taking steps urgently to get better weapons out to the troops, if better weapons were at all possible, had long been a desperate necessity: never more so than at that particular moment.

Suddenly, the attitude of the government changed. Overnight it shifted from one of lethargy to one of absolute urgency. The Chancellor of the Exchequer, William Gladstone, unexpectedly went down to the House of Commons and announced that he had wholly agreed the Hardinge Memorandum and that Whitworth's experiments would be paid in full by the government. By this time, however, the collective wisdom of most senior army officers now considered that battles were won with the weight of artillery and not with rifles. Would it be possible therefore for Whitworth to study cannon design as a matter of priority perhaps while waiting for the completion of his gallery? The view that artillery came first was an opinion also widely held among French and Prussian officers, and Joe pleased Hardinge and the War Minister by readily acknowledging that he too could fully understand the military logic behind their thinking. However, he himself had come to the view that the best way to proceed would be to mock-up some small-bore weapons ready for use in the gallery so that he could then perfect a system of rifling. Having thus satisfied himself about the mechanics of his work, he would then set-to and machine a cannon barrel.

Curiously enough, Whitworth's plan to proceed in this way received encouragement from some unexpected sources. One such ally was Henry Bessemer, the steel man with whom Whitworth had recently discussed gun steel and the making of barrels. During their last conversation Bessemer explained that it was his experience at the Vincennes military academy plus his promise to Louis-Napoleon personally that gave him the stimulus to perfect his Bessemer steel process. 'It was', he admitted, 'the spark which kindled one of the greatest industrial revolutions that the present century has to record'. It was indeed.[16] Within three weeks of the gun trials at Vincennes, Bessemer's famous patent '*Improvements in the Manufacture of Iron and Steel*' was submitted to the Patents Office on 10 January 1855.

Back in June 1854, when the Chancellor of the Exchequer announced that the Government was willing to fund the building of Whitworth's experimental shooting gallery, Joe lost no time in searching for a suitable site. Not surprisingly he was unable to locate such a place other than his own estate at Fallowfield, Manchester. The conditions both he and his architect laid down were pretty exacting. It had to be a brick tunnel with a tiled roof over 500 yards long. Joe was quite determined but his decision to build a gallery on his own estate must have been viewed with some apprehension by his neighbours although they were some considerable distance away. Nevertheless, he went ahead. The difficulty was that it had to be on perfectly level ground and almost a third of a mile in length: it needed a solid concrete base and its brick walls were to be 20 feet high and 16 feet apart. Adequate openings for light were provided along the south side of the tunnel and as Thomas G. Baring MP, the Junior War Minister, said in the House of Commons, 'Mr Whitworth was allowed permission to erect at the public expense all the apparatus he required – and not at small cost, I may add – but something like £16,000 was spent, and very properly spent'.[17]

Unfortunately, in order to save both time and money, the exceptionally high walls of the gallery were inadequately buttressed and an unusually fierce gale one night not only felled some trees but demolished a considerable length of the gallery almost as soon as it was built. Naturally the flattened walls and its tiled roof were immediately rebuilt but commencement of Whitworth's experiments were unavoidably delayed until March 1855. Meanwhile, the War Office behaved in a somewhat heavy-handed fashion and appointed two army officers to shadow Whitworth's work at The Firs, thinking no doubt that these officers could oversee the experimental work and keep the War Office informed. Such a hope proved forlorn. Joe didn't like the idea and made it absolutely clear that he personally had sole charge of the experimental work. The officers appointed were a Captain Jervis MP – who proved to be a thorn in Whitworth's side for at least ten years – and a Captain Lutzen, one of the weapon experts attached to the hostile Nasmyth Small Arms Committee, both of whom were requested by the War Office to remain in Manchester while the research continued.[18]

It was an unprecedented arrangement, firstly because an unpaid backbench MP had been delegated to Manchester on behalf of the War Office and secondly because Whitworth himself, not liking the War Office's choice of two antagonistic army officers, requested that the gunsmith Westley Richards be allowed to assist him and be officially recognized. The Treasury, on taking advice from the War Minister, were very happy to have the whole exercise professionally co-ordinated and readily agreed to pay the costs. Not only did they allow the royal gunsmith, Westley Richards, to have one or two of his own staff at The Firs, but it also meant that Whitworth's own organization would have the best possible supply of essential WR gun parts from the beginning.

For some months past Joe himself had been very clear how he wanted to commence his gun experiments. In fact while the shooting gallery was being rebuilt his own tool and gauge-makers were able to demonstrate their undoubted skills by putting together a series of 'segmentalized tubes' made into mock hexagonal gun barrels. Their appearance must have been strange indeed for they were made by cutting lengthways six radially-fitting segments, sweating them together in the form of tubes and held by external hoops. The assembled pieces were then reheated and the whole red-hot assembly twisted until the rifling had acquired the desired spirality. In effect they were disproportionately heavy and thick walled but made to provide the best available polygonal rifling of various lengths and bore sizes. For the first time ever Whitworth had thus been able to broach to within reasonable limits hexagonal spirals. Next he machined the projectiles to fit the hexagonal bore, historically creating to within very fine tolerances the first accurate '*mechanical fit*' rifling system. In this way Whitworth was able to provide for himself the basic requirements of a gun laboratory and by using recognized scientific procedures he slowly began to unravel the inexplicable mysteries which had so far denied gunmakers the ability to make accurate guns.

Unlike the best scientists, however, who try to set out with open minds, Whitworth and Westley Richards started their research with a string of well-entrenched prejudices. Well ahead of Joe's ideas for instance was his commitment to replace soft-lead-coated or solid-lead missiles (which so easily fouled-up gun barrels) with hard bullets and hard cannon shells. It was an objective which of necessity compelled his adherence to the use of his '*mechanical fit*' system. Furthermore, because of the horror he experienced after witnessing the crude hammering of shot into gun barrels, he instinctively wanted to do away with the use of a ramrod and go for breech-loaders. But his co-researcher, Westley Richards – whom Brunel later claimed had first given Whitworth the idea of hexagonal rifling – wanted none of it: the '*mechanical fit*' system plus breach loading was for him going too far too quickly. Truthfully, when Joe answered the very same point put to him by Sir John Hay MP during an 1863 House of Commons Select Committee, Whitworth replied, 'Westley Richards did all in his power to try and persuade me to abandon the thing, but I saw its value, in consequence of being able to apply self-acting machinery for producing projectiles'. Sir John, who was at that moment questioning Joe's right to have patented the hexagonal idea, then asked: 'You do not acknowledge any obligation either to Mr Brunel or to Mr Westley Richards then?'

'I do not say that', Whitworth retorted honestly. 'I am very much indebted to Mr Westley Richards for all the information that he gave me in respect to the manufacture of rifles generally'.

'But you owe nothing to Mr Brunel?'

'Nothing whatever', replied Whitworth.

Mr Hussey Vivian MP, also a member of the committee, followed this up by asking rhetorically: You do not desire to detract from Mr Brunel's merits, but you do desire to assert that you at the same time adopted the same idea without concert?

But before Joe could properly reply, Sir John Hay, thinking the question needed a little more hob-nailed subtlety added: 'No communications passed between you, did they?'

'None whatever,' answered a tired Whitworth, a trace sarcastically. 'It appears Mr Brunel was before me and I am very pleased to think so.'[19]

Bearing in mind that these exchanges in the Select Committee took place some eight years after the start of Whitworth's experimental work at The Firs, Joe's answer must have been seen in the context of the public argument which was then raging about field artillery and naval guns rather than small arms. Isambard K. Brunel had, on 20 October 1852 to be precise, requested Westley Richards to make for him an hexagonally-bored rifle but Westley Richards's production facilities at the time were not up to it and the very poor example which he was able to show Whitworth was of little value. After Brunel's death in 1857 his son set about establishing his father as the original inventor of the '*mechanical fit*' hexagonal system. By 1863 he had managed to collect the papers together and submitted the whole case to a Select Committee of the House of Commons for their jurisdiction as to the eligibility of Whitworth's patent.

While it was clear to everyone why Brunel's son wanted to establish the patent in his father's name, the same clarity doesn't explain why so many writers and historians want to knock Whitworth's own explanation of what he actually patented. The fact is, he himself never claimed the original idea. What Whitworth did patent was the total system and the method by which it could be made. Indeed, he recognized that there were many such systems in the past and admitted he first saw similar rifles in the Museé des Invalides. He may possibly have confused this with the Vincennes gun collection which he had also visited at one time, but he had made the point. Long before these weapons were made, however, the Military Engineering Department at the University of Padua and the Venetian Arsenal worked on similar ideas.[20] The best specimen, albeit a much more modern example, was a hexagonally bored rifle made by a Sergeant Major Robert Moore of the RA in 1843, regretfully now lost according to the Tower of London authorities. But so far as Whitworth's own patents were concerned, in all fairness they were really an announcement by him that he had actually *made* a hexagonal spiral of sufficient quality to guarantee an accurate shot, notwithstanding Sergeant Moore, I.K. Brunel, Westley Richards, the Venetians and others. In a letter to Lord Panmure, the War Minister, dated June 1857, Whitworth wrote:

> I do not wish to claim for myself the sole merit of trying that particular form of barrel. It has been tried in many isolated cases, but the advantages of the

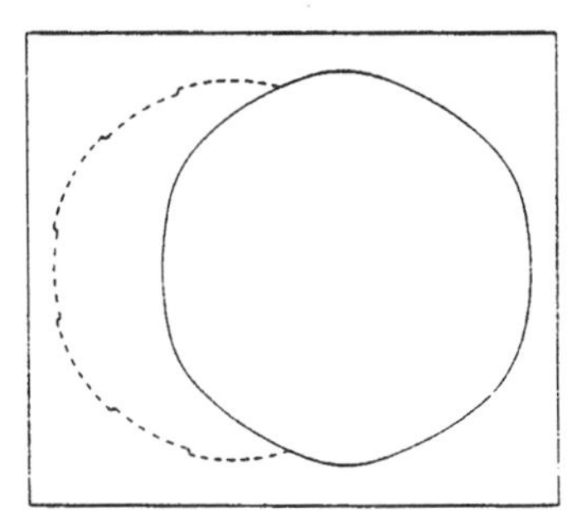

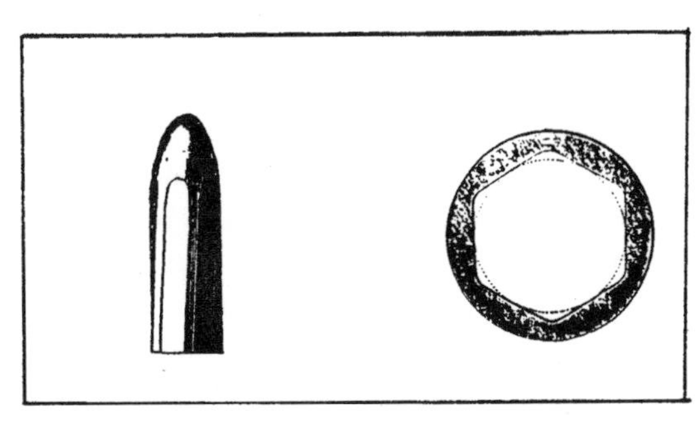

Fig. 9 The superb accuracy of the most advanced of modern small arms as exemplified by the polygonal bore (left), developed for the 1990s by the German gunmaker HK, offers some atonement at least, for past bitter disputes between Whitworth and the War Office. World leaders Heckler and Koch rightly claim for their polygonal system an increase in muzzle velocity and the elimination of wear; two of the advantages claimed 130 years ago by Whitworth. The Whitworth hexagonal bore and shot is shown on the right.

complete polygonal system for barrels and projectiles had not been practically developed.

In 1987, 130 years later, the polygonal system is now successfully used. A similar diminishing of Whitworth again arose over his ideas and patents for a breech-loading rifle. It was said at the time he had been inspired by the Parisian gunsmith, Lefaucheux, and the improved Pauly system which the Parisian had developed. Not so. A careful study of the design steps which probably led Whitworth to his first breech-block rocker-mechanism indicates that his original interest in breech-loaders almost certainly started in the United States with a breech invented by Christian Sharpe in 1848. A further modification of his rudimentary ideas occurred perhaps after he saw the work being done on revolvers by Colonel Colt at Pimlico in London. The final design, however, was Whitworth at his best. It was a prime example of his own design maxim based on simplicity and although it was five years ahead of its time it was well within the manufacturing capacity of contemporary machinery. The reason it did not get anywhere in Britain was that the military authorities wanted neither breech-loaders nor Whitworth, but had Joe allowed his draughtsmen to develop the design it undoubtedly would have attracted a great deal of international interest.[21]

Though his experimental equipment was ingenious, from October 1855, Whitworth struggled to overcome extremely complex phenomena. What in modern terms could be described as hypersonic measurements – that is to say, observing the flight-flow patterns around various bullet configurations – or perhaps simulating the ballistic impact of a flat-nosed missile crashing through a massive steel plate: all this without any of the scientific paraphernalia of a modern laboratory. Uppermost in Whitworth's mind no doubt was the fact that he had to validate his ideas by experimental results but in the absence of laboratory experience he realized that he was totally dependent upon his own ingenuity. Looking back it is astounding just how accurate his results were. First of all he suspended tissue-paper screens every thirty yards along the whole length of his shooting gallery to record the trajectory and flight stability of his flying bullets. In another experiment he erected bags full of bran to catch his bullets mid-flight, thus he could then examine the spin effects of his rifled barrel and check the bullet's speed of rotation. He got up to all kinds of tricks to measure speed and the difference in explosive energy, initially absorbed by barrel friction using his own *mechanical fit* system compared to that of orthodox cylindrical rifling. He came to the conclusion, applicable both to rifles and his three-pounder, that the Whitworth system absorbed 2 or 3 per cent of the explosive force whereas the more orthodox guns absorbed some 20 or 21 per cent: this great difference being accounted for by the fact that orthodox rifling required the shot to be first expanded before forcing the then oversized bullet and cartridge through the barrel.[22]

Later authorities, like Longridge and many who followed, were baffled to know how he did it but readily endorsed the relative accuracy of Whitworth's incredible figures. But whichever way the results are viewed it must surely be a tribute to the infinite care and intelligent assessment Whitworth gave to all his experimental work that the criteria he established mid-nineteenth century still remain more or less valid today. In 1946 the American, Dr Harold Edgerton, perfected stroboscopic equipment for ultra high-speed photography. Remarkably he was able to photographically 'stop' bullets travelling at 1,500 ft per second and scientists were then able to analyse in every detail flying objects travelling beyond the speed of sound.[23] Back in 1855 Whitworth and his associates calculated the speed of their bullets to be about 12,000 yards per minute (600 ft per second) and revolving at about 250 revs per second. One hundred years on, modern scientists using precise methods considered Whitworth's calculations probably correct to within about 5 per cent. It can only be described as an astonishing performance.

About the same time Joe was coming to his own conclusions about the flight characteristics of missiles, the French physicist, Jean B. Foucault, developed techniques for measuring the absolute velocity of light. He too accomplished great accuracy and got within one per cent of what many years later was proved to be the precise figure. Foucault also researched the properties of rotating bodies. He concluded that a considerable force was required to deflect any such body and that in the absence of an external force a rotating axis will always retain a fixed direction in space.

All this Whitworth was finding out for himself a long way removed from Foucault and armed only with tissue-paper screens and bran bags. It was once described by *Punch* as engineering wizardry. Subsequent armoury textbooks which are based on Whitworth's published reports are now legendary.[24] For instance, the critical length of the projectile compared to its diameter; the essential spirality per foot of barrel; the diameter of bore, or in his case the across-flats measurement, the weight and the quality of the charge; even the minutiae went down in immaculate style and remained basic gun criteria for sixty years or more. If moral decency still exists the War Office together with the academic world should now behave with a degree of magnanimity and posthumously credit Whitworth with the recognition his gun tunnel and gun research deserves. As D.W. Bailey, the American rifle historian and a leading authority on the Whitworth rifle, wrote in the magazine, *Guns Review*, March 1969:

> Whitworth's most important contribution to the gun making business and more generally to the development of rifled small arms was that he reduced a great deal of confusion to order by systematic experiment and created a foundation of proven facts from which he created a system which exhibited the great superiority of his work. This system created at once the basis upon which myriad imitations and improvements were made and the stimulus to make them. He was the founder not so much of the Whitworth rifle as of the greatest and most fruitful period of experimentation and development in the British gun trade: the benefits of which we are still repeating today.[25]

By comparison with most 1854 laboratories The Firs gallery must have been crudely equipped but it was here that Whitworth stumbled across his most profound understanding. In a purely instinctive way, foreseeing all modern scientific procedure, Joe realized his results depended on repetitive consistency and that he must change only one element at each stage. This realization must have accounted for his successful experimental sequence. It now sounds idiotic, but in his curious meccano fashion, Whitworth actually caricatured Einstein's *Deterministic Mechanics* to the extent his work still remains – in outline at least – theoretically correct.

The coming together of Joseph Whitworth and Westley Richards proved to be a rewarding relationship. It was an amicable arrangement too and the fact that the Birmingham gunsmith had his own company which supplied parts like gun locks and trigger mechanisms, enabled the gallery programme to have a good start. Westley Richards was twelve years younger than Whitworth. Born in Birmingham, he took over his father's business around 1847 – the same year his wife was killed in a riding accident leaving him with a two-year-old daughter. He never remarried. He and Whitworth remained personal friends throughout, although on occasions it became clear that their ideas differed. The Enfield rifle, for instance, had a 0.577-in diameter bore while Whitworth wanted to reduce his experimental barrel to 0.450-in 'diameter' or even smaller if possible. Westley Richards, presumably supported by the two army officers who represented the War Office at the gallery, wanted to keep to the Enfield equivalents so that the experiments were a genuine comparison. Whitworth, however, stuck to his original intentions with the result that within six or eight months he was using extra long bullets with 0.451-in calibre mocked-up barrels for all his rifle experiments. The initial indications were so good that Westley Richards in the end was convinced that the smaller bore was superior and thereafter he himself manufactured rifles of that calibre.[26]

While the officials witnessing Whitworth's experiments were satisfied that the results on small arms were correctly recorded, Joe's own ideas in regard to heavier artillery barrels were also making good progress. When he looked back it must have seemed incredible that he had actually used his 500-yard gallery for trials with 3-pounder guns. Seemingly, he devised ways to carry out limited distance experiments by using the most beautifully machined hexagonally bored segmental tubes mounted on heavy cast iron frames. His 3-pounder tubes were 1.575 in across flats but tentatively, he also experimented with much larger segmental tubes measuring some 3 in across flats for use with 12-pounder shells. Naturally they were never fired with a full charge but without question on this very limited scale Whitworth must have been very excited with the early results. He would have been less than human if he wasn't now impatient to let his guns do the talking.[27]

RIFLE RESULTS DO THE TALKING

> In conclusion, my Lord, I feel myself justified in stating with confidence that the polygon construction of barrel and projectiles possesses far greater advantages than any other construction with which I am acquainted. It is equally applicable to small fire arms and large pieces of ordnance.

Letter from Joseph Whitworth
to Lord Panmure, War Department,
Pall Mall, June 1857

On 23 April 1857, *The Times* reported that the Government School of Musketry, Hythe, Kent, 'has established beyond all doubt the great and decided superiority of Mr Whitworth's invention. The Enfield rifle, which was considered so much better than any other, has been completely beaten. In accuracy of fire, in penetration, and in range, its rival (the Whitworth) excels it to a degree which hardly leaves room for comparison.'

These particular trials represented the first of three landmarks in the development of the rifle. All three were to do with the handiwork of Whitworth yet at no time was his work recognized as the most significant small arms engineering of the century. The Minister of War, Lord Panmure, attended the trials throughout though sadly Whitworth's mentor, Lord Hardinge, had died seven months earlier. His death robbed the occasion of Whitworth's most illustrious supporter, the most senior officer to whom the War Department would listen. Hardinge, together with General George Hay, had seen for themselves during one of their trips to Whitworth's estate, The Firs, the full realization of his experimental 0.577 calibre short barrel hexagonal bore – one of which was rifled twenty turns in twenty inches – and still it didn't strip the rifling. Using only half a charge of 35 grams of powder its lead alloy bullet penetrated through seven inches of elm; and at a reduced distance of twenty yards a steel bullet went through a wrought iron plate 0.6 inches in thickness. When the two generals reported this to the War Department they were, quite frankly, disbelieved. Nevertheless, it was the first time anywhere in the world that a rifle bullet had gone straight through an iron plate!

In his report to Lord Panmure, Whitworth claimed that:

> Owing to the combined facilities afforded by the polygon system of rifling; the *mechanical fit*, and quick turn, I was enabled to make the most satisfactory experiments with regard to the penetration of my hard metal projectiles through iron.

Whitworth liked to recall that when he and his team turned up at Hythe armed with his hexagonal bores (otherwise they were exactly the same as the Enfields) his guns exceeded all records: the Enfields were withdrawn from the contest at 1,400 yards, unable to hit the target. When War Ministers actually witnessed the Whitworths doing as well at 1,100 yards as the Enfields did at 500 yards, and when they saw the Whitworths now going through sixteen inches of elm planks as against the Enfield's seven inches, they left the gunnery, earnestly asking Joe to write to the Ministry setting out the progress made at The Firs since his experiments began in March 1855.

Whitworth was delighted to do so, sending a full report in June 1857. It was over 22,000 words in length.[28] He explained the new principles his experiments had established. Written with absolute clarity the 'gun thesis' he created still stands. It is truly remarkable to now recall that as late as 1928, French military researchers confirmed that hexagonal *mechanical fit* field guns equalled, if not bettered, conventional artillery. Mathematically there is still a case to be made in favour of *mechanical fit* systems, assuming, of course, that the whole system and its economic manufacture is available and used as one complete system (see fig. 9).

Within his 1857 report to Lord Panmure, Whitworth sets out the following tenets:

> On trying the barrel with four turns, in comparison with the military rifle having half a turn, I found to my great satisfaction that it gave an equal elevation.
>
> The results led me to suppose that the effect of the combined progressive and rotary motions of the projectiles cause such a displacement of the atmosphere, as the ball (bullet) progresses, that the body revolves in what is almost a vacuum, so that any increase of rotary velocity meets with little or no increased resistance, and does not affect the elevation.
>
> I also found, as I expected, that I had no difficulty in firing projectiles of any desirable length, without their having a tendency to turn over.
>
> One of the most important advantages attending the use of the long projectiles is, that it admits of a reduced diameter.

But Whitworth now had every reason to feel embittered by the treatment he suffered. In 1857, James Nasmyth, at the age of forty-nine, retired to his country retreat, Hammerfield, there to pursue his interest in astronomy. His small arms committee was renamed the Whitworth and Enfield Committee although Whitworth himself didn't take the chair: neither, it would seem, did the War Office thereafter pay much attention to the committee minutes. The reason Whitworth refrained from taking the chair was that he recognized how ludicrous it would have been for him to have signed the committee's decisions recommending his own system of rifling and gun manufacture. In the event, he need not have worried; any influence the committee had faded with Nasmyth's going.

Immediately after the Hythe trials Whitworth concluded he should do everything possible to persuade Enfield to reduce the bore size of its 0.577 calibre rifle by at least 25 per cent: for his own guns he decided on a 0.450 calibre – a 22 per cent reduction. It was a correct decision, proved time and again both at the gunnery trials and by his own research. It cost Whitworth personally a great deal of money as he tried desperately hard to convert the War Office but they would have none of it. In utter disgust Whitworth smiled wearily. 'After a lapse of eighteen months', he lamented, 'a Committee of Officers reported to the Government in 1859 that the bore of my rifle was *too small* for a military weapon'.

Three years later, much to his surprise, the Army Ordnance Committee during his absence reported that practically every small-bore gunmaker had 'copied to the letter the three main elements of success adopted by Mr Whitworth, viz. diameter of bore, degree of spiral and large proportion of rifling surface'. The final mockery, however, had to wait a further seven years. Whitworth himself was then able to write, none too agreeably, '. . . in 1869 a Special Committee reported to the War Office that the calibre of a breech-loading rifle should be 0.45 in, as appearing to be the most *suitable for a military arm.* This conclusion', Joe growled, 'coincides exactly with what I recommended in 1857', twelve wasted years earlier.

The second landmark created by Whitworth occurred when Queen Victoria fired the first shot to open the NRA prize meeting at Wimbledon, on 2 July 1860. It was an extraordinary event yet the press – and every writer since – dismissed the accomplishment as so much gossip, or at best, royal minutiae. It was nothing of the kind. The shot demonstrated for the first time that a gun could be made to *consistently* hit bull-centre shot after shot. The gun used was a Whitworth hexagonal bore 0.451 across-flats muzzle-loading rifle mounted on a mechanical rest and fixed at a distance of 400 yards from the target. Whitworth recalled the event by explaining that 'a silken cord attached to the trigger was handed to Her Majesty by me, and the rifle was discharged by a slight pull on the cord. The bullet struck the target within one and a quarter inches of the centre'.

This remarkable achievement was made possible because the barrel of the gun had been drilled from the solid and afterwards broached using Whitworth's new techniques.[29] History was being made. The Manchester men attending Wimbledon had fired the gun many times scoring a 'bull' each time. Regrettably,

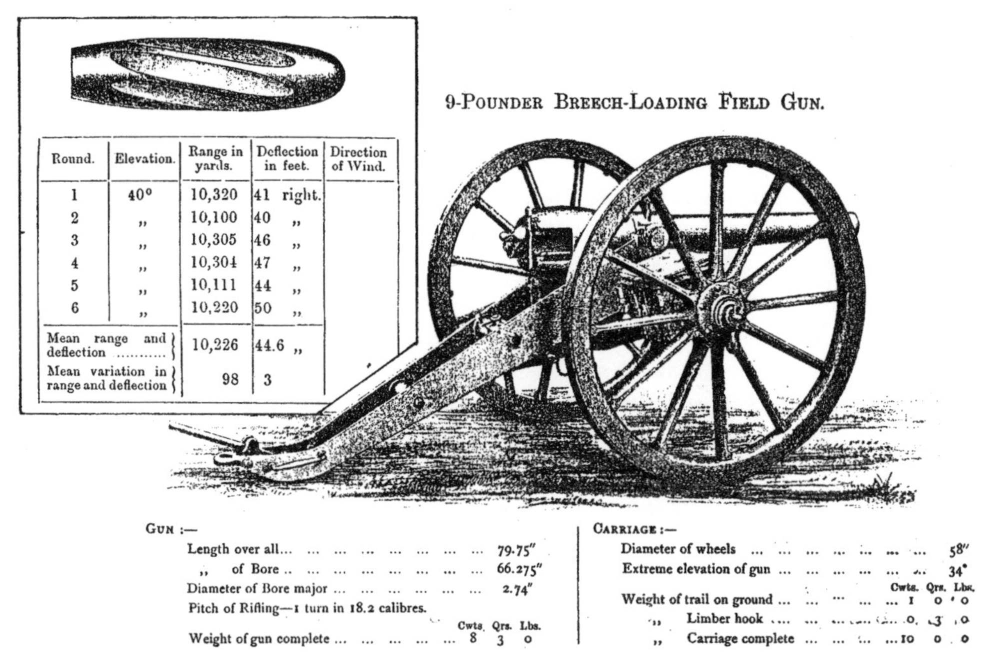

Round.	Elevation.	Range in yards.	Deflection in feet.	Direction of Wind.
1	40°	10,320	41 right.	
2	,,	10,100	40 ,,	
3	,,	10,305	46 ,,	
4	,,	10,304	47 ,,	
5	,,	10,111	44 ,,	
6	,,	10,220	50 ,,	
Mean range and deflection		10,226	44.6 ,,	
Mean variation in range and deflection		98	3	

Fig. 10 Whitworth's most impressive gun. The (range and accuracy) trials of this Whitworth breech-loading 9-pounder at Southport (9/10/1872) astonished the world.

of the military observers present all but Prince Albert were scared off by the hexagonal bore. Albert, however, made no secret of pressing the Minister to go for Whitworth; the fact that neither the Minister nor his department ever did annoyed him intensely. Even more vexing, the Prince knew that had Whitworth been permitted to use his own brass cartridges he would have changed over to a *breech-loader* and destroyed the opposition by even greater margins. As it was, the Whitworth *muzzle-loader* won every contest for thirteen years until 1870.

The 'royal shot' at Wimbledon represented four years of development work by Whitworth, made possible by his *invention* of the twist-drill and adjustable broach. It was this cardinal secret which finally removed barrel-making from the blacksmith's hammer although the old method lingered until the coming of cold-drawn techniques. (The latest 1970s method, ironically, is now back to using super-high-speed horizontal hammering machines!) But the twist-drill in fact represented the third (probably the greatest) of Whitworth's great rifle landmarks.

How then did perfection of the twist-drill come about? Two years after he patented his first horizontal drilling and broaching machine, Whitworth patented his second series of designs, on 12 June 1857, all of which incorporated much more sophisticated feed mechanisms. They too failed to overcome the 'wandering' problem (drilling a hole eighteen inches deep from both ends of a barrel, the holes inevitably failed to accurately meet at the centre), hence Whitworth conceived the brilliant notion of *twisting* a plate-drill its whole length thus giving the drill both axial location and a much improved swarf removal.[30] This was a tremendous breakthrough which revolutionized not just barrel manufacture but once it became known most workshop procedures too. Curiously, although he patented his horizontal drilling machines he chose not to patent the *twist-drill.* Instead he kept the drill and his broaching technology tucked away in Sackville Street. It proved a wise strategy. In the event he openly talked about his methods from 1859 onwards, saving for display at the South Kensington 1862 Exhibition the first ever examples of rifle barrels drilled and broached from the solid. His work was rightfully acclaimed by most leading engineers at the time as 'truly masterful', not least of which his new tensile broaching equipment figured prominently.

Prior to the South Kensington Exhibition the political vacillations of 1858 compelled Whitworth to reconsider his situation. Should he in fact discontinue his interest in guns? It was as fundamental as that! Lord Derby, the Prime Minister, had appointed General Jonathan Peel MP (brother of Whitworth's friend, the late Sir Robert Peel) to be his Secretary of State for War. Jonathan Peel loathed Whitworth, both politically and for his gun systems: but more about that shortly. The fact he was considered the most right wing blimp in Derby's Cabinet actually helped Whitworth, but in the most bewildering fashion. Peel informed Whitworth in January 1859 that no further experiments would be funded by the government using the Whitworth system of hexagonal rifling. The letter was written with absolute bluntness and offered no reasons why the government wanted so suddenly to end Whitworth's work. Joe was stunned.

Although the letter was signed by General Peel, Whitworth was yet to learn its real author. Certainly he then didn't know of the veiled relationship between William Armstrong (the gun manufacturer) and Peel and that it was Armstrong who had insisted that Whitworth be dropped completely. Naturally, no one outside the Cabinet had realized why Armstrong was in such a strong position to do these things. In fact on two occasions only did Joe himself refer publicly to Peel's letter. The second occasion was during his evidence in 1863 to the House of Commons Select Committee on Ordnance when he was asked to recall why he had actually entered the armament business. He replied that it was when he decided to fight Armstrong and Peel. It was then he revealed the depth of his bitterness. 'I did not have previously the most distant idea of becoming a manufacturer of rifled arms,' he said, 'but when I received this letter from General Peel to inform me that no more experiments were to be made with guns on my principle *I determined at once* to become a manufacturer and to prove that my system was right. With respect to the rifle it has already been shown that it was so; and I think it will be admitted that I was right with regard to ordnance also.'[31]

Whitworth's reactions were a clear indication he had been deeply hurt; especially so because the Minister was a brother of his earlier political hero,

Robert Peel. But if it did nothing else, General Peel's letter almost radicalized Joe overnight, raising his political awareness remarkably. And once he got to know what was going on between Armstrong and Peel it naturally sharpened his understanding of William Armstrong's privileged position relative to the War Office. It also demonstrated perhaps more than anything else the hostile competitiveness which was slowly building up between Armstrong and himself.

Fortunately for Whitworth, Lord Derby's Government lasted no more than a brief sixteen months. Sworn in February 1858, it lasted until June 1859 when Lord Palmerston came back in and out went General Peel. It was inevitable. Lord Derby had fostered the most disparate camarilla of modern times by deliberately setting up within his Cabinet a number of hostile relationships in an attempt to make this particular coalition work. One example: he made Disraeli his Chancellor of the Exchequer then brought in two extreme zealots in charge of the army and the navy, General Jonathan Peel and Sir John Pakington. Both of them detested the very sight of Disraeli, the very man with whom they would have to deal had they wanted more money for guns and armoured ships. From Whitworth's point of view the story is worth telling.

Going back to the formation of the Second Derby Administration, Whitworth knew that he personally was in trouble immediately he read in the *Manchester Guardian*, 27 February 1858, that Peel was in the Cabinet. General Peel had been a professional soldier, pro-Lord Raglan but very much anti-reform; he was profoundly anti-Manchester School politics. Disraeli said of him: 'General Peel's eyes lit up with insanity when reform was mentioned', whereupon Peel responded that 'certain politicians tailor their principles to suit calculated requirements'. He went further: during the Reform debate he argued: '*There is nothing so elastic as the conscience of a Cabinet minister*'. Peel's quiet vitriol was scathing.

Lord Derby had insisted on making Viscount Hardinge (son of Whitworth's friend, the late Field Marshal Hardinge) Peel's number two at the War Office to salve his own conscience in terms of Whitworth. It was a nice gesture but of little help: the whole business of armament manufacture was soon to look as though a private mafia had taken over at the War Office once the wheeler-dealing between the War Office and William Armstrong got under way. In fact within ten days of taking office General Peel had personally put to Cabinet a plan whereby all future gun manufacturing would be channelled through Armstrong. The Prime Minister, however, sensed something risky about the idea and he actually wrote to Peel advising caution. *Nevertheless the plans went through*, albeit secretly. Surprisingly, the matter was not seriously debated until Lord Derby and General Peel were accused of underhand scheming in the early sixties.

The fact that Peel's scheme offering Armstrong exclusive rights had actually gone through Cabinet was extraordinary but that it never leaked to the House was even more astonishing. Historically, it coincided with the publishing of the latest results attained by Whitworth's field guns, all of which made the situation even more cryptic. Hunch-like, as if he anticipated a censure motion when the details of the now famous Whitworth six-mile cannon shot became known, the Prime Minister's office suggested that the Ordnance Special Committee should urgently visit both the Armstrong works at Elswick and the Whitworth factory in Manchester to consider all available systems of rifling. And although he was reluctant to do so, General Peel immediately directed the late Hardinge's son, Charles S. Hardinge, to write to Whitworth to ask if the necessary facilities would be offered to the Committee. Joe replied on 26 September 1858, signifying his pleasure in providing all that the Committee required. 'Come to Manchester anytime', he wrote, but sadly (contrary to Lord Derby's wish) he was crudely snubbed. General Peel didn't want the Committee to go, nor did the Chairman of the Select Committee and when the truth became known that Peel's Office had finally made arrangements with Armstrong only and not Whitworth, it seemed that the Minister had chanced his anti-Whitworth prejudice once too often.

Both *The Times* and the *Manchester Guardian* thought that the General's attitude towards Whitworth was offensive and contrary to the national interest but perhaps the most damning confirmation of this whole warped business came from Admiral Sir William Wiseman, the Chairman of the Ordnance Special Committee, when he tried to explain to the press why they had visited the Armstrong factory only and not Whitworths.

'At first', he said, 'we thought it would be necessary to visit both manufacturies in order to ascertain their method of manufacturing guns: but we only visited Mr Armstrong because we had no proposal from Mr Whitworth before us for constructing guns'. Of course they hadn't. General Peel had secretly prevented the War Office from contacting Whitworth. Colonel Lefrey, the War Office technical adviser, when he was questioned simply said, 'Mr Whitworth was so secret we would have got nothing from him'. 'How curious', snapped the man from *The Times.* 'I have Whitworth's statement here explaining what he is doing'. Four years later the matter was raised again and Whitworth wrote to *The Times* on 11 October 1862, confirming that at the time he had many interesting guns to show the War Office if they had wanted to see them.

Back in 1858 the Ordnance Special Committee, having treated Whitworth's work as a 'trifling irrelevance', went on to make its single most important recommendation that the Armstrong field guns *be approved.* The Secretary of State, General Peel, couldn't wait to report the decision to Cabinet. Imagine his shock that same evening on being *publicly advised* by the Prime Minister not to be so anxious; that he should proceed a little more slowly, particularly in regard to guns heavier than, say, 32–pounders.

'There may be superior cannon available in the future', the Prime Minister wrote to his Cabinet colleague. Unprecedently, he made it an open letter, dated December 1858. Certainly it was a somewhat perverted procedure for Lord Derby to have set out the Cabinet minutes in open correspondence – but then so were the following events even more perverted. Lord Derby was in a hurry. He had realized his administration couldn't last much longer. In the event, he and General Peel were to last until June 1859; less than six months in which to finally exclude Whitworth and bring in Armstrong.

The first thing they did was to ask Armstrong if he would sell his gun patents to the Government. Three days later, the reasons became clear. General Peel had said, 'Only Armstrong knew how to make coiled-wrought-iron gun barrels', therefore the Government felt compelled to follow it up and ask Armstrong if he would also *manufacture* the complete guns. The whole thing was beginning to take on a curious twist, doubly so when Armstrong '*generously*' offered to transfer his patents to the Government without payment – a gesture described by Peel in his letter to the Prime Minister dated 15 January 1859, as 'the handsomest offer ever made by a private individual to the Government'. Armstrong again wrote Peel personally, suggesting that he himself should be appointed Director of Rifled Ordnance on a *part-time* basis at a reduced salary of £3,000 p.a. plus expenses. Accordingly, the Cabinet agreed the arrangements, awarding him the title of Engineer to the War Department at a financially agreed salary of £2,000 p.a. *plus expenses.* In all it amounted to £3,000 anyway. His appointment was dated 23 February 1859 – his salary being back-dated to 1856 to compensate him for the work already done – but of far more importance to Armstrong were the special conditions which accompanied the job.[32]

In the first instance Armstrong had demanded that a letter be sent by the Government to Whitworth personally saying that *no* further experiments would be publicly funded using the Whitworth system of hexagonal rifling. Secondly, it was agreed that the Armstrong Engineering Co. at Elswick should continue as a private company and that a new gun factory called the Elswick Ordnance Co. be built next door. The idea was to separate in the public mind Armstrong the government gun-buyer from Armstrong its gun-supplier, particularly as he personally would place the contracts and fix the prices on behalf of the War Minister! It was neat, it was cartelist; the Attorney-General considered it was legal. Indeed, the third part of the package gave Armstrong a knighthood. As one MP said, 'even before a single gun was produced'.

The new company was registered on 25 January 1859, just ten days after the funding contract was signed. One of Armstrong's two adopted sons, George Rendell, was made general manager. His other adopted son, Stuart Rendell, a young barrister who later became an MP before going into the House of Lords, negotiated all the details. He therefore loyally defended Armstrong taking a full share of the profits – a blatant variation of their first agreement.

In terms of the first full year's output at Elswick of one hundred guns, comprising in the main, 32–pounders, the total price paid by the War Office was £40,000. The company also received £36,000 ex-gratia payments in addition to some £65,000 personal compensation paid to Armstrong. Soon afterwards, Elswick constructed one hundred and sixty 110–pounders at an average cost of £684 each as against the £424 paid to Woolwich Arsenal for each of five hundred and seventy five similar guns made at the royal arsenal during the period

1859–62. Also revealed during the evidence given to the 1863 Select Committee on Ordnance, was the fact that Woolwich Arsenal, the state armoury, constructed 12–pounder muzzle-loaders for £87 each; compared to the £170 paid to Elswick. Incredibly, both these prices for identical guns were negotiated by Armstrong for Armstrongs and undersigned by John Anderson of Woolwich.[33]

Four months after Lord Derby and General Peel were defeated, in October 1859, Whitworth determined he would go it alone as an independent gun manufacturer. It was partly speculative, partly defiant, coming as it did days after the Navy decision to go Armstrong.

When the Duke of Somerset, the new Palmerston Minister for the Navy, announced on 14 October 1859 that the Royal Navy would henceforth be equipped with Armstrong 7 inch bore 110–pounders, built at Elswick at the price of £700 each, Whitworth feared he would have to look elsewhere in the world if he was to redeem both his self-esteem and the vast investment he had ventured upon his own hexagonal gun systems.

During the year 1860 Whitworth's constructed an entirely new generation of heavy field-guns made with steel barrels and designed to operate as both breech and muzzle-loaders. They were high quality weapons – suitable, he thought, (when converted as deck guns) for the Royal Navy – but admittedly more expensive than Armstrong's. His list prices (although Whitworth agreed all his gun prices were negotiable): for a 4.5-in bore 32-pounder he charged £400; for a 5.5-in bore 70-pounder, £700; and for his new very big gun, a 7-in, 120-pounder – its hexagonal barrel was 13 ft long – the price at £1,350 was almost double the Armstrong-Elswick price. On a more competitive note, however, Joe must have been pleased to learn that although his shells and solid bolts were hexagonal in shape he could at least mass produce both kinds at far lower prices than either the state arsenal or Elswick; this encouraged him to set aside part of his Sackville Street gun factory for this special purpose.

Although Whitworth was surreptitiously encouraged by Palmerston's new ministers towards the end of 1859 to submit his field guns for trial, it was in fact 1861 before he was approached directly and asked if he would officially compete against the Armstrongs. It was very much a political situation. The Cabinet was divided – for and against Whitworth's hexagonal system. Few ministers and MPs had the courage to plunge for something new therefore the circumstances tended to settle on small arms rather than field guns, political personalities rather than policies.

Whitworth sided with those of his Manchester friends who supported Palmerston despite the barracking the Prime Minister received in Parliament. 'What! That utterly exhausted old painted pantaloon', raged Disraeli. John Bright was even more explicit. He wrote in his diary 'Oh! That aged charlatan'. Nevertheless, Joe ignored the jibes and stood by his expectations.

The Cabinet lasted six years. *Pantaloon* or not, the Prime Minister suited Joe; he thought he could do business with his ministers. At the end of one critical gun debate, for example, in June 1861, Palmerston himself entered the Chamber deliberately to reassure Whitworth's supporters: 'I am not at all insensible to the great importance of furnishing the army with the best possible weapon', he said. 'It will be the duty of the Government – a duty which they will sedulously perform – to ascertain with the greatest accuracy what is the best weapon'. Twelve months later, on 17 June 1862, he again intervened to overturn a Select Committee recommendation, thus preventing Whitworth's rejection for a second time.[34]

Palmerston's ministers did two things for Whitworth. Unbelievably and not commonly known, they actually placed an order for his rifles and secondly, they terminated the Armstrong contract. When Palmerston came in, in June 1859, he quickly installed Sidney Herbert in place of General Peel as Secretary of State for War and in an unprecedented act of faith Herbert immediately ordered from Whitworth 10,000 rifles. They were to be a cheaper version of Whitworth's very successful 0.45 Hex.bore Match rifle, highly subsidized by the maker at twenty shillings each. They were roughly half price but because someone in Cabinet had later opposed having the Whitworth gun, Herbert had to tell Joe that the price (even at twenty shillings) was *too dear*, and therefore he was compelled to cancel the contract. In expectation of government orders Whitworth had equipped his new rifle factory with his latest horizontal drilling and broaching machines. The plant was unique and capable of producing far superior rifles – his first commercially available rifles were made August 1859 – and by 1865, the Manchester Ordnance and Rifle Company had gone on to successfully make its first experimental 0.300-in bore sporting rifle.

The second thing Palmerston did was to appoint Sir G.C. Lewis MP Minister of War. He, Lewis, immediately terminated the Elswick contract, thus bringing about the voluntary retirement of (now Sir) William Armstrong.

At the age of fifty-three, Sir William was anxious to rebuild his own engineering establishment; a tremendous feat which he managed with considerable poise. Sadly, his gun contracts were never fully redeemed before government law officers again moved in and brought charges of conspiracy and corruption against both Armstrong *and* the Ordnance Department. It was by then the year of Whitworth's death, 1887. The difference this time was that the charges followed extensive reporting by the press of naval gun failures which the younger end of W.G. Armstrong's design staff tried hard to overcome but failed. Ironically, had they adopted the original gun barrel recommendations proposed by Whitworth, they could have succeeded.

It was always the same. The validation of Whitworth's ideas habitually came long after the event. To prove the point and perhaps conclude the saga of his rifles: nowhere illustrates the 1859–63 situation better than the cross-examination of Whitworth during the 1868 Select Committee on Breech-loading Rifles.

The Chairman, Lt.-Col. H.C. Fletcher, asked Whitworth why some of the supposedly Whitworth rifles sent out to India after the Mutiny behaved differently from the others. 'I do not know', Whitworth replied. The man must have blushed with shame. Of course he knew: they were all manufactured by different methods; some by himself, some by Westley Richards and some by Enfield. Of the 8,000 rifles sent to India, 2,000 were made hexagonal bore by Whitworth, who also supplied the hexagonal ammunition; the rest were bored and rifled octagonally by Westley Richards and later made up by Enfield for use with cylindrical bullets. The Chairman asked, 'Is it not the case that Westley Richards uses octagonal rifling?' 'Yes', replied Joe, 'he had a licence from us. We did not wish to part with the (hexagonal) *mechanically fitting* bullet.' What he had really explained – though he couldn't bring himself to admit it – was that he did not wish to allow Westley Richards or Enfield or anyone else the use of his twist drills or drilling and broaching machines. That in fact was the truth: why the 2,000 Whitworths shot brilliantly, why the other 6,000 fouled up and were poor by comparison. The 2,000 were drilled from the solid, the rest were hammered split tubes 'made on the old principle' into which were forced *incorrectly* shaped bullets.

The next questioner was a Captain Mackinnon: 'Would you put fouling down to a fault in the barrel?' 'Yes', said Whitworth. 'We bore them out of the solid and we never correct our barrels – they do not need it. They are *all* right. We cannot detect any difference when they are fired accurately from the machine. That is the great advantage of this plan of manufacture and I think it is a great pity that it should not be followed up'. Captain Mackinnon continued, 'Would not the cost be considerable?' Whitworth was reassuring. 'Steel barrels to be made as perfectly as they could be made would probably cost about twenty-five shillings each'. 'To be bored out of the solid?' queried the incredulous Captain. 'Yes', confirmed Joe, 'I think we had two pounds each for the first that were made and there have been some made at thirty shillings each. I think they might now be made at about twenty-five shillings each if made in great numbers and of steel. Iron barrels cost from eighteen shillings downwards. I am waiting until the breech-loading system is settled and then I mean to try again'. 'Do you mean the mechanism of the breech?' – 'I mean until it is decided what kind of breech-loader is to be used', concluded Whitworth.

Every time he appeared before a Select Committee he had the feeling he was pushing against locked doors. Why on earth did these people reject the best ideas? Even his closest friends found it difficult to help him. Mostly they were either pacifists or anti-militarists. Had he been able to analyse his own situation he would have seen more clearly the decisions he needed to take: first to design and manufacture his own cartridges and secondly to decide the type of breech-loading system he required. These two aspects were fundamental to the future of both his small arms programme and his field artillery; more so in terms of naval guns. Gunnery officers wanted to avoid having to swing the gun barrel inwards everytime they were loaded.

Sadly, amid the clamour and disorder of the period, Whitworth lost sight of his objectives. It was wholly uncharacteristic. He fully realized that without properly designed ammunition his guns would never sell. And without a definitive decision as to the length and detail of his hexagonal bullet and cartridge case the type of breech he wanted could not be determined. Each problem was an integral part of the same decision. On the positive side, he was all set to manufacture the very best in rifle barrels; he was absolutely satisfied about that but in regard to the mass-manufacture of bullets and cartridges he knew it would be silly to risk going it alone. He couldn't help but feel outwitted when the War Office declined their support.

When Whitworth opened his Sackville Street factory his output then totalled five hundred rifle barrels per week. He was then faced with the question of having to make considerable investment, all of it risky and highly speculative if his gunmaking was to remain a private venture. The fact that the War Office did not make a decision until 1872 when the government finally approved the 0.450-in calibre Martini-Henry breech-loading rifle (it incorporated all Whitworth's principal features except the hexagonal *mechanical fitting* system) almost persuaded Whitworth then and there to drop the whole business. Nor is it hypothetical to theorize that had Sidney Herbert and Sir George Lewis, the War Ministers back in 1861, seized the opportunity – as they were twice urged to do by Prince Albert just prior to Albert's premature death – and had they promised to fund Whitworth's tooling-up of the Boxer cartridge alongside Whitworth's own hexagonal genre, history (according to the facts contained in the War Office archive) would have been very different. In the event, the War Office shied away leaving Whitworth to build a somewhat limited production plant capable of manufacturing just sufficient ammunition for his own guns. As he himself subsequently made clear, from 1862 onwards his future work concerned the development of heavy artillery rather than small arms.

The fact that the Enfield armoury, the Birmingham SA and the London SA companies were unable to bore from solid bar good quality rifle barrels prior to 1872, forced them all to order their ready-made barrels from either Firth's of Sheffield or Whitworth himself. The fact that the trade actually existed verified the commanding lead Whitworth had established. Even Thomas Greenwood, an ex-apprentice of Sir Peter Fairbairn and a personal friend to whom Whitworth had passed knowledge of his twist drill – but not the know-how attached to his secret drilling and broaching procedures – failed to design and build a successful barrel drilling machine. The same also applied to both sides during the American Civil War.

Evidence for this comes from Thomas Greenwood himself.[35] In 1871 he responded to a Russian invitation for the tooling-up of their *Berdan* rifle and for him to supply over 1,100 machine tools. The two armouries for which he contracted were at Tula, 100 miles south of Moscow and at Izhevsk, 700 miles east. For help, he wrote from St Petersburg to his expert assistant in America, James H. Burton. His letter, dated 19 March 1871, corroborated the fact that Whitworth's barrel machinery was not available for sale. 'They (the armoury at Tula) are to make 300 guns per day', he wrote, 'producing everything but barrels and forgings for the "shoe" which they will get (for some time at least) from the barrel makers ready bored'. And by way of authentication, they were, for a short time, supplied either by the Whitworth Rifle Co. or the Belgian state armoury at Liège (using Whitworth machines).

To summarize, it is perhaps true that had Whitworth 'not been so stubborn' (as some writers have suggested) and had he manufactured more orthodox rifled guns and gun barrels, he would have been a far wealthier man. On the other hand, had he not wholly pursued his *hexagonal mechanical fit* theories he would never have produced the world's most accurate weapon. In that sense, the 1860s were for him, paradoxical. They were also intensely galling. Practically all the gun principles he researched (short of his hexagonal rifling) were, over the years, endorsed by the War Office and saucily introduced by his competitors.

As General George Hay said to the *Mechanics Magazine*, May 1860, 'Mr Whitworth had solved the problem he undertook, namely, how to project to the best advantage, a given quantity of lead with a given quantity of gunpowder, and there is no gun in England at this moment which will fulfil that condition to the same extent as the Whitworth rifle'.

'With these facts' the magazine wrote, 'from the very highest authority, it will be impossible for the War Department to continue the manufacture of the Enfield arm to the exclusion of the Whitworth'. How wrong they were!

BIG GUN POLITICS, SUPREME ACCURACY AND FLUID-COMPRESSION STEEL

> The Whitworth 12-pounder has sent *shells* through iron, which until now no *shells* had effected; and his 70-pounder shells went through oak and iron each four inches thick; and to crown all, yesterday his 120-pounder sent *shells* even through the 'Warrior' itself!
>
> *The Times*, 26 September 1862

It is sometimes asked: if Whitworth's field guns were so much better than the others, why is it that today's military and naval historians seldom mention Whitworth by name?

The simple explanation can only be that the British government never approved the hexagonal system for use by the British armed forces. But if that sounds too smart an answer, it should also be explained that whenever they were used by a foreign government and *fired in anger*, the guns were rarely replenished with Whitworth's specially designed hexagonal *ammunition*: hence they invariably failed to equal their potential. The same thing also happened at home on the firing range: the officers in command repeatedly used the nearest to hand. The projectiles were unsuitable and a poor performance was inevitable. Whitworth himself tried to prevent this happening but without the endorsement of the government and without financial help for manufacturing his special shells the task was beyond him.

The primary reason here for such an explanation is to put right the injustice of excluding Whitworth from the historic record and to remedy the myths which have circulated ever since. One such myth credits William Armstrong with the invention of a special *built-up* barrel system (i.e. a series of shrink-fit tubes one on top of another) and the crediting of the German engineer, Krupp, with another – the solid *steel* barrel. Compounding these assertions it is still said that the world's governments in 1862 were limited to a simple gun choice (assuming, of course, they had finally rejected using solid cast-iron) between the Armstrong method and Krupp's steel. To assert this limitation of choice is to offend not just Whitworth but also a Captain A.T. Blakely, another reputable gun engineer who also manufactured guns using the so-called Armstrong system long before William Armstrong. Perhaps the following excerpt taken from a letter written by the Whitworth Company and published in the *Mechanics Magazine*, 2 December 1862, settles the controversy. The points made were later agreed by both the Woolwich and Armstrong camps as fair comment.

This correspondence arose from an agreement by Whitworth that he should experiment with a 120–pounder gun using his flat-fronted projectiles. The problem, explained Whitworth, was that his own Manchester works could not, at that time, make a 7-in gun. Would Woolwich Arsenal make it for him – leaving him to rifle the bore? All was agreed and eventually the gun proved a winner. The headlines needled Armstrong, so much so that he accused Whitworth, on 15 November 1862, of unlawfully using the Armstrong patented barrel design. Whitworth's staff replied as follows:

> . . . 7 December 1861, Mr Whitworth was informed that the War Office had sanctioned the manufacture at Woolwich of a seven inch gun . . . to be made under his own directions. Its breech was closed by a screw, of a kind *not*, we believe, previously used, except by ourselves in our 70-pounder guns. It is a triple screw, having three different diameters on a common axis; these take simultaneously into three internal screw threads.
>
> It is said that the gun was made on the coil principle and therefore Mr Whitworth was indebted to Sir William Armstrong. This obliges us to state what is known of the coil principle in this country before the Armstrong gun was introduced. Sir William's first gun was made, we believe, in 1855. His application for a patent for his gun was made in February 1857.
>
> Mr Whitworth, in the specification of his patent of December 1854 describes guns made of segments and hoops, which, he says, may be put on in a second series. The hoops used by Mr Whitworth were made of welded coiled iron. He may, therefore, be said to have anticipated Sir W. Armstrong in using the coil principle, though we fully admit that others preceded him. Armstrong also asked if Mr Whitworth claimed the invention of the solid bar for the inner tube? Certainly not; it was well known before. But it must be admitted, that while Sir William Armstrong has advocated the use of

> cylinders formed of welded coiled bars, Mr Whitworth has deprecated their use, and we have always used a solid bar of homogenous metal, bored out, for the inner tube of the guns made out at our works.
>
> We cannot close this letter without expressing our great regret that the success of Mr Whitworth's late trial appears to have called forth a feeling of animosity which we have no desire to reciprocate.

Five years prior to this controversy a similar dispute arose mainly because the ambitious needs of the War Council exceeded Whitworth's ability to deliver the engineering required. At the time he had built an experimental 3-pounder field gun which was quickly taken by the army authorities to their Shoeburyness gun butts for trial. The results were very impressive indeed; Lord Hardinge was unable to hide his elation. Both he and General Hay expressed the view that in their opinion Whitworth's polygonal rifling system was superior to any other scheme being tried out anywhere in the world. For them, the *'mechanical fit'* system was an absolute must and they proceeded to persuade Joe that he should concentrate upon much heavier artillery as soon as possible. Whitworth no doubt explained to them the practical difficulties which then prevented the accurate machining of an hexagonal bore especially in poor quality steel, whereupon Hardinge suggested that perhaps the Royal Foundry at Woolwich could cast *brass* blocks suitable for Whitworth to machine 24–pounder howitzer barrels. The Chief of Staff really was trying very hard and although he expressed certain reservations Joe agreed to do the work.

The royal castings duly arrived at the Chorlton Street works and Whitworth's machine men got to work. In really no time at all (it was then February 1857) – exactly eleven months after the generals' visit to the Fallowfield gallery – the brass howitzers were finished and the first gun sent to Shoeburyness for trial. With a charge of 2½ lb of powder and an elevation of 14° the gun duly despatched its elongated projectile very accurately to a distance of 3,240 yards. A vast number of gunnery experts had been invited to express an opinion and they were genuinely astonished by the results. A few weeks later, the second of the brass barrels was tested but it was first subjected to a rather spectacular piece of theatre in a very confined space on Whitworth's own estate at Fallowfield. The date was 26 June 1857 and the object was to demonstrate the effectiveness of hexagonal rifling and to do so visually in much the same way as Bessemer had done. That is by attaching coloured streamers to the surface of the shell; the ribbons would then fan out centrifugally once the shell was shot into the air, thus proving its spin and nose-first stability. It was probably flamboyant and unnecessary but it was the sort of confidence-building stunt Joe had to practise if both the press and the ministry were to be convinced.

Whitworth was in his element. His guests were also keen to try out his experimental shooting gallery. John Scott Russell followed by Henry Maudslay, William and Frederick Siemens, E.T. Bellhouse – plus another dozen mechanical engineers of national repute – all queued to prove, by each scoring a 'bull' time after time, that they themselves were the world's finest shots – by kind permission, of course, of Whitworth's hexagonally bored rifles. They were most impressed: 'Never seen anything like it', they said. Next came firing a steel bullet straight through a steel plate. Incredible! Whitworth then invited them to try out his whaling gun. It had a receding breech; rather too heavy to be held at the shoulder, but perfect when placed on a rest. 'It is designed to shoot flat-headed whales', he explained to a somewhat surprised audience, 'which until now . . . men had not dared to harpoon'. He had recently learned that an American captain had tried to shoot them with arrows but only three out of every forty shot were actually killed. 'I didn't like what was happening,' he said, 'so I designed this whaling gun – machine tool engineers desperately needed whale oil.'[36]

Finally his audience trooped back to the brass howitzer. Cast as a 24-pounder it had been rifled under Whitworth's personal supervision. The last shot he tried before tea was 96 lb in weight and was fired with eight ounces of powder. It was a long polygonal shell – its length over three and a half times its diameter – the one feature Whitworth insisted bestowed the shot with its characteristic stability. 'The gunnery experts don't like it,' he told his friends, 'because, they say, the *diameter* is too small relative to its weight to do sufficient damage.' Absurdly, the Horseguards seigniory argued that diameter had to do with explosive power. He then warned his guests to be on the look out for anti-Whitworth criticisms of his demand for small diameter shot, especially from senior army officers in London. And sure enough, eleven years later, when those present ultimately read the 1868 Select Committee Report they must have recalled Whitworth's warning. One example was ludicrous. A certain Colonel Halliday – a recognized War Office rifle expert – put a typically bizarre point of view when he was being questioned in Committee by Earl Spencer as to whether a 0.450 calibre bullet would merely injure a man rather than kill him. 'Having to look after a great number of wounded enemy', said Colonel Halliday, 'may be as great an inconvenience to one as looking after a great number of wounded men of your own.'

'You seem to fear that a .450 calibre bullet might pass through a man and not make a sufficient hole?' proffered the Earl.

'Yes,' the colonel replied. 'The orifice made by a small bullet, I think, is likely to be much less effective in doing little more than temporarily crippling a man.'[37]

Back at The Firs, however, on 26 June 1857, the engineers' memorable day out was coming to an end. Whitworth proposed that everyone should now avail themselves of the carriages waiting to take them back to Piccadilly, Manchester, where their colleague, William Fairbairn, was due to unveil a monument dedicated to James Watt, the engineer. He, Whitworth, was very sorry, he said, that there was 'not time to partake of the refreshments I have provided'. John Scott Russell did no more than clamber on top of the howitzer, face the assembled guests and proclaim: 'On behalf of everyone present may I express our thanks to Mr Whitworth for the lessons he has taught all of us today. It is our unanimous feeling, as members of the Institution of Mechanical Engineers, that we should thank our retiring Chairman for the manner in which he has discharged his duties in that office. The friends around me have asked me to say to him that his brother engineers owe him a deep debt of gratitude for having spent the whole course of his useful life in the advancement of their profession. We hope he will now persevere in what is now, for the first time in England, thanks to Mr Whitworth, a new engineering science. By depending upon his own experiments, he will furnish a new series of weapons worthy of the mechanical art in this century.' Scott Russell then stepped from his gun platform to loud cheers. Whitworth was obviously moved. He stood silently for a moment, emotionally distracted, not quite sure what to say, before quietly suggesting that perhaps Mr Scott Russell would kindly invite them all to see his, and Brunel's, magnificent ship, *The Great Eastern*. Russell needed no prompting. 'Delighted to afford the opportunity', he replied. 'I will communicate with the Institution and write you personally', hinting that the pre-launch banquet aboard the ship would probably be on 8 August 1857. 'But don't forget,' he reminded everyone, patting Whitworth's brass casting, 'this particular gun barrel will be going for trial at Ainsdale Sands, near Southport, next month. Watch out for the results.'[38]

When similar four inch guns were tested on the range at Shoeburyness the missiles were confidently shot into the sand butts. But at Ainsdale the firing range was open ended. Unfamiliar with the efficacy of the Whitworth system the gunnery team primed the brass gun with what they thought was a safe 2½ lb of powder and bang – the low elevation sent the 24-pounder shot a distance of nearly two miles before it hit the sand and richocheted to the right, hop-bouncing a further two miles before it crashed through the wall of a house north of a village called Waterloo. The thing rolled on to the carpet. Miraculously it did no greater damage than to demolish the window and frighten the life out of an astounded lady sat beside the hearth.[39]

The third 24-pounder brass howitzer machined by Whitworth was thus treated with much more respect when it too was sent for trial in November 1857. It shot both cleanly and accurately and if compared with any other gun on the basis of pound for pound of explosive, it out-distanced all competition. As Whitworth himself said when interviewed by the *Mechanics Magazine* in March 1860:

> The brass howitzer guns which I rifled in 1856 stood every proof to which they were subjected. I could not now improve upon them as muzzle-loading guns and I feel confident that they are as efficient as any rifled cannon of like calibre that have been made. In fact, of the rifled cannon, as of the rifled musket, constructed on the principles which I have adopted it may be said that practically, they must all shoot alike – a result which necessarily follows accurate measurement and good workmanship in making them.

Encouraged by the success of the brass howitzers, Lord Panmure, the new

Secretary of State for War in Palmerston's Cabinet, set in motion a works order at Woolwich Arsenal to provide Whitworth with three more castings. But this time they were to be cast-iron. Not only that; by comparison with the brass castings they were huge – big enough to make 32-pounder barrels. The Woolwich artillery people were very keen to try out cast-iron using the Whitworth system. Whitworth, however, wanted to use steel. He had already learned of the unconfirmed experiments carried out in both the United States and in France refuting the use of cast-iron 32-pounder barrels similar to those he was being asked to machine. While in the case of the brass howitzers he had been hesitant, this time he was positively apprehensive about the safety of the trials. Naturally he conveyed these misgivings to Lord Panmure but apparently the Woolwich experts were confident that all would be well and on that understanding Joe reluctantly went ahead with the machining of the gun barrels.[40]

Sadly the trials proved disastrous. Whitworth's long-held misgivings about the use of cast-iron for gun barrels were established beyond doubt. For very understandable reasons he had instructed his works foreman to take special care with the machining and when the barrels were finally inspected they were considered to be first class. And although the castings had already been allowed to weather for a long period they nonetheless lay idle for a further period until January 1859 before being taken by the army to the Kent coast for trial. The first two barrels burst into fragments as soon as they were fired. The effect was withering, not only for Woolwich's expertise but also for Whitworth's reputation. Fortunately, by June, the set-back had somewhat diminished in importance and the third gun, now experimentally upgraded to a 68-pounder, was taken to Portsmouth for its trials aboard HMS *Excellent* as a naval gun. An elongated shot was used making it the equivalent of an 80-pounder. Indeed because he had such massive confidence in his 'mechanical fit' system he personally had suggested using an overweight missile, albeit flat-fronted and made of hardened steel, mainly because it was to be aimed at 4-inch thick wrought-iron plates made up as a mock armour-plated frigate. The shot itself was a success and the missile went straight through the dummy ship's armour plating: but alas, the propelling charge was far too much for the cast-iron barrel and that too burst asunder.

It is a fair assumption that Joe had realized that the gun would burst like its two predecessors, so wanted to put everything into his one-off chance of going through the armour-plated frigate first time, therefore by using his enormously overweight shot he won the challenge but lost the gun and almost his reputation. As he himself afterwards stated in the *Mechanics Magazine*:

> The fact that the ordinary cast-iron service guns which I rifled as an experiment in 1858 proved too weak to be used as rifled pieces has been much dwelt upon; and it was perhaps an error of judgement to apply my system experimentally to cast-iron blocks without strengthening them. I may mention, however, that my flat-fronted shot went through the ship's 4-inch

> plate, the range being 450 yards. In no other instance, I believe, has a single shot been driven through a 4-inch plate.[41]

Clearly Joe regretted having agreed to the experiment in the first place but rightly celebrated the success of his flat-fronted shot. He would have been the first to agree, however, that he should have put far more thought into the whole business but apparently the bursting of cast-iron gun barrels at Woolwich was commonplace. As Sir J. Emerson Tennant wrote, almost in mitigation of Joe's uncharacteristic lapse from his normal attention to design principles:

> For guns of a large calibre, the necessity has not yet been dispensed with of strengthening the barrel by surrounding it with concentric hoops of the same metal – for the terrace on the façade of the Royal factory at Woolwich – which by a stroke of grim humour had acquired the name of 'the cemetery' . . . is thickly strewn with the carcasses of bursted cannon, of every known species of iron and of almost every attempted construction, torn into fantastic fragments by the untameable fury of gunpowder.[42]

Away from all thought of Woolwich Arsenal, the political pressures across Europe tended to emphasize Britain's indecisive ideas about its armoury while the erratic situation at Westminster continued to threaten Whitworth's own future quite subjectively. With equal irrationality the Government then decided to have a shoot-out between Armstrong and Whitworth at Shoeburyness, seven miles east of Southend, on 25 September 1862, the winner to take all! The Armstrong guns were well beaten yet the War Office recommended they be adopted for immediate service in the field. Obviously this was just as much a political decision as was General Peel's decision in July 1859 when he ignored Whitworth's astonishingly accurate 5.8 miles shot from one of his 12-pounders. The rest of the world could not believe it, yet the War Office merely stepped up its elaborate pretence not to notice as Whitworth's results became more and more incredible.

The Times newspaper and the *Mechanics Magazine* had reported the best 1859 results from Southport and Shoeburyness as 'truly astonishing'. Neither paper had expected the range nor the accuracy to be 'so devastatingly precise'. At an elevation of 35°, even two of Whitworth's 3-pounder shots reached five and a quarter miles, missing the target centre by a mere three yards! At two miles, the same gun actually hit the centre twice out of five shots.

At Southport, Whitworth's 12-pounder shots ended his 1859 contribution. At an elevation of five degrees his shells hit the target at a distance of one and a quarter miles: the target on this occasion less than two feet wide! Neither Armstrong nor the other gunmakers attained anything like these spectacular figures. Towards the end of the 1859 special trials for 12-pounder guns, the *Mechanics Magazine* reported: 'The target was placed one thousand yards off; it was six feet square and had a bull's-eye two feet square. Whitworth fired ten shots. The first two passed close over the mark; but each of the succeeding shots were sent through the middle part of the target, two of them leaving their holes in the bull's-eye.' The magazine concluded its report with an analysis of the heavier field artillery.[43]

The most interesting results occurred when the whole business of repeat gun trials resumed at Shoeburyness on 25 September 1862. In the presence of Cabinet ministers, the Iron Plate Committee and a large assembly of high-ranking army and naval officers, a *hybrid* 7-in calibre gun constructed by Armstrong, *its bore hexagonally rifled by Whitworth,* was placed on a platform at a distance of 600 yards from the Warrior target – a third longer than any distance in the past. The gun weighed just over 8 tons as against its competitor, the Horsfall smooth-bore cannon which weighed some 24 tons. The performance of the Whitworth rifling system was remarkable. The target was constructed to represent HMS *Warrior* – the hull being 4½-in thick iron plate backed by eighteen inches of teak plus a further five-eighths thick inner skin of metal – all supported on massive angle-irons.

The Times reported each shot – the first 'struck the left centre of the target within an inch almost of the white spot at which it was aimed. The second hexagonal mechanical fit projectile was 131 pounds (in weight). The effect of this shot astounded everyone. It went completely through everything, bursting apparently when it encountered the last resistance of the inner skin'. From Whitworth's point of view it was the perfect result. *The Times* then posed the all-important question: 'Are we at last to develop a really good gun which can send its shot through any armour, or is armour to gain the day? The Armstrong is out of the question. What is wanted is a wrought-iron gun – a muzzle-loader of course – capable of throwing a shot to smash any armour plate, or else such a flat-headed shell as Mr Whitworth uses, which can penetrate the plate and burst inside it.'[44]

In the event, Parliament suggested that the Board of Ordnance should learn from the *real thing.* Thus, over a period of three years they monitored very closely the American Civil War, Vice-Admiral Kuper's bombardment of Kagoshima on the coast of Japan and the battle of Duppel during the Schleswig-Holstein affair. At Kagoshima, the twenty-one Armstrong guns mounted in Kuper's ships did, in fact, suffer continuous problems which rendered their breech mechanisms unusable; but it was their inaccurate shooting in the end which proved to be the gun's nadir. As a result, in early 1864, all naval 7-in deck guns were replaced by 20 and 40-pounders and although neither gun was a particular success a modernized version of these 1870s 4.7-in 40-pounder breech-loading Armstrongs has remained the basic model from which contemporary naval deck guns have developed. As one Select Committee MP remarked during questions about Kagoshima, 'Whitworth's ideas may have been right after all.'

Fed up with events he couldn't influence – Whitworth was then long separated from his wife and was probably still living alone at The Firs – it was inevitable that he raked over the gun success his superior engineering expertise demanded and tried to overcome his wretchedness by restructuring his works management. He brought in exactly the kind of experts he required – yet he never took full advantage of the engineering design skills he had by then assembled. Had he done so, he would almost certainly have been in a position to offer the British Government more advanced guns when the Admiralty withdrew the failed Armstrong deck-batteries following the abortive naval bombardment of Kagoshima in August 1863. Had Whitworth, twelve months earlier, gone back to the drawing board, his unfinished 'rocker-block' breech mechanism (based as it was on his 1855 rifle patent) plus his *fluid compression* steel barrels and hydraulic recoil buffer arrangement, he would now be credited with an epoch-making world-first. In the event, he let it go! Instead, the French gun company, Schneider-Creusot, further developed not Krupp's ideas, but Whitworth's 1862 undeveloped (nonetheless exhibited) ideas and won for themselves world acclaim.

Whitworth was convinced as early as the mid-fifties that gun barrels, to be hard-wearing *and safe*, must be steel. He recognized that Armstrong's 'coiled-tubes' represented a significant advance in gun construction but what theoretical understanding there was concerning the elasticity of metal reinforced his own intuitive belief that he must make every effort to find a way of making a superior gun steel. Krupp produced a cast steel barrel but it was no better than steel made from carbonized iron bars. At the time neither Bessemer nor Siemens-Martin steel was good enough. Both were unsound because less than pure materials were used in their manufacture causing the heterogeneity of cast ingots. Hard spots, cavities and cooling veins proved major faults until the silica problem was solved. Much prime work was done at Middlesbrough and by Armstrong's own staff but from 1859 onwards surely it must be wrong for some modern steelmen to dismiss so contemptuously Whitworth's fluid-compressed steel which was so important *in its own period*. The two characteristics gunmakers wanted were strength and ductility – Whitworth's method provided both.

It was this lack of uniform solidity in the mass of the ingot which first pointed Whitworth towards his fluid compression – the idea of casting steel ingots under pressure. Again it was pure inspiration which prompted him to search for a hydraulics man with gun experience, and to make him his new managing director. J. Menassah Gledhill proved an exemplary choice. Indeed, it was he – according to Professor R.H. Tweddell – 'who first suggested forging the ingot after compression in a suitable hydraulic press'. More positively, Professor F.C. Lea (in January 1939) after careful consideration of what alternative technical skills existed during the 1858–69 period, concluded that Whitworth's mechanical methods were a legitimate advance and that his results assisted the actual development of a more advanced metallurgy a decade later. The fact that Whitworth used a hydraulic ram to press down on the molten metal and that he continued the pressure after the gas ceased to escape meant that he not only prevented fracture by internal stresses but alerted future metallurgists to possible remedies. Fluid compression also produced a metal that was compact and sound throughout its length.

Almost twenty-three years later, the most remarkable testimony to these developments came from members of the United States Navy Gun-Foundry Board. Following their visit to Whitworth's (Openshaw) factory in 1883 they reported:

> In speaking of the Whitworth establishment as unique and of that place as a revelation, reference is specially made to the subject of forging. As to the assorting of iron and the treatment of the metal in the furnaces, there is no intention to draw distinctions; but as to the treatment of the metal after casting, there can be no doubt of the superiority of the system adopted by Sir Joseph Whitworth over that of all the manufacturers *in the world*. . . . It is only from personal observation that the merits of the system can be fully appreciated. The Board witnessed the operation of casting, followed by that of *liquid-compression,* the enlargement of hoops, the drawing out of cylinders and the forging of a solid ingot. The unanimous opinion of the members is that the system of Sir Joseph Whitworth and Company surpasses all other methods of forging, and that it gives better promise than any other of securing that uniformity so indispensable in good gun metal.

This report has special significance. The Board were steel experts in their own right and having just returned from a tour of European steelmills they unanimously placed the Whitworth system in the leadership of the world. Even more notable, two of the visitors were gunmakers associated with the Midvale Steel Corporation plus William Sellers himself; the remaining two were American steelmasters.

The Board members were also interested in a paper on the measurement of gun barrels which Whitworth had presented to the Institution of Mechanical Engineers seventeen years earlier, on 31 July 1866. The paper arose from criticisms levelled against Whitworth's use of his new ductile *mild* steel for a 7-in bore, 70-pounder gun barrel. 'His steel guns are too soft,' the critics asserted. Stung by these uninformed censures, Whitworth invented an instrument for micro-measuring the bore-size of a gun barrel both before and after proving tests. Not only did his fluid compression mild steel guns wear less and suffer less distortion but he actually established that he could *reduce* the overall tonnage of metal and still retain the equivalent strength.

The American visitors were very impressed. What they could not fathom, however, was: 'why do British gun engineers pretentiously refuse to benefit from Whitworth's work?' Fifty years later, Professor Lea discussed the same point: 'Whitworth himself could not understand how army officials could delay adopting steel for guns and continued with the conversion of cast-iron guns. He showed conclusively that by using fluid-compressed steel, his own particular gun construction and the form of shot and hexagonal rifling which after considerable experimenting he adopted; if all four were combined the results obtained were far better than the guns then in service.'[45]

ARMS, MORALITY AND THE AMERICAN CIVIL WAR

At the time the American Gun Board were shown over the Whitworth factory they were intrigued by the part Whitworth had played in the American Civil War. The fact that he supplied both sides was well known because both the US government and the arms industry studied for ten years the battle performance of practically every single gun used during the war.

Whitworth's principal argument why he supplied both sides was his anxiety to prove his guns superior to all others under all conditions – especially when they were fired in anger. He realized he was open to attack, and sometimes he denied the charge; other times he tried to salve his conscience by adopting the sham reasoning that by supplying both sides he was being neutral. He enlisted Cobden's free-trade axiom 'ask no questions – apply no restrictions' but that also was pseudo-reasoning even if it was 'applied equally to both sides'. As an ethic of neutrality it was then – and still is – a bogus concept. The whole business defies Whitworth's usual logic but he was convinced that it was the right thing to do. The fact that Lord John Russell's Proclamation of Neutrality was never rigorously enforced enabled shipyards and gun-makers to quietly supply arms with impunity.[46]

As the war got under way so the situation in Manchester slowly deteriorated. Within twelve months of the American South opening fire on Fort Sumter, in April 1861, the cotton-starved Lancashire towns became riddled pauperdoms. Once their looms were silenced, cottonmen became ragmen. Within seven days of the start, President Lincoln declared a blockade on all ports thus sealing off the South but so far as cotton was concerned he had little need. Jefferson Davis, the Confederate President, had banned all cotton leaving the South anyway. He honestly believed his catch-phrase 'Cotton is King' and reasoned that if four million Lancastrians depended on cotton, Lord Palmerston would soon be forced to intervene on behalf of the Confederacy. It was a grave misconception and the South desperately needed currency to pay for guns and ships. Although Lancashire was brought to its knees with at least 250,000 families on five shillings per week relief (a flat loaf was fivepence and meatbone 'scrapes' were tuppence-ha'penny per spoon) it was then that Lord Derby launched his charity to eke out survival. But it was the American South which shifted its ground first. Jefferson Davis appealed for European credit before having to launch his 'cotton-bonds' in return for armaments and ships. Baring Bros. in Paris and London, Baron Rothschild in Vienna and Van Wart and Son in Birmingham all responded and made credits available to the Confederacy. At least European gunmakers were now assured of being paid.

Lancashire industrialists expressed divided loyalties, stretching Whitworth's moral dilemma to the limit. Whatever was done had to be done surreptitiously. Manchester people – aided by Americans living abroad – raised money (mainly for the Federal North) thus quite early, agents working for both sides placed orders with Whitworth for a variety of field and naval guns. Almost at the same time that the *Reynolds* newspaper demanded (29 September 1861): 'England must break the blockade or her millions will starve', the *New York Tribune* reported that the American ship *Bermuda* had beaten the blockade into Charleston Harbour and was carrying eighteen heavy field guns including two Whitworth 124–pounders. Shoulder rifles had been ordered from Birmingham as early as May 1861 and the first ten thousand from Whitworth's by August. Curiously, Armstrong also supplied both sides but much later. Officially, no Armstrong gun went from Woolwich Arsenal but certainly guns from his Elswick factory found their way to America whereupon a team of British army officers already in the United States were asked to observe their performance.

John Bright, now MP for Birmingham, led British opinion in support of Lincoln. 'The quickest way to get cotton through to Lancashire,' he said, 'was for the North to win the war.' 'Strengthen the blockading of the Confederate Southern States,' he added. Richard Cobden, his close ally in the House, didn't hold with blockades of any kind – for him, they were an offence against his beloved free trade. Instead, he wrote to his American friend, Senator Charles Sumner, Chairman of the Foreign Affairs Committee, 'It is the suffering and the misery that your blockade is bringing on the masses in Europe that turns men against you'. But as a polemic it had little impact; both North and South were convinced that the war wouldn't last, so they concentrated on purchasing the best armaments available in Europe. The argument, however, did have one compulsive aspect; the fiercer the debate became the more money the fundraisers collected; the more guns both Armstrong *and* Whitworth were contracted to supply. And though the South was running well ahead in the contribution stakes, Lincoln's War Department was well satisfied with the response confirmed by the American Ambassador in London.

Technically, Whitworth's gun draughtsmen derived a great deal of satisfaction from converting field guns for suitable mounting aboard Confederation warships. Their ability to cripple enemy ships at distances far beyond the fire power of the Union frigates spread fear from one side of the Atlantic to the other. As 1864 approached, armoured Confederate steam-assisted sailing ships (fitted with Whitworth guns) were considered the most deadly accurate batteries afloat yet their performance made little impact on the British Admiralty. John Brown, the Clydebank shipbuilder, estimated that one hundred and eleven British ships (totalling 60,000 gross tons) were purchased and armed by Confederate naval forces but that a mere fourteen carried Whitworth guns. Perhaps this was the reason for the Admiralty's lack of interest – who knows – but two of the most interesting of these ships, the CSS *Georgia* and the CSS *Shenandoah*, both proved the effectiveness of their Whitworth armaments.

Take first the CSS *Georgia*. This single-screw clipper (one funnel, 600 tons, 200 HP) was built by Denny Bros at Greenock under the name of SS *Japan*. It was launched on 10 January 1863 and purchased by Captain M.F. Maury by means of Confederate Cotton Certificates. Before leaving Scotland, 150 tons of steel plating was added to the hull, slowing the ship considerably. On arrival at Liverpool, further weight was added in the form of five Whitworth guns; two 100-pounders, two 24-pounders and one 32-pounder. They were mounted on specially constructed deck frames designed by Whitworth's staff. Within her first twelve months at sea – despite being overweight, slow and awkward – her gun accuracy alone had taken prizes at sea to the value of 406,000 dollars. Unfortunately, the *Georgia* consumed too much coal, Captain Maury returning her to Liverpool in May 1864. The Whitworth guns were taken off and Lord John Russell (because her presence offended British neutrality) ordered her back to sea, whereupon she sailed for Lisbon only to be captured by the US frigate *Niagara*, off the mouth of the River Tagus. Quite illegally, the US Navy then sailed her to Boston, USA, before her owner, Edward Bates, received £6,000 insurance via a British court.

The case of the *Shenandoah* was even more remarkable. Built in Scotland for the China trade it was a single-screw, 1,200 tons, three-masted sailing ship. Although only 250 HP, under ideal conditions using both steam and sail she could just about manage eleven knots. As she reached London, in October 1864, the Confederates bought her at the quayside and fitted eight Whitworth guns including four 7-in 68-pounders – the curious calibre suggests they were muzzle-loaders. Considering the ship was a mere 220 ft in length and went on to capture at least forty of Lincoln's supply ships, it speaks volumes for the small amount of ammunition she could carry and the fact that her gunners would have had to make each shot deliver something. In August 1865, the captain sailed her back to Liverpool not knowing that the war had been over almost four months. The guns were stripped out but what happened to them? It is strange that not one of Whitworth's naval conversions survived.

Naval operations during the Civil War were somewhat minor compared with the war on land. From Whitworth's point of view, while the Confederate experience of his muzzle-loading swing deck-guns taught him a great deal it was the reports he received from the major battles which proved the most valuable. Of the estimated one million shoulder rifles supplied from Britain, Whitworth supplied about 65,000 hexagonally rifled muskets, the majority being his 0.45 calibre muzzle-loading target rifles.[47] Most American commanders reserved these Whitworths for 'sharpshooting' (i.e. used by specially trained snipers at long range) and when they were used with the correct hexagonal ammunition they were brilliant but on most occasions, troops on both sides tended to make do with the nearest ammunition to hand. Not surprisingly, the guns quickly fouled up and performed badly.

Whitworth's field artillery suffered a similar experience until May 1863 when the Confederates began to make their own hexagonally mechanical fitting shot and shell at Richmond, Virginia. When fed with these more precisely made projectiles, the results were quite astonishing. Observers' reports from both armies – especially those from the North – confirmed not only the necessity for the correctly shaped shells but that they also made a strange whirring sound as they flew through the air. If mounted on the correct Manchester-made field carriage, the Whitworth results on the battlefield were identical to those obtained at Shoeburyness – they were excellent!

Three British artillery officers were sent from the British Military Attaché, Montreal, on 9 May 1862, into the battle areas to observe both the Armstrong and the Whitworth guns. The officers were led by a Captain Mahon RA who reported inaccurate firing due to the inexperience of the men involved. The fact that, at 2,000 yards, the targets suffered little damage they attributed to the *miscellany of shot* being used. Charles Knap, an American artillerist, giving evidence before a Senate Committee in 1864, said of the Whitworth: 'As a toy it is the most wonderful gun in the world, but it is not fit for actual service for it requires very delicate manipulation. . . . It is a perfect thing to show the state of the art, but for actual service, in my opinion, it is not worth carrying into the field.'

Although the gun most preferred by the United States was the American Parrott, the most passionately named guns on both sides – both for and against – were the Whitworth 12 and 32-pounders. Of the Manchester 2.75-in 12-pounder, General W.H.C. Whiting, Commander of the Southern forces around Wilmington, pleaded for a replacement of his lost 12–pounder Whitworth. 'The efforts of the enemy to stop our steamers are increasing . . . (our one Whitworth gun) . . . has saved our vessels and millions of money going to the Confederate States.'

The New York Tribune reported in September 1863, that one-third of the guns which laid Charleston in ruins were Whitworth 12 and 32-pounders. James Bulloch, chief negotiator in Britain on behalf of the Confederates, personally favoured the Whitworths. He sent eulogies about them back to his War Minister enclosing actual quotations from Whitworth for 32-pounders at £400 each and hollow shells priced at £35 per hundred. In Bulloch's opinion the deal was a bargain but expert judgement led to ministers recommending the purchase of the more orthodox Armstrongs from Elswick, or their acknowledged inferior copies, the Clay gun, made by the Mersey Steel and Iron Co.

The two best informed (Civil War) studies concerning field artillery quote artillery officers from both sides agonizing over the problems suffered by the Whitworths. The Newark Study particularly speculates that in the absence of contemporary explanations as to why the North in the main failed to use Whitworths, the principal reasons were (a) difficulty of supplying their uniquely shaped projectiles which demanded precision manufacture, and (b) instinctive human reluctance to accept a weapon so different from those in use for several centuries. They also quote two statements both of which are pertinent yet somewhat contradictory. The first, referring to the final campaign against Richmond, on 7 May 1864, is from a letter a Colonel Abbot wrote to Brigadier General Hunt declaring:

> I also think of taking two 12-pounder Whitworths along. They make excellent sharpshooting to dismount guns. *They are very light,* and may be of service for such special uses.

The second statement was written by General E.P. Alexander some years after the war. It relates to the guns used by McIntosh's Battalion after Gettysburg.

> One muzzle-loading six-pounder and six breech-loading twelve-pounder Whitworths were distributed through the army and often rendered valuable service by their great range and accuracy. They fired solid shot almost exclusively, but they were perfectly reliable and their projectiles never failed to fly in the most beautiful trajectory imaginable. Their breech-loading arrangements, however, often worked with difficulty and every one of the six was at some time disabled by breaking some of its parts but all were repaired again and kept in service. As a general field-piece its efficiency was impaired *by its weight and the very cumbrous English carriage on which it was mounted* and while few in the army may often be valuable, the United States three-inch rifle is much more generally serviceable with good ammunition.

Warren Ripley, an American authority on Whitworth guns, recalls General Gillmore's chief of artillery on Morris Island, Brigadier General John W. Turner, once remarking:

> There appeared to be much difficulty experienced at times in loading these guns by the projectile wedging when part way down. It could then be rammed home only by heavy blows of a handspike or by attaching a powerful purchase.
>
> They were very unsatisfactory in point of accuracy, shooting very wild, seldom hitting Fort Sumter at a distance of 3,980 yards. In comparison with the 8-inch Parrotts in the same battery, they fell far short in accuracy and subsequently one of them became disabled by the gun apparently sliding through the reinforcement to the rear. A displacement of nearly an inch took place closing the vent completely. The other, being considered unsafe after this, further use of it was discontinued.[48]

The search for a more positive understanding as to the potentiality of Whitworth's hexagonal system can now be progressed only if an identical gun and sufficient shot were to be made available using modern technology; but other than engineering inquisitiveness there seems little purpose. Of the twenty-two or twenty-three Whitworth (heavy) guns which are known to survive only three or four are still good enough to provide evidence of any kind. The most significant failure, however, both on the firing range at home and during the American Civil War was the failure by the Manchester Ordnance Co. to provide at the right price sufficient *mechanically fitting* ammunition. It was a monumental blunder and responsibility for it must be down to Whitworth himself. This deficiency of properly designed shot provided all the reasons and the instinctive caution for the military mind on this occasion to reject Whitworth's unorthodoxy.

Of course, the manufacture and the distribution of military weapons is at the forefront of any discussion concerning international politics and human behaviour. It is unquestionably a moral obligation for any government to defend its own people. But how it is done can be subject to a variation of values.

Ethically engineers and scientists should apply the same moral code when they make military weapons for their own government as they would when asked to supply the same weapons to countries overseas. Moral judgements at this level are not easy and there is ample evidence that Whitworth himself was torn between supplying foreign governments and his own conscience. Of necessity the overseas contracts he fulfilled must have been shorn of his famed rationality and managerial judgement and probably explains why he hesitated when it came to building his own full-sized ammunition plant. In the end he decided not to do so and it proved to be his biggest mistake as a gunmaker.

Much of Whitworth's own background was draped in a kind of Methodist-Quakerism, therefore somewhat pacifist, but the first inkling his friends ever received about his gunmaking followed a leaked whisper about the huge shooting gallery he had erected in among the fashionable estates of the south Manchester suburb, Fallowfield. It was as though he had invented war itself. But in justification of what he was doing he tried hard to convince his critics that his own weapons would not make war but would be a deterrent against war. At heart he was an instinctive objector against the obscenities of international aggression, yet when the time came for himself to make guns, no one more than he recognized this self-abuse of his own logic. But his defensive musings were now taking on an original twist. He reasoned that the superb fire power and deadly accuracy of his own guns would stop aggressors in their tracks – or so he believed. Innocence personified perhaps. Curiously he anticipated with such exactness the very same 'peace-through-fear' arguments the nuclear people use today. Jarringly, he was even brass-hatish enough after the launch of his 'Big Bertha' type guns to declare as far back as 1866:

> The greater the precision with which firearms may be used at long distances, and the more their powers of destruction are increased, the more reluctant will civilized nations become to use them against each other.[49]

Three years later at the age of sixty-five speaking to his own engineering institution, Whitworth again echoed the words he had written in an earlier report describing what was then his new heavier artillery:

> Were it not that the increased destructiveness of war must tend to shorten its duration and diminish its frequency – thus saving human life – the invention of my projectiles could hardly be justified; but believing in the *really pacific influence* of the most powerful means of defence these long projectiles I call the 'anti-war' shell.[50]

Again the words are remarkably perceptive of the 'weapons for peace' arguments. The Americans actually christened their nuclear bomb 'an anti-war bomb'. In fact it could only have been the '*believed pacific influence*' – to quote Whitworth's words about his own gun – which kept the world's nuclear physicists on a rational keel while they were designing the most powerful and terrifying holocaust imaginable. It couldn't be otherwise. World-class engineers and scientists, whatever language they speak, share a very fine scientific esperanto which spells out the finely tuned rationality of their thoughts. Whitworth himself, relatively speaking, must have been in exactly the same position in 1868 when he astounded the world by making a gun which could hurl a 310-pound projectile a distance of 6½ miles with terrifying accuracy. For mid-Victorian years it was a deadly piece of artillery. By then Whitworth knew that one of his guns could be made to lift 500 pounds or more high explosive a distance of 12 or 14 miles bang into the centre of a predetermined target. It was an awesome notion adding yet another string to the strategist's bow.

Joseph Whitworth very much valued the continuing friendship of John Bright MP, the peace campaigner, whose earlier strictures about his gun-making still rankled. But deep down he genuinely wanted to rationalize the work which had taken over his life. Nor was he alone among military engineers and naval architects in thinking aloud their own moral senses, especially during the times when international peace was threatened.

One such year was 1869 when a threatened Franco-Prussian conflagration aroused many Christian thinkers in the armament business to vent aloud their self-criticism and to confess shame at their wayward morality. Part of the reason for this sudden guilt was the fact that the Germans had nominated one of their own royal nationals for the Spanish throne. It must have been the flimsiest reason ever for the French in 1870 to declare war on Prussia. Interestingly, not only was it French engineers who expressed their anguish but because Louis-Napoleon had earlier recruited some British engineers including Whitworth and the naval architect, John Scott Russell, this critical self-questioning phase invaded even the Royal Society in London and the Institution of Mechanical Engineers.

John Scott Russell, for instance, was not only a close friend and adviser to Louis-Napoleon, he was also a consultant to both William Fairbairn and Whitworth in regard to their French contracts. At the time of the 1870 war Russell was working on a new Channel ferry-steamer and some other French naval work but like Whitworth he was not averse to speaking out about the immorality of war and the rôle played by military engineers. Writing in *MacMillan's Magazine* in 1871, Scott Russell posed the very question:

> Are all our ideas of modern civilization and progress mere delusive dreams? Are refinement, invention, wealth, science, all worthless as an end of human beings; and are war and conquest the only worthy direction and aim of manful human exertion? Is all machinery and engineering worthless, save the machinery and engineering of human slaughter? Is it possible that all this knowledge and all this divine gift and this profusion of human genius had no other aim and end but a mighty Armageddon of Christian nations, and that the moral of human modern civilization is expressed in these words – Behold with what skill modern Christians slay one another?[51]

Of course the cynics immediately point to the double standards practised by both Whitworth and J. Scott Russell. Both have designed and supplied military weapons – Scott Russell has even built battleships. But again, it is the eternal moral knife-edge upon which military engineers and scientists have always perched. If, in their own mind the one ameliorating question – am I making aggressive weapons – is softened by the belief that their own weapons are wholly defensive they feel comfortable. Add to that Whitworth's theory that potential aggressors fear retaliation by superior weapons, it almost objectively becomes incumbent upon engineers to design ever-more fearful deterrents.

By and large the British press, particularly *The Times* and *Examiner,* happily gave Whitworth every support and campaigned for the British government to adopt both his rifles and his artillery. But some Victorian writers and parliamentarians, still angered by the sheer criminality and gross mismanagement of the Crimean War, rather over-dramatically lumped the likes of Whitworth with the more sinister 'merchants of death'. In Joe's case his weapons were not used in the Crimea and the criticism was somehow unfair. At that time, being the experimentalist gunmaker he was, Joe Whitworth never really justified such a sibilant Shavian image, let alone an 'arms king' title. And in all honesty, in the beginning neither did William Armstrong, his long-time gun adversary. Of course they both became extremely wealthy. Whitworth made most of his money as a toolmaker; little or nothing out of guns. Armstrong, a lawyer in the beginning, later made a fortune, first from artillery and then from rebuilding Britain's naval power.

But discussion about these matters was not confined to engineers and scholars. Manchester itself reverberated with a new engineering and scientific moralism. Ever alive to the reputation of his own church, the Cross Street Chapel, the Revd William Gaskell led the crusade. William Fairbairn and James P. Joule, two of Manchester's immortals in the history of science, together with a number of other leading engineers; all were active members of the Cross Street Chapel and frequently referred to the question of science and morality. It was trenchant debate at its best.[52]

Following Whitworth's 'weapons for peace' arguments, James Joule spoke out forcefully against the use of bogus theories and asserted there was no conflict between his (Joule's) own scientific contribution and his Christian belief. Nor did he see why others should experience difficulty either. 'Science can be misused', he argued, 'as well as being properly applied.' Referring to 'The improvement of the art of war and of implements for mutual destruction', he clearly pointed the finger at Whitworth and others: 'I know there are those who think that these improvements will tend to put an end to war by making it more destructive. I cannot think that such an opinion is based on common sense. I believe war will not only be more destructive but be carried on with greater ferocity.'

James Joule concluded his reproach with devastating clarity: 'In reference to this subject we must deplore the prostitution of science for the aggrandizement of individuals and nations, the result being that the weaker is destroyed and the stronger race is established on its ruins.'[53]

CHAPTER TEN

Infidelity, Education and Whitworth's Legacy

At the age of fifty-three, Whitworth's intensely active life was making him fretful. Unable to ride strictures of any kind, whether from the press or from colleagues, he became quarrelsome. He told friends he was not well – as indeed he wasn't. The doctor prescribed rest but it was like telling a compulsive gambler not to take chances. The year 1856 was unremitting and among those closest to him probably Fanny, his wife, had taken the brunt.

The Whitworths had been married for thirty-one years. In reality, for the last ten, Joe had been married to the job rather than Fanny. He had travelled a great deal and saw very little of either Fanny or The Firs, his home. By 1856 they were virtual strangers. Joe had grown with his engineering accomplishments – he was by then an international celebrity – but by comparison, Fanny had been left to diminish in size and no doubt resented her declining rôle in the eyes of her once cavalier canal-boat lover. Now they were both desperately lonely, quite separate people living under the same roof – albeit a very spacious roof – both desperately in search of companionship and affection; he looking towards different, younger crinolines while she was probably left to find her solace straight from the bottle.

The Firs, known locally as the *big* house at the end of the long drive, with its own fifty-two acre estate and farm, never suited Fanny's personality. It was the epitome of a successful industrialist rather than the natural habitat of a simple canal lass. The Firs was her rightful home – of course it was – but it never felt like home. She didn't fit into this grand scale nor did she see the necessity for such *entretenir* masquerading – it wasn't her style. Frankly, the distance between Fanny and Joe daily grew wider, though it is doubtful, looking back, whether she ever had the self-confidence and drive to fly in the face of Joe and do things her way. Had she done so, very probably he would have admired her much more. Like most Victorian engineers, Joe failed in romanticism. He liked people who delivered that which they were committed to deliver. Engineering was notoriously a tough industry where traditionally an engineer always had to deliver or get out – and Joe was no exception – he expected the same rules to apply to all things including his home life.

For us, much of the Whitworths' life together must be conjecture. A few intriguing strands, however, when pieced together do provide a colourful picture. For example, the final breakdown of their marriage and Fanny's departure from The Firs can be dated, if the simple coincidence of events is acceptable as evidence. Prior to Christmas 1856, invitations sent by the Mayor, Sir James Watts, were addressed to Mr and Mrs Whitworth although the local newspaper, October 1856, reported Joe without Fanny both for the inauguration of the Free Trade Hall and the opening of St Mary's Hospital in Quay Street, Manchester. Later on, mid-1857, the Mayor's invitation list meaningfully omitted Fanny's name completely.[1]

The significance of these invitations is strengthened when Whitworth was invited by HRH Prince Albert to join himself and the Queen at Osborne House, Isle of Wight, from 16 December 1856. Albert, personally, wanted to try out Whitworth's latest rifles and asked him to bring one or two down to the estate for a shoot. Joe had been requested by the Prince's private secretary to keep him informed as to when his 0.45 rifled musket would be sufficiently perfected. This he had done whereupon the Prince responded the following day. Whitworth also informed Lord Panmure, the War Minister, who indicated that he would await the New Year before travelling to Manchester. In regard to the arrangements at Osborne House, however, the Queen had noted these events in her journal but had the Royal Visitors Book at Osborne also been available it would have confirmed that Fanny did not accompany her husband. Had their marriage survived reasonably intact it is inconceivable that Fanny would not have been delighted to accept this particular Royal invitation and would have travelled with Joe to the Isle of Wight.

Two other happenings seemed to verify that Fanny finally departed The Firs about the same time Joe left for Osborne House. If it was the case that she preferred to stay with her sister at Tarvin, Cheshire, rather than remain at Fallowfield, it was fitting she should move in with her sister at least a week before Christmas and secondly, when Major General Charles Grey, the Prince's secretary, contacted Whitworth concerning the opening by Prince Albert of the Art Treasures Exhibition at Old Trafford on 5 May 1857, his arrangements assumed Whitworth to be spouseless.

A good indication of the wretched unhappiness which gripped The Firs that particular New Year was Joe's own despairing cry; one of almost desperation. As soon as he got back from Osborne three days before Christmas he immediately sent a message to his close friend, George Wallis – the man with whom he had travelled to the United States in 1853. In his message, dated 21 December 1856, Joe appealed to his friend to join him:

> I intend to be present at your lecture tomorrow evening and I shall be very glad if you will return with me and take a bed. For some time past I have been unwell but I am now improving.
>
> Yours *very* truly – Joseph Whitworth

It wouldn't have been easy for him to have done that. The note describes graphically a man in search of someone in whom he can confide. Its immediacy suggests that Whitworth was realizing for the first time that his thirty-year married partnership had just ended and that he needed sympathy and companionship. The truth is that 1856 had brought to a critical pitch the long-standing differences between Fanny and himself. In the beginning they had thrived on a threadbare existence: absolute frugality. Fanny understood that and could cope; but now wealth and cleverness drove them apart.

The Firs had lots of rooms and plenty of space. Had Joe and his wife wished they could have lived separate lives in the same house but the irritants were too great. Nor could they avoid guests staying with them. In their situation some sort of pleasant hospitality was frequently required, an atmosphere seldom possible when harmony between the hosts has long departed.

The experimental shooting gallery occupied much of Whitworth's time. Now that the autumn leaves were gone it was just visible from the new wing of the house. Not that cook or the housemaids needed reminding: the coming and going of gunsmiths and army officers kept them fully occupied. Westley Richards and Edwin Chadwick were favourite regulars. In fact all the guests found The Firs an interesting place and welcomed Joe's invitations. What with measuring machines and working models of various things scattered throughout the house, one or other occasionally brought to the table, dinner was always an unusual experience. But Fanny was never comfortable with any of it; neither did she contribute conversationally. At the age of fifty-six – she being almost three years older than Joe – it was probably she who decided to quit. Mercifully, they departed their separate ways without a great deal of acrimony.

There is no evidence of either abuse or bad temper which is surprising considering that, unknown to the other, each had a younger paramour waiting in the wings. In Fanny's case, when Joe first became satisfied that his shooting gallery was ready to go ahead in his absence, he asked his senior works foreman, James Booth, to join Westley Richards at The Firs to supervise the proceedings; Westley to look after the guns while James Booth would see to the engineering aspects. Both were widowers. James Booth had worked for Whitworth since he was twenty-nine years old. Five years younger than Fanny, he thoroughly enjoyed – when given the chance – her more mature comeliness and didn't complain when Joe, his employer, requested that he stay over at The Firs more frequently once the gun trials started.

Some time later, 1861 in fact, Whitworth was still in the process of reorganizing his works management team but failed to recognize the sterling service James Booth (sometimes called John) had given him for the past twenty-six years. One imagines Whitworth was still unaware of Fanny's secret flirtation with his Mr Booth although somewhat suspiciously James, very soon after the team changes, quit the factory and probably moved in with Fanny, by then living at Forest House, Delamere, Cheshire, a nicely situated country residence less than six miles from her sisters and family at Tarvin. James Booth, his loyalty forever unswerving, exactly as he had behaved while in Joe's employ, dedicated the same caring attention to Fanny until the day she died, 28 October 1870. Sadly, she had to end her life by having that Victorian know-all of doctor's aphorisms, *diseased liver*, pegged to her character. As if by way of scorn, less than twelve months prior to her death (some fourteen years after she and Joe had separated) she became the first Lady Whitworth: not exactly an act of reward but by virtue of the fact that Joe was knighted well ahead of the new laws permitting divorce.

But what of Fanny's life after 1856 when she eventually departed The Firs? It is as much a question concerning Joe's character as hers. What provision did he make? Unlike most separated wives Fanny suffered no financial problems. Incompatibility usually meant a discordant relationship stretching over many years, the outgoing partner without resources hanging on for the best settlement. It was not so in Fanny's case. Mr Aston, Whitworth's personal solicitor and company adviser, seems to have made generous arrangements. Within two years of leaving The Firs, Fanny had settled in her new home, Forest House, happily provided with a reasonable income. And considering that any financial settlement in Victorian times was largely dependent upon male generosity, it is fair to suggest that Whitworth, on this occasion, exhibited an unselfish nobleness not usually acknowledged either by his friends or his obituarists.

But before going on to discuss Whitworth's own much longer but still secretive affair with Mary Louisa Orrell, it is perhaps relevant here to describe the years prior to Fanny and himself moving out to The Firs in 1845 or 1846. For some eight years previously they had lived two miles nearer town at 62 Upper Brook Street.

These houses were fine, square-built 'town houses' of red brick with imposing front doors up a few steps. They were built about 1812. Some twenty-odd years later when the Whitworths moved in, Upper Brook Street was a smart, pleasant road approaching Manchester from the south. It was reminiscent of the days when 'private cabs with spruce coachmen on their boxes took up their owners and drove them with a show of dignity to their offices'.[2]

The 1841 Census however casts an intriguing insight as to the Whitworth household at the time. Fanny Whitworth is absent from the list. Resident with Joseph was Petsey Lewis, a twenty-year-old servant and Martha Lightfoot, a twenty-year-old milliner. The same applies to the 1851 Census when at The Firs, only two servants were listed, neither Joe nor Fanny being included. The explanation of course may be perfectly simple. In 1851 we know that Joe was in London attending the Great Exhibition and it would have been quite feasible that when he was away from home Fanny preferred to stay with her sisters at Tarvin.

Interestingly, the writer Jane Carlyle together with her companion visited the Whitworths at The Firs in 1846. She confirmed she had spent the day at his house in the country; meaning no doubt his new estate amid the green fields of Fallowfield, a leafy Manchester district within the town boundary.[3] She went there by cab from Carlton Terrace, Greenheys, yet according to an 1830 map the house she visited was in fact, a good-sized farmstead named Ardern's Place.

The cab would have reached the estate by passing a small house (spelled at that time The *Firrs*) later to become The Firs Lodge. When she got there, oddly enough, she was greeted not by Fanny Whitworth and her husband but by Joe and the Manchester Town Clerk, James Heron. It was an interesting but somewhat different foursome for lunch than she had expected.

Within six months of moving to his new house Whitworth had engaged the architect Edward Walters to design and build what was tantamount to an entirely new house, leaving very little of the old property, Ardern's Place, standing. The work was finished in 1850 and Whitworth named it The Firs.[4] At the same time he acquired the adjacent farmland which altogether made an attractive estate of some fifty-two acres. The architect had utilized to the best advantage the natural contours of the site and built what one builders' journal has described as 'an extremely interesting building'. Until 1991 it was the official residence of the Vice-Chancellor of the University of Manchester, and as one of its famous post-Scott tenants, Sir W. Mansfield Cooper, remarked:

> The house was leased [1882] to Mr. C.P. Scott [the editor of the *Manchester Guardian*] . . . thus it could tell many an intriguing story of the great days of Liberalism in England.[5]

Indeed it could! Long before then, many of the country's leading radicals frequently gathered round Whitworth's table at The Firs for an after-supper nightcap, not just to celebrate in later years the Reform Bill of 1867, but for the same MPs who earlier had demolished Robert Lowe's anti-reform arguments, to now refurbish their case for when the time came to again kill his fresh opposition to engineering education; and to the provision of better elementary education for working people. Men like John Bright and William E. Forster, the Minister of Education, were much beloved visitors to the house along with Henry Cole and T.H. Huxley, all of whom happily responded to Whitworth's call for more effort to be put into the demand for technical education.

Naturally, having himself built the house, the architect Edward Walters, especially during the early years, remained a firm family friend and a frequent guest. But much more than that, he became a considerable influence encouraging Whitworth to broaden his already wide political and educational interests. As an architect he had been sent (in March 1832) to Constantinople, the entrance to the Black Sea, to supervise the building of a small arms factory. His friend, W.H. Barlow, was already there working for Maudslay, laying down a railway system. While the two friends were in Turkey, Richard Cobden arrived on holiday but was taken ill. Edward Walters looked after him, in return for which Cobden persuaded his Manchester business friends to commission Walters for the design of their new buildings; thus his contribution was probably the most outstanding of the Victorian period. The literary journal, *The Critic*, summed it up, in December 1871, when its editorial declared:

> To Mr Walters, we, indeed Manchester, owes a debt of gratitude for the wonderful change which he wrought in the appearance of the town. The time was ripe for such a revolution in artistic thought.

This last point was no doubt referring to the fact that it was Edward Walters who introduced the Italian Renaissance style to Manchester and did so brilliantly. His Manchester and Salford Bank – on the corner of York Street and Mosley Street – was of beautiful Italianate design, the best of Walters's pure palazzo tradition; although it was his Free Trade Hall in 1856 which became his most adored edifice possibly because of its political connotations. *The Critic* asked his friend, C.H. Benson, what he thought of Walters's work. 'That of a genius', he replied, listing all the richly carved stonework which made Manchester's cotton warehouses worthy of Milanese opera.

Of earlier times at The Firs – the years Fanny and Joe were together until 1856 – life at the house was largely dominated by Joe's shooting gallery and the local consequences brought about by the Crimean War. Edward Walters was still a regular guest along with the many other outstanding Liberals for whom Whitworth's two cooks, Mary Charles and Rebecca Lee, had to cook regularly in addition to their usual culinary feats. Two years previously, Cobden and Bright had persuaded Walters and Whitworth to invest in their newspaper, *The Morning Star*, reputedly to give the 'Manchester School' theorists a daily voice. It promised to be an imaginative newspaper with a good editorial staff, but its base was too narrow and in late 1856 it folded prematurely. From among the Whitworth coterie, Walters particularly was least able to afford the considerable sums they all had invested and lost. Whitworth, no doubt, helped him out.

Since 1847, Whitworth had been determined to acquire a country estate well away from Manchester, particularly an estate near Darley Dale, deep into the Derbyshire countryside between Manchester and Derby. Why he favoured Darley Dale is not clear but after two years negotiations, come 1856, he finally secured the Stancliffe estate at a cost of £33,850 (between £1.5m and £2.0m at today's values).[6] Edward Walters was again very interested in wanting to modify this new baronial residence in line with Joseph's vision[7], but with extraordinary perception Whitworth drew away his friend and persuaded him to again team up with W.H. Barlow with the idea of persuading the Midland Railway Co. to divert their proposed Ambergate to Manchester track through the Derbyshire Dales. They succeeded and, by 1860, Walters had designed and built (in Derbyshire stone) at least eight stations alongside the Midland's track including Darley Dale itself – the whole thing (especially Buxton) a piece of railway construction still revered by railway enthusiasts everywhere.

From the beginning, Whitworth had very clear ideas what he expected of a country estate. But it was his confidence in being able to envisage a finished concept, even when the initial material looked poor – as it did at Stancliffe – that again proved Whitworth's instinctive talent as a visualizer. It gave Stancliffe Hall and its grounds an intriguing dimension throughout its development. Who but Whitworth would have *seen* a tree-lined suntrap emerging from a part-disused quarry? Who but Whitworth would have visualized that within twenty years of his starting from chaste banks of solid rock *The World* magazine would describe his dream in such laudable terms? In June 1877, the magazine wrote:

> When Whitworth first came to Stancliffe, the house stood on bare hillside, without attractions other than magnificent scenery, a plentitude – even to super abundance of air, and with stone quarry. Keenly appreciative of the advantage of a bracing atmosphere, he avoided the comparative stuffiness of the village and chose a dwelling place open to the four winds of heaven. Probably his abode was bleak enough at first; but year by year thought, industry and money combined have transformed the rugged hillside, scarred and rent by the quarrymen, into one of the most beautiful landscape gardens in England. Vast cavities have been taken advantage of in the interest of 'the picturesque'; hollows have been filled up, mounds have been raised, and ravines scooped out, that the eye may ever find a charming foreground for a landscape picture by wooded Derbyshire hills, and the purple moorland. Shrubs, indigenous and exotic, have been planted in thousands and surprise the eye by their luxuriant growth in the most unlikely spots. The rocks and precipices are clothed with greenery of every conceivable shade and form; and many have cunningly constructed wind walls designed with that happiest of arts which represents accident.[8]

With ever greater veneration, *The Gardeners' Chronicle* fleshed out this phenomenal transformation still further. Astonishingly before his time, Whitworth blasted holes in the rock to enable him to transplant mature trees. He actually succeeded. *The Chronicle* describes the result of his work thus:

> The main roads are bordered with a wide shrubbery border filled with a profusion of choice Rhododendrons, Azaleas and other flowering trees and shrubs, intermixed with spiry Conifers, bronzy Retinosporas and elegant Birches. The rocks themselves are light fawn, verging into rich chestnut-brown and are carpeted with Pernettyas and Vacciniums. Of the larger plants occupying pockets on the rocks are glorious masses of white and yellow Brooms, gorgeous bushes of Gorse, thickets of Rhododendron, Daphnes and Hollies. Conifers are everywhere, mostly flame-like or pyramidal in outline.[9]

Quite clearly, judging by these later reports, the estate, even during the early 1860s, was a magnificent show of trees and bushes. The hard work, albeit very expensive work, put in by Whitworth and his manager, Joseph Dawson, was at last beginning to attract the gardeners' press. Since 1853, in fact, Whitworth had running through his mind various schemes as to how he would root fully grown trees in rock. Transplanting them in huge cast-iron tubs was one idea. His mind was continually racing away: maybe because at this time it was a sad and difficult period for him when he and his first wife, Fanny, were continually at loggerheads, just before they finally separated in 1856; the year the Darley estate became his own. In all probability she played no part in any of it, nor seemingly, did she ever set foot inside the lodge gates. What actually motivated Whitworth, what particular objective gave him the enthusiasm to keep working at the estate for some eighteen years or more is an open question. What is more positive, perhaps; the day Mary Louisa became mistress of Stancliffe, in April 1871, the whole scheme began to look more definite – the railway connections more regular – although even in middle age Whitworth still thought little of riding horseback (together with one of his grooms, either Tom Davies or Tom Bateman) the forty-odd extremely hilly miles between The Firs and the Stancliffe estate.

One other discernible aspect threaded its way through these distinctive years at Stancliffe: it was the definitive, though gradualist, influence exerted on Whitworth's life by Mary, his new wife. As already mentioned they shared a common interest in educational issues and as we shall learn shortly, Whitworth had it in mind to hand over Stancliffe to the state for use as a residential college and retirement home for professors of engineering. And as these matters were seriously discussed in London with both architects and the Ministry of Arts and Science from 1867 onwards, it is inconceivable that Mary was not familiar with Joe's ideas.

Indeed, being the person she was – daughter of Daniel Broadhurst, a very active Liberal and the Manchester City Treasurer; herself a somewhat mature Mayoress of Stockport at eighteen years of age; accepted politically on equal terms with all Whitworth's chums, Fairbairn, Edward Tootal, Chadwick, John Bright, plus men like Edward Walters. She knew them all, some possibly before Whitworth. It is difficult under these circumstances not to suspect that had Joe proposed a college for the education of women all would have been well; but because he saw the whole thing in terms of engineering, she, possibly, became an inhibiting influence. Nor was she entirely detached, a decade later, when her husband (they were then well married) let it be known that he had abandoned his plans for the rebuilding of the Stancliffe Hall. It was again *The World* magazine which reported in 1877:

> The models for the great house that was to be are now consigned to the lumber-room, the childless master of the garden on the hill is determined to rest content with the pretty house he has already.[10]

The fact that Mary Louisa had become a widow so young but did not remarry for twenty-two years is a clue to the kind of woman she was; it is also an indicator of the kind of companionship she preferred. She reputedly circulated among talented, articulate, radical thinkers including much older women like Elizabeth Gaskell. Though Mary herself was probably much less talented, she was, nonetheless, as forthright in her advocacy of education for women and the feminist cause as Elizabeth Gaskell. Mary loved high fashion clothes and 'social gossip' – presumably the opposite in taste to Whitworth's first wife – but her somewhat haughty, some said aloof, behaviour as the so-called mistress of Stancliffe was little different from other middle-class Liberal progressives and pro-education campaigners during the Victorian period.

In reality Mary Louisa was a prodigy of a brilliant political pot-pourri. Joe's daydreams went back to the late 1840s over at Fairbairn's place, The Polygon. The Fairbairns' wine and cheese parties glittered internationally; Unitarian intellects vied with 'one-nation' Tories from Peel to Disraeli; Liberals from Bright to Gladstone, from the Potters to the Heywoods, plus of course the brightest jewel of all in Whitworth's eye, the youngest of the Tootals – Mary Louisa herself. Their relationship quivered from the start.

The puzzle: why did Mary Louisa wait a decade or more for Whitworth, not knowing whether he was going to outlive Fanny? It was, in the 1860s, an absorbing, yet frequently insoluble Victorian dilemma. 'Till death do us part' meant what it said. Mary and Joe could never marry nor (even *if* Mary was an expert gold-digger) could they satisfactorily settle the question of inheritance as long as Fanny existed as Joe's wife. As things turned out, Joe outlived Fanny by seventeen years. Mary, on the other hand, had already remained an unmarried widow for twenty-one years despite the almost certain fact that she was pursued by admirers from the first day she became widowed. Recognized as an attractive habituée among the young Liberal literati; married at the age of eighteen into one of Stockport's wealthiest cotton families, yet here she was, hanging on for a man who was neither a Don Juan nor a scintillating conversationalist. Articulate – yes, and wealthy – but twenty-three years older than herself and married into the bargain. Why then, did she wait? What sort of pre-marriage relationship did they enjoy?

Victorian writers often wrote of nouveau industrial aristocrats – the purveyors of a new world – and certainly Whitworth during the 1860s would be considered top of such a list. Just as young graduates of today attach glamour and prestige to scientific discovery so Mary and her contemporaries would have attached similar prestige to being seen with the likes of Whitworth – an internationally known engineer. Although it would, perhaps, be stretching it too far to make him a 'scientific idol' – for one thing he didn't look the part – nevertheless, the ushering in of a new engineering culture which so excited the Victorian intelligentsia was part of Whitworth's attraction.

From 1857 onwards, Joe led an extremely active life, frequently travelling to London and occasionally to the continent. He could afford the luxuries sufficient to persuade Mary along. Palpably, his new status, that of being a wifeless celibate, was there to exploit. It would be unreal not to assume that they both enjoyed The Firs. Mary's visits assisted Joe to puff up his ego, thinking to himself that his Firs estate was so much superior to Throstle Grove House, the family mansion Mary had enjoyed for two years until the premature death of her husband, Alfred Orrell. Joe, more than anything, wanted her to think she was going up in the world. He would have felt dreadfully degraded had she ever found out that Throstle Grove House and the Orrell family were deep-rooted parts of his own ragged-trousered boyhood. Such knowledge he kept very secret. How he had hated the deferential servility of it all. The Orrells were to him (as a boy) the grand master and mistress of the big house. God forbid that Mary should ever find out! 'Old man' Orrell, Mary's late father-in-law, had tyrannized the poverty-stricken district in which Joe had been brought up. Joe's own father, in fact, had good reason to remember Mary's former in-laws. The 'old man' was a strict disciplinarian who preferred to either cane or whip his cotton mill employees rather than 'dock' their wages. He was once seen caning his own son, Alfred – Mary's late husband – in the mill yard. It can be safely assumed that whatever other secrets the couple shared, Joe's boyhood was not one of them![11]

Mary Louisa's own parents were very different. They were both soft, warm-hearted people and gave Whitworth much pleasure. Indeed, it was very sad news when, on his return from London in April 1859 Mary told him that her father had died. As City Treasurer, her father had been of tremendous help to Whitworth but Joe's memory of him was the simple sincerity of their friendship particularly in the company of Mary's mother, still very much an unaffected member of the Tootal family. Joe got on with them all very well, especially Edward Tootal, Mary's favourite uncle and Whitworth's earliest friend from among Manchester's business community.

But it was Henry Tootal Broadhurst, Mary's elder brother, who impressed Whitworth most. Once Henry became the senior partner in the family firm, Tootal Broadhurst Lee, he worked hard making it the leading cotton giant of its day. His ideas remained identical with those of Whitworth; he deeply admired the engineer's campaign for the promotion of technical education. On the day of their father's funeral Whitworth noticed Henry's son, the seven-year-old Edward, sitting quietly observing the family scene. He got into conversation; the boy was fascinated. And as Edward grew older he too became a devotee of Whitworth. As the Chairman of Tootal Broadhurst Lee he introduced discounted shareholdings for the benefit of his employees. This, in essence, really was Whitworth's teaching, as indeed was the effort he put in, ten or fifteen years after Whitworth's death, when he, Edward, persuaded Winston Churchill to contest Oldham, Lancashire, as a free-trade Liberal and to fight the seat on a pure Cobden-Bright reformist ticket. Whitworth would have loved it!

After her father's death, Mary spent more time with her mother at Ardwick Place; round the corner from the Fairbairns. She also filled in time by entertaining her literary friends at her cottage in Grasmere. For Whitworth, life wasn't quite so leisurely. As President of the Mechanical Engineers, anxious to promote his gun interests and to spend as much time as he could with Henry Cole and company in London perfecting his various schemes for the advancement of technical education, he was absent from The Firs and from Mary (and also his works) for considerable periods. In reverse, of course, he would frequently invite his London friends to stay with him at The Firs and though the decade was event-packed all the way through, the last two years were punctuated by two particular events which overshadowed all others. The first happened on the first day of November, 1869; he and William Fairbairn received their baronetcies together. The second event – the sad death of Joe's estranged wife, Fanny – occurred twelve months later, on 28 October 1870; but just how he and Mary received the news – perhaps it is not too scurrilous a thought to guess that they received it with some relief.

Less than six months after the death of Fanny, in fact, the sixty-eight-year-old baronet married Mary Louisa at St James Church, Piccadilly, London, on 12 April 1871. Despite the bride's youth, being twenty-six years younger than Joe, the wedding turned out a modest affair conducted by Mary's cousin, the Revd James Carter. The couple's best man was Joe's old friend, Edward Tootal, while the other signatory was her brother, Henry Tootal Broadhurst.[12] The one interesting guest, missing on this occasion, would have been Mary's twenty-three-year-old daughter, Mary Orrell. She herself had just married a Glaswegian merchant but after two or three years of marriage she devoted herself to 'helping the sick poor of Glasgow'; eventually setting up the original Nursing Association for the training of nurses. If she was, in fact, 'a chip off the old block', young Mary was a credit to her mother, herself by now dedicated to winning the right for women to be educated.

Soon after Mary and Joe married, Mary decided to remain at Stancliffe rather than use The Firs as their regular home. The reverse would have been more obvious considering the majority of her family, the Tootal Broadhursts, lived in the Manchester area but plainly she came to adore – and to prefer – their own Darley Dale estate. Since 1856, both estates had been managed by a Joseph Dawson, a very competent person born but a few yards from The Firs. He started work for Whitworth as a twenty-three-year-old head gardener but on becoming estate manager for both places Whitworth provided him with the loveliest of houses on the estate at Darley Dale, a house which Dawson later named Fircliffe, presumably in recognition of his dual function. Dawson and his family became family friends, broadening their interests as Whitworth first introduced his pedigree farm then his thoroughbred horses. But flowers and trees remained his favourites. Again *The Gardeners' Chronicle* reported:

> The beauty and richness of colouring were superb, almost beyond belief. The planning has been carried out under Sir Joseph Whitworth's superintendence most effectively, and judiciously by Mr Dawson, whose zeal and intelligence have affected wonders, and whose courteous attention we would here gratefully acknowledge.[13]

Local Darley Dale folklore has it that the Whitworths were hardly the most popular of estate owners, nor do local families ever recall hearing it said that 'the Whits' were regarded as good employers. Terence Kilburn, a Darley Dale historian, has written studiously of such matters and concluded that 'the wholesale burning of Sir Joseph Whitworth's personal papers shortly after his death robbed future biographers of this valuable family history'.[14]

The possibilities are endless. Maybe Mary Louisa behaved like Queen Victoria's daughter, Princesss Louise, and destroyed her husband's personal papers.[15] If true the results have been equally dire. Had the royal diaries survived, hopefully they would have told us something of the casual friendship between Prince Albert and Whitworth; his personal impressions and quite possibly, something of Joe's first wife, Fanny. Terence Kilburn, fortunately, has unearthed some interesting (folklore-ish) anecdotes which help fill in certain gaps. His researches are fascinating.[16]

Whitworth's kitchen garden, for example, was adjacent to a cottage and field owned by a certain 'Jakey' Millward. Though Whitworth gradually bought out most of the smallholdings around Stancliffe Hall, 'Jakey' refused to comply with Joe's requests. Not used to being rebuffed, a war of retribution ensued – Whitworth for instance built an 8-ft wall 20 ft from Jakey's cottage. Still he didn't sell, so Whitworth cut off his water supply! Another example concerned the carriage drive built by Whitworth between Stancliffe Hall and West Lodge – a matter of some 400 yards. Joe wanted all his visitors to have a tour of the estate – albeit enforced – so he extended the drive fully two miles. This brought him into conflict with another landowner, Samuel Holmes. When he too refused to succumb to Whitworth's blandishments to allow his circuitous drive to slice through his land, Joe appealed (unsuccessfully) to the Local Government Board. That was 1873, when, it is now said, Whitworth developed a compulsive desire to surround himself with high stone walls. Five years earlier, Whitworth's American associate, Charles T. Porter, visited Stancliffe and reported 'He had a *democratic* park. It had no wall, and wire fences were as yet unknown, so he could not keep deer. We observed the very pleasant house beautifully located in the valley, but he [Whitworth] told us he was planning to remove it and build a baronial hall in its place.'[17]

During the mid-nineteenth century it was highly modish for industrial leaders to plan model estates. Whitworth was no exception. His original ideas were similar to those of I.K. Brunel at Watcombe Park in Devon and the estates built by the Yorkshire wool families. The most influential model estate to animate his ideas however, followed the appointment by Sir Titus Salt of William Fairbairn and a whole team of leading architects to create in the Aire valley outside Bradford, Salt's own idealistic dream, Saltaire. His mills were to be Renaissance palaces like those in Manchester but his model cottages were, as expected, well built and practical, very much the standardized style which followed the Great Exhibition. Whitworth's own cottages at Darley Dale were almost the same as these, similar to a thousand others across Lancashire and Yorkshire. None had water-borne sanitation but the scullery was given a water tap. It is still said in Darley Dale that Whitworth 'specially requested that no doors should be put at the front or side because he did not wish to see women gossiping idly to one another, or staring at his carriage as he passed by'. Not so. The plans were taken from the same drawer used by Lord Derby and others and were probably designed by George Dance. But quite properly, some of these legendary tales do carry a grain of truth: rich estate owners spying on their employees while erecting protective walls for themselves was not just an eccentricity exclusive to Whitworth but was, it would seem, a universal idiosyncrasy common to all country estates in Victorian times.

Once Whitworth reached his seventy-third year he seemed able to relax more and enjoy Stancliffe as an estate, particularly his new stud farm and trotting ponies. The Hall itself had been described by journalists as 'quiet and unpretending' but 'meticulously hung on many of its walls were pictures by artists Whitworth most admired'. William Etty was clearly his favourite while he and Mary both enjoyed their collection of Thomas Creswick's landscapes, especially those painted in the Lake District and Derbyshire. David Roberts RA, sometimes referred to as Scotland's Canaletto, was another favourite from whom they had collected a number of watercolours. They enjoyed their landscapes and they themselves willingly sat for commissioned portraits.

Joe sensibly recognized his latest heart 'palpitations' to be a sombre warning and that no longer could he keep up the phenomenal pace he once set. Again the historian Terence Kilburn noted that lately 'Sir Joseph seems not to have enjoyed fulfilling his manorial rôle of attending church. He harboured great contempt for the rector, the Revd Frederick Atkinson'. Here, Kilburn was alluding to Joe's worship at the Saxon church of St Helen, Darley Dale, and his disagreement with the vicar about education in the village. Kilburn continued: 'A long cherished dream of Sir Joseph's was a scheme for a Village College in Darley. At its most ambitious the plan included an infants, primary and comprehensive school with gardens and a playing field. There would be an emphasis on technical subjects and the most able scholars would be offered entry into Owens College in Manchester. Not surprisingly, the rector strenuously opposed such ideas and in doing so sacrificed the goodwill he could well have nurtured in Sir Joseph for the benefit of his parishioners'. The fact that Whitworth didn't grapple with the Revd Atkinson more vigorously suggests that he was becoming more philosophical – or tired – although the miserliness of his subsequent contribution to the local church-run schools indicates his embitterment.

Towards the last decade of Whitworth's life, Edmund Yates, writing in his series 'Great Men at Home', captured a winsome view of Joe's semi-retirement when he wrote:

> The advantage of sitting and living in a large room containing abundant cubic feet of air has induced the master of Stancliffe to foresake his snug study and write habitually in his billiard room. Here when suffering from fatigue, he will sit quietly while Lady Whitworth reads to him – not a report of the latest scientific Congress, but the latest new novel – the more stirring and so-called 'sensational' the title – his interest being manifested by the occasional caress vouchsafed to Lady Whitworth's 'Willoughby' pug; an animal which in its own gentle way tyrannises over the entire household. When in his usual vigorous condition, Sir Joseph who loves neither cards nor chess, will sometimes play a game of billiards on his well-known *three legged* billiard-table with cast iron top.

> Of this table – a good one to play upon – he is very proud indeed; almost as proud as he is of the steel tip with which his horses are shod so as to allow the frog [the tender middle of a horse's hoof] to touch the ground.[18]

Of the house itself, little has been written, a surprising void considering Britain's foremost architects and designers have, at some stage, contributed much of their combined skill to its present shape and size. Maxwell Craven and Michael Stanley, writing in their book *The Derbyshire Country House,* describe Stancliffe as 'an important and irregular house (re)built by T. Roger Smith in 1872 for the munitions magnate, Sir Joseph Whitworth, Bt. with Jacobean effects. E.M. Barry made alterations in 1879 and a winter garden was built in 1885. The house was famous locally for the iron billiard table in its cavernous interior. The original house was 17th century of which the south range survives, much altered'. The Craven and Stanley description continues by recalling that a manor house on the site dates from the fourteenth century and notes that a William Heathcote purchased it in 1799 for £10,500; a comparatively low price compared with the £33,850 paid to Heathcote's heirs by Whitworth in 1856 after two years' negotiations.

The magazine *The Architect,* when reviewing an international exhibition of architectural drawings, 25 May 1872, enthused excitedly when it proffered the following opinion:

> The drawing of Sir Joseph Whitworth's mansion, 'Stancliffe', by Mr. T. Roger Smith, is very effective and displays a most excellent design; thoroughly true in style (that which we understand as the François Premier, as our neighbours term it) and very picturesque in composition. This is the stuff of which our mansions should be designed. Neither the emasculated Italian of the Palladian or Vitruvius on the one hand, nor the ascetic and ecclesiastic aspect of the Early Mediaeval on the other, it becomes sufficiently Renaissance in the best sense, with the freedom of Gothic in every use of detail, to be in our estimation the best of all styles for the expression which one naturally expects in nineteenth century secular and domestic architecture.[19]

Clearly, from what has been said more recently, the major additions to the house contributed by T. Roger Smith deserve praise. His general style, both at Darley Dale and elsewhere, is not only reminiscent of the elegant classicism associated with the French Renaissance but confirm Smith's considerable attention to detail. His semi-circular dormer sash-windows and ball-shaped finials together with his other first-rate embellishments seemed to prove his desire to surpass even the best Loire chateaux. His gatekeeper's lodge at Stancliffe, for instance – the West Lodge – must surely rank as the most dignified Victorian-built house in Derbyshire and certainly deserves the many professional tributes it receives. The more acclamatory references, however, offered by *The Architect* in regard to the Stancliffe estate as a whole should perhaps be venerated rather less considering that T. Roger Smith was, at that time, editor of the magazine!

The interior of the hall and its decoration provides another story as absorbing and as revealing as all the speculatory gossip combined. It explains much of the Whitworth saga at Stancliffe. The fact that the work was done by the foremost royal designer, John Gregory Crace, feeds the one capricious thought that Mary's vanity often overruled her husband's earthiness. It is suggested that Mary Louisa engaged architects and furnishers as soon as she and Joe got married, having herself first declared a preference to live at Stancliffe rather than The Firs. It was also she, no doubt, who insisted on creating a country residence in keeping with her own ideas rather than to allow their architects to design – as Joe would have it – a future retirement home for engineering academics.

Unlike Whitworth's works staff, Mary usually got her own way. The T. Roger Smith additions to the house were completed in 1873 and soon afterwards John G. Crace was engaged for the furnishings and decor. Mary had privately remembered that in 1857 Crace had redesigned her own Abney Hall near Manchester, in preparation for Prince Albert staying there. Naturally the very idea nourished the egoistic interplay which occasionally flickered between the two newly-weds; Mary being perky enough to remind Joe that she and her first husband, Alfred Orrell, once owned the now famous Abney Hall (it was then called Throstle Grove House) and that the particular bedroom suite prepared for the Prince Consort was once her own bedroom. She enjoyed teasing; it was Joe who was moving up the social ladder – not herself. Indeed, within a further five or six years, the architect E.M. Barry was engaged to again modify and extend the house, this time probably to make the entire concept a more coherent whole. As for Joe himself – now in his late seventies – he enjoyed the house as much as Mary.

Whitworth's own friendship with J.G. Crace was somewhat different. It started much earlier when Whitworth had been invited by Pugin's aides to try and speed up the enormous backlog of woodcarving the designer required at the House of Commons. It was during this work that he got to know J.G. Crace quite well, an entirely new companion through whom he later renewed his friendship with an old acquaintance, Richard Redgrave, RA, after a gap of some thirty years. Redgrave had started life as a young engineering draughtsman working for Joseph Bramah during the same period Whitworth first worked in London. They had much in common and became friendly; now, many years later, Joe found himself regularly among this very talented group and thoroughly enjoyed their company. The group, mainly brought together by Henry Cole – adversely described by Lord Derby as 'Coles magic circle' – not only included men like Crace and Redgrave but young scientists and military men like George G. Stokes and – a little later – John Donnelly. As for Whitworth, he never lost sight of his main purpose for cultivating Henry Cole and company – which was the development of technical education in Britain. He realized only too well that the so-called 'magic circulets' were not only the architects of the new colleges of science but also the brain power behind the new Department of Science and Art – at the time a struggling subsidiary of a not too sympathetic Board of Trade. Joe never gave up: his consistency was the dominant reason why Cole, Redgrave and Stokes particularly, all became directly involved with the Stancliffe estate. But more about this shortly – all will reappear.

Meanwhile, back in Manchester, at the Whitworths' other estate, The Firs, a domestic staff was retained at the house to look after Joe (and very occasionally Mary) together with his overnight guests from London during their working sojournments. In the past his guests were largely military people and engineers; these days they were more concerned with parliamentary politics and education rather than guns. His experimental shooting gallery had been partly dismantled – even his smallest artillery trials were no longer suitable for Fallowfield anyway – but two other leanings were now becoming increasingly paramount among his thoughts: how to attract a wider readership for quality newspapers and how he personally could assist young scientists develop their potential talent: a question ideally answered when a John Hopkinson emerged in 1871 from Cambridge as both a Whitworth Scholar and a leading Prizeman in mathematics. In regard to the press, however, Joe's engrossment has never before been discussed but as a major investor in the *Manchester Guardian* he received prior wind in 1872 that a twenty-six-year-old Oxford scholar, Charles Prestwich Scott, was to be appointed its editor. Joe decided to wait and see how he got on. In the event, he liked him very much and when the time came helped both him and the paper considerably.

Both Scott and Hopkinson were non-conformists, active dissenters. Both men – each in his own way – were instrumental in forcing the Government (by its 1871 Act) to bring to an end the necessity for all Oxford and Cambridge dons to pledge their adherence to the Church of England. The University Court supported Hopkinson's refusal to sign by insisting he remain a fellow of Trinity which left the government little option but to end religious discrimination. 'They made a little lion of me', John Hopkinson is reputed to have said, 'and made me roar against the disabilities of the non-conformists'.[21] Good for him. John went on to become a brilliant, internationally known scientist, helped enormously by Whitworth employing him nominally (without any strings attached) as his London agent. It enabled John to undertake important university research while receiving a wage – a rare privilege among academics. Interestingly, a decade later Whitworth wrote to Hopkinson (still his personal assistant) from his hotel in Cannes (13 November 1883) where he was convalescing from a recent illness. The letter indicates the state of play and refers to his continuing to employ John as a P.A. The letter read:

> Dear Dr Hopkinson.
>
> I have signed the agreement dated the 12 November which I enclose [His agreement to continue Hopkinson's employment].
>
> Have you seen General Reilly or Colonel Alderson?

I see that the Marquis of Hartington [the Secretary of State for War] is to be in Manchester on the 27th. Will you see if General Reilly will do anything relative to his visiting the works?

Had I better write a letter to the Marquis inviting him to see the works? Can you arrange to be in Manchester on the 27th when you could see the Marquis? Let me know under the circumstances what you think is best to do.

The weather here is fine and I hope I shall soon be better than I have been.

Yours sincerely, Joseph Whitworth.[22]

C.P. Scott (and indirectly *The Manchester Guardian*) also became beneficiaries of Whitworth's extended generosity when he invited him in 1882 (Scott was by then married) to become – for as long as he lived – the tenant of The Firs at a mere peppercorn rent. Scott and his wife could have free range of the whole estate. It was a unique offer, incomprehensible perhaps to those who never attempted to understand Whitworth's rooted belief in the true function of the quality press and the need for Britain to raise its general level of understanding. Indeed, the combined striving of Scott and the *Manchester Guardian* staff created a new era of edifying journalism and newspaper strategy. As for Scott himself, he was totally committed. He declared publicly his determination to advance – even beyond the 1867 Act – the cause of electoral reform, women's rights and Home Rule for Ireland. He remained editor of the *Manchester Guardian* for fifty-seven years – an all-time record – during which time he rid the paper of any hesitancy once the bane of genuine radicals. Long before he became a Liberal MP in 1895 his radical intent had been clearly established.

The significant point here was Whitworth's support for Scott politically. More than anything he wanted to help the cause Scott espoused. The fact that he chose an unusual method of helping Scott personally not only amplified his purpose but it gave the young editor a psychological freedom so essential to his task. It also gave him space in which to meet his political friends in comparative privacy. In some ways, of course, by giving Scott a lifelong tenancy, Whitworth made himself a 'hostage to fortune' (he couldn't foretell what Scott would do in the future) nevertheless this one single act typified Whitworth's loathing for those so-called 'newspaper greats' he had sometimes met and who traded in nothing more than mere tokenism.[23] The only proviso Whitworth imposed was that The Firs, after the death of Scott, should become the property of Owens College – a wish wholly honoured when the time came.

OWENS COLLEGE AND THE WHITWORTH SCHOLARSHIPS

> We [Britain] are beginning to lose ground for want of better educated engineers
>
> William Fairbairn 1867

During the course of the 1867 Paris Exhibition it slowly dawned upon British engineers that William Fairbairn's prophesies had already become fact: France and Germany were exhibiting an engineering technology well ahead of Britain. Fairbairn went further. 'We require to unite theory and practice';[24] but his indisputable advice largely fell on deaf ears. Sadly, the majority of master engineers could see little connection between science and engineering.

'We need good practical men – not geniuses', was their unwitting response when they were asked to help finance the founding of an engineering faculty at Owens College.

The activists behind the idea of a science-based college called a special meeting of Lancashire engineers at the Manchester Town Hall, on 11 December 1866. A second meeting, seven weeks later, was asked by Whitworth, the elected treasurer, to provide £10,000 in support of an engineering professorship and a new engineering library. Under the rather wordy catch-phrase – 'Owens will be a science-orientated modern liberal rival to the ancient universities' – Whitworth, Charles Beyer and John Robinson each threw in one thousand pounds followed by the others present until a total of £9,505 in promissory notes lay on the table. This sum was later augmented by a further £1,250 from Beyer followed by £5,200 from a Mr James Ashbury. In March 1868, Mr Osborne Reynolds of Queen's College, Cambridge, was thus appointed the first professor of engineering.[25]

At the same time as Whitworth and his engineering colleagues were canvassing support for the sciences, a more general – but equally passionate – campaign was being waged to raise a further £100,000 to provide entirely new buildings on the recently acquired Oxford Road site. And though the cotton famine had drained from the area much of its wealth, the Lancashire cotton towns responded generously. Of course, the engineering case advocated by Fairbairn and company still piqued and the question of science laboratories remained a prickly issue; worst of all, the most narrow-minded conditions were attached to possible donations. 'A technical school, yes, but what was the necessity for a university to teach engineering science?' 'Why did the university need the authority to confer its own degrees?' None of these questions were surprising; it had taken Whitworth himself some considerable time to grasp the essential difference between an arts based college and having a university led by scientists with their own integrated research laboratories at the heart of the matter.

The *Manchester Guardian* and the *Spectator* went further and warmly supported 'a north of England science-based university'. The Principal of the college responded approvingly. He reiterated what was by then a majority opinion. 'Our special line should be the study of experimental and applied science . . . we should not fear comparison with Germany'. It was a marvellous breakthrough – not yet for Beyer and Whitworth and engineering – but a just reward for the considerable influence exerted at Owens by Henry Roscoe and the other Liebig-Bunsen trained chemists from Heidelberg. Little wonder the talented, but jealous, somewhat anti-science arts-peacockery slyly referred to a place called 'Manchester-on-Heidelberg'.

Thus heartened by the success of the science lobby so far, a more positive engineering attitude was soon revealed. The year following the Manchester meetings, 1867, Whitworth, accompanied by Beyer and Fairbairn, left Manchester for the International Exhibition in Paris. They were joined at the exhibition centre by Lord Granville and Lyon Playfair; an ex-cabinet minister and the Government's adviser on science. Not by accident this influential fivesome came together only to learn that of the British engineering exhibits only Whitworth's were awarded the Grand Prix. Playfair was at once convinced of the reason for the sparsity of British 'golds'. 'Our country', he said, 'has shown little inventiveness since 1862: there is a lack of industrial education for the masters and managers of factories'. Lord Granville concurred but again emphasized the need for scientific education in engineering. Six months later he visited Manchester and told his audience: 'In the application of science and industry our European competitors were making far greater advances. The men of Manchester ought now to come forward and push this question of science as far as they possibly could.'

That same evening, 26 August 1867, Lord Granville accepted Whitworth's invitation to stay the night at Fallowfield. He shared Joe's cab as they drove back to The Firs. In the semi-dark and soft leather seats they discussed how best Whitworth could set an example to engineering and other employers to advance the cause of technical and science education. A number of schemes already occupied Joe's thoughts (including probably his scholarship scheme) but no one was better placed than Granville to offer advice as it was he himself in 1864 – then Palmerston's Lord President of the Council – who first informed the Owens College partisans that the state would not assist financially. Professor John Tyndall referred to this in 1867 when he told a Parliamentary Select Committee: 'The facilities for scientific education are far greater on the continent than in England. Those industries (engineering) into which the scientific element enters will one day be outstripped. *As sure as knowledge is power this must be the result.*'[26] The *Edinburgh Review* entirely agreed with Tyndall when it reported on the Parliamentary Inquiry:

> The inquiry now is not what we have been, but what we relatively are; not whether we have gained a high place and reputation, but whether we can retain them. To rest upon our oars is to drift backwards; and not to be the first is soon, in this age of activity, to be the last.

The pressures on the government in favour of state funding were beginning to mount. One or two leading opponents from the past were changing their views. Henry Cole, for instance, now that he himself had a pecuniary interest in state education turned turtle. He recorded in his diary (19 April 1869) being asked by Scott Russell to agitate for technical education. 'I declined as incompatible with my office', he wrote. Two months later he had lunch with Whitworth and Lyon Playfair and Whitworth asked them both to make known their views publicly. 'Playfair is not willing to agitate', Cole entered for the 20

June, 'and I upbraided him' – thus confirming that Cole himself had (privately) moved closer towards Scott Russell's idea for a 'Ministry of Public Education'. The fact that these pertinent issues were raised in this more open fashion was due not just to Whitworth's presence but to the effective initiatives he had taken the previous year. The press had welcomed his scholarship scheme with tremendous applause: it immediately established him as someone willing to back his advocacy with his own money; in a non-interventionist free market climate it gave him unequalled moral integrity; it even endeared him – 'temporarily you understand' – with his arch-critic, Robert Lowe MP.

The publicity concerning Whitworth's Scholarship Scheme was timed to perfection. Soon after Christmas 1867 it was apparent that even with the generosity of the surrounding Lancashire towns the Owens College Appeal would fail to meet the cost of the new buildings, nor would it endow the quality of teaching required. The fund-raisers quickly realized that once again they must seek help from the Government – some people thought it was a worthless exercise – nonetheless they were granted a meeting with the Lord President of the Council on 5 March 1868. The delegation was led by Alfred Neild and included three engineers: Whitworth, Beyer and Murray Gladstone. They were received courteously but all they could wring from the Minister was another meeting at which the Prime Minster promised to be present.

This further meeting took place at Downing Street on 24 March 1868 but this time the delegation was considerably strengthened, not – as previously – wholly made up of Liberals, but this time it included leading Disraeli supporters like Sir Philip Egerton. Conscious that the theme would again be 'self-help' Whitworth consulted his friend Lord Granville. They agreed that before he travelled to London, Whitworth should seize the initiative. Six days prior to the meeting he wrote to Disraeli personally offering:

> to found thirty scholarships of the annual value of £100 each, to be applied to the further instruction of young men natives of the United Kingdom, selected by open competition for their intelligence and proficiency in the theory and practice of mechanics and its cognate sciences, with a view to the promotion of engineering and mechanical industry in this country; and I venture to hope that means may be found to bring science and industry into closer relation with each other than at present obtains in this country.[27]

It was a magnificent proposal; exceedingly generous. In the end it cost Whitworth and his legatees about £128,000 (£5.25m at 1994 values). Whitworth genuinely believed in what he was doing but in writing to Disraeli personally just prior to the meeting he clearly intended it to partially answer the 'self-help' line repeatedly put by successive governments. That it did, but unhappily it also provided ministers with the perfect example of what could be done by personal gift. Nor did it move Disraeli in terms of state aid for Owens College but the much higher level pro-engineering-science debate which followed ensured there could be no turning back. That aspect was down to Whitworth.

Joseph Thompson, in his *History of Owens College*, portrays the agonizing Prime Minister excellently when he described the Downing Street meeting thus:

> Mr. Disraeli, who was accompanied by the Chancellor of the Exchequer, Rt. Hon. George Hunt MP and the Duke of Marlborough (Spencer Churchill) Lord President of the Council, received the deputation courteously. It was an interesting scene and characteristic of the chief actor. The room was well filled and many had to stand. The Premier slipped in noiselessly and sat with his back to the window. He kept his eyes down when the gentlemen spoke and the addresses were delivered, but he was not insensible to what was going on. Observing Mr. Grote, Sir Philip Egerton, and others standing, he addressed them by name and requested them to be seated. In his reply he assured the deputation of the great importance attached to the subject which they laid before him. The college had evidently done good work and was destined to make its influence work. It had his fullest sympathy, and would command the greatest consideration from his colleagues when he brought its claims before them. 'But', he said, 'If Her Majesty's government, in the exigencies of the state, should be unable to comply with your request, I am sure that the public spirit and the generosity of Lancashire will not allow the interests of the college to suffer'. This was done in his grandest manner. He had a slight cold, and held in his hand a large cambric handkerchief edged with black, which he freely used as a lady would use her fan, as a valuable aid to effect. The impression left on the minds of the hearers varies with their idiosyncrasies: some were hopeful, others feared the politeness was a cover for refusal. Nothing came of the application.[28]

On 2 April 1868, Lord Montague MP stated in the House of Commons that 'Mr Whitworth has made a most munificent offer for the promotion of technical education, which the Privy Council has gratefully accepted.' This pleasing announcement naturally caused much excitement, and the daily press commented fully upon it. Two days later, Whitworth himself announced the rules and conditions for the scholarships. Though the details had been finalized in conjunction with Henry Cole and Lyon Playfair his letter to Cole as the Secretary of the Science and Art Department asked for the Department to administer the whole scheme and that a competent authority should award a Wh. Sch. (Whitworth Scholar) degree analogous to the existing faculties of divinity, law and medicine. The candidates were to be subjects of Her Majesty, whether of the United Kingdom, India or the colonies, who were not more than twenty-six years of age, and the scholarships were tenable for two or three years. Successful candidates would be required to spend the period of holding the scholarships in the further satisfactory study of the theory and practice of *mechanical engineering*, according to the spirit of the endowment; and the student should state where he proposed to do this. If he wished to complete his general education instead of continuing his special scientific study, he might be permitted to do so. He might go to the universities or colleges affording scientific or technical instruction, or he might travel abroad. The successful artisans should be encouraged to study *theory*, and should be aided in getting admission to machine shops and other practical establishments.

It is interesting to note that although the Whitworth Scholarship Scheme has gone through a number of administrative changes since 1869 it not only still survives but that the letters Wh. Sch. are still revered. Nowadays, sadly, the number of scholarships are down to ten per year and one third (£1,300 p.a.) of their original value, nevertheless once each candidate completes his or her degree course to the satisfaction of the IMechE Awards Panel each award holder is still entitled to use the designatory letters Wh. Sch. and to receive a Whitworth medal. Since 1984, under the jurisdiction of the Secretary of State and the IMechE, the scholarships are much closer to the conditions originally suggested by Whitworth one hundred and twenty-five years ago, that is to say, a candidate to be eligible must have discontinued full-time education at sixteen, served at least two years' engineering apprenticeship and completed the first year of an undergraduate degree course.

Towards the end of 1868, the year Whitworth finalized the details of his scholarship scheme with the help of the Science and Art Department, he also discussed with Henry Cole and Richard Redgrave a possible future for Stancliffe Hall. His long-term idea envisaged that one day the whole estate would be taken over by the Science and Art Department for use as an engineering college and retirement home for professors. If such a scheme was acceptable he clearly recognized that the existing hall would require extensive alterations so he engaged Redgrave to draft possible designs. It is interesting that Cole should have entered into his diary, on 6 January 1869, 'Whitworth came and approved Redgrave's design for his house', which was followed on Sunday 11 April with a captivating memo: 'Whitworth called for breakfast. We went to Windsor. Had lunch with General Gray (Queen Victoria's secretary). Discussed Owens College and the Redgrave plans for the house'. Intriguingly, a further entry, 1 May, confirms that 'Mr Whitworth said Professor George G. Stokes (a Cambridge mathematician and secretary of the Royal Society) was making another plan for his house'; while somewhat dispiritedly, on 22 June, he recorded, 'met with Playfair and Whitworth. Whitworth doesn't like his house'.

Departmental notes subsequently written by Cole revealed that Whitworth's ideas came up against the fact that it then wasn't possible for someone to hand over a house and land to the state – in Whitworth's case he possibly wanted to hand over two estates, The Firs and Stancliffe – hoping that once the state had accepted them as a gift, the Science and Arts Department would thereafter fund their maintenance.[29] It was an extremely imaginative idea but years ahead of its time. Only a hint remains why Cole and Whitworth visited Windsor but the most likely explanation centres on the Duchy of Lancaster and the late Prince

Albert's notion that the Duchy itself could provide a technical university. Sadly, it would seem Redgrave's drawings of Stancliffe have not survived: had they done so we would have known much more about Whitworth's intentions. As it was, the departmental discussions were overtaken by Whitworth's marriage in 1871, whereupon his bride, Mary Louisa, contacted the architect, Prof. T. Roger Smith, with some very *different* ideas as to the future of Stancliffe.

In some ways Mary's choice of architect was surprising considering that T. Roger Smith, George Stokes and Redgrave were already close colleagues of Henry Cole and were all four committed to the further development of a technical university. They knew the kind of legislation which would be required should someone like Whitworth offer the government a whole estate suitable for use as a college; the outline of a Bill was clear in their minds as early as 1872 and a draft Bill was presented to the House of Lords in 1874. Its purpose would enable the government of the day to accept gifts of land and buildings so long as they were intended for educational purposes but due to the controversial nature of the legislation it was not brought from the Lords to the Commons until 3 August 1875. By that time the T. Roger Smith additions to Stancliffe Hall were completed and Mary Louisa was anticipating at least twenty pleasurable years of residency. The immediate need for a Bill had somewhat receded.

The further conversations Whitworth had with Cole and his so-called 'magic circle' had also been overtaken by the start of the most remarkable interplay between Gladstone and Disraeli. In December 1868, Gladstone defeated Disraeli to become Prime Minister for the first time. Naturally, the educationalists were cock-a-hoop; they assumed that their long wait for state aid for technical education was over. Not so. Gladstone behaved no differently and offered the same reasons for refusing money as Disraeli. But at least he changed the Cabinet significantly: albeit hesitantly, he brought in John Bright at the Board of Trade and Robert Lowe as Chancellor of the Exchequer: as the gossip suggested, he balanced lions with tigers. Hopefully he also brought in Lord Granville as Colonial Secretary, an appointment destined to lift hearts at Owens College who expected so much from the Science and Art Department. But as things turned out they got nothing and despondency returned as the years rolled on. Five years later, when Disraeli regained the premiership, he repeated not just the words of Gladstone but exactly as he himself had uttered them in 1867: 'Technical education there must be, but not from the Treasury purse'.

Despite this disingenuous attitude towards the sciences and engineering education shown by the Gladstone-Dissy axis the Victoria University of Manchester (as Owens College became) eventually climbed above its earlier resentment that industry should be made to fund the sciences, and applied itself to the creation of an entirely new movement in the national life of England. Tribute should be paid to the three men most responsible; George Faulkner, Charles Beyer and Joseph Whitworth. As Dr. A.C. Magian stated in his *History of Owens College*: 'At the end of the eighteenth century Oxford and Cambridge were the only universities in the country and had steadfastly refused admission to Dissenters. Kings College, London, was founded in 1829 by Earl Spencer and the Tory Party and kept up the religious tests. But the Victoria University, which arose out of Owens College of Manchester, was established by the active cooperation of Liberals and Tories, of Churchmen and Dissenters, of lords and commoners and of men and women of every shade of opinion and from every walk of life. It enabled youths who could not afford the expense inseparable from life in the older universities to obtain a university education and a university degree.'[30]

It must also be said that much of the success in those early days was down to the German influence in Manchester. Charles Beyer from Plauen in Saxony was the leading example. Not only did he give more money to the college than Owens himself, but the inspirational lift he gave engineering science was equal, in fact, to Whitworth's own immense contribution. The degree of excellence conceded the college internationally soon after its official opening in 1873, centred on chemists such as Dr Edward Frankland, Henry Roscoe, Carl Schorlemmer, Wilhelm Dittmar and Julius Dreschfeld, all of whom were products of Playfair, Bunsen and Liebig via Heidelberg and Giessen. These men were but a few of the constant stream of extraordinary talent freely moving between Germany and Manchester.

Charles Beyer's total bequest in 1875 of over £115,000 (£6.5m at today's values) ensured that professors would be a little less dependent upon direct emoluments from industry – a move which tended to free the Manchester academics from the dictates of industry.

Scholastic freedom thus became an important issue particularly when the Gladstone-Dissy devotees argued that science and engineering laboratories should be wholly funded by industry. Both Beyer and Whitworth attached great importance to academic freedom. So too did Professor Henry Roscoe but that was before he entered Parliament and then had to supplement his income by working as a *consultant* to industry. As a younger chemist he argued vociferously against the dreadful pollution of rivers from the outflow of waste chemicals. Once he was elected to Parliament in 1885, however, not only did it end an era in Manchester but Roscoe successfully opposed Birkbeck's River Pollution Bill. He argued that the Bill would 'imperil the very existence of many of our important industries if the liquid discharges from chemical works were ended'. It was the classic case against parliamentary placemen.

Little or no writing about Whitworth and education, however, can be concluded without mentioning the consequences in Manchester of the Education Acts and the Technical Instruction Act. Both these Acts came in after Whitworth's death in 1887. His earlier influence throughout the formation of this legislation had played its part and some visible proof still remains. The original Manchester School of Technology, for instance, built on the site of his old gun factory in Sackville Street was, in the main, due to the efforts of his trustees, R.D. Darbishire and R.C. Christie. In 1896, there was a partial amalgamation of the Technical School and Owens to prevent overlapping but six years later a new Municipal College opened in its own right, a proud remembrance of Whitworth's endeavour.

Curiously enough the one college project which really carried the Whitworth stamp was outside Manchester. In 1878 – at the age of seventy-four – Whitworth collaborated with Charles Manby, Secretary of the Civil Engineers, and Henry Bessemer, to set up a College of Practical Engineering at Muswell Hill, North London. The college opened in September 1881 with John Bourne, the steam engineer, appointed Principal of the college. In terms of its technical education it was an outstanding success but the local authorities at the time were reluctant to bail out the London engineering employers who, like their Manchester predecessors, failed to recognize the necessity for technically qualified staff and the college was compelled to close in 1890.

Professor W.H. Armytage, in his book *A Social History of Engineering*, explained the sequence of events leading up to the Muswell Hill College. 'The Institution of Civil Engineers made an inquiry in 1870 into the education and status of civil engineers in the United Kingdom and foreign countries and found that there were only seven centres in Britain where an engineering education could be obtained. In March 1871, the House of Commons ventilated the whole question and the government went ahead'. Coopers Hill College was the first, Crystal Palace the second, 'but it was left to the private munificence of Bessemer, Whitworth and Charles Manby to initiate a third venture: a college of practical engineering at Muswell Hill'.[31]

Certainly it was the overwhelming wish of the House of Commons that 'something should be done' but Gladstone proved the biggest stumbling block; he refused to overrule the distaste of the Treasury to help Muswell Hill. Indeed, it was left to Sir William Mather MP, a great Manchester Liberal and electrical engineer, to persuade George Goschen, Salisbury's Chancellor of the Exchequer in 1889 to allow the county councils to levy a penny rate for technical education and to grant half the duty the Treasury collected on the sale of whisky to assist the building of science laboratories in technical schools. Unfortunately, the penny rate and the 'whisky money' came six months too late to save John Bourne and Muswell Hill – the shutters were already closed.

During the last twenty years of Whitworth's life the sheer divergency of his non-engineering interests tended to minimize the personal attention he could give to the running of his factory. Just prior to 1860 he had partly corrected this by himself becoming company Chairman and by appointing J. Manny Gledhill his Managing Director.[32] Although he had already made Billy Hulse a partner, he recognized – and warmly supported – that Hulse would shortly be leaving to set up his own machine tool factory in Salford. All the managerial changes he had made had been beneficial, which encouraged him to go further and make the firm a limited company. But again, his intentions were far from orthodox. Following advice from a whole range of experts, he dedicated his company to the principle of shared management – 'One Nation' industrialism. His ideas were profoundly innovative. He was again making history, exploring paths others thought too risky to follow. He wanted his employees to share the wealth they were creating; he wanted a share-owning democracy much in advance, as it happened, of the very limited parliamentary democracy which existed at that time.

The articles of association Whitworth registered in 1874 were truly remarkable. His company objectives as he set them out read as follows:

> The establishing, managing and assisting of Schools, Libraries, Banks, Dispensaries, Infirmaries, Provident Societies and Clubs for the benefit of persons employed by the company.[33]

In other words, the first thing Whitworth wanted his company to do was to provide technical education for his employees, particularly his apprentices. Secondly, he wanted them to have a works doctor and an ambulance room but most important in his view, his company should be legally empowered to bank any savings his employees wished to have deducted from their wages and for the company to then convert such money (if mutually agreed) into company shares. This latter point was something to which he attached great importance: he prized very highly that his employees should themselves participate in the policy-making of the company.

When these far-reaching changes finally went through, in spring 1874, the company payroll had reached 780: its board of six directors included the entire works management. Whitworth himself, of course, was in the chair and very clearly it was he who decided these matters. Indeed, the lawyers had made sure that so long as he held one-third of the share capital he would exercise supreme control in the management of the business. In 1875, the 'purchase consideration' of the company was stated to be £350,000 of which £300,000 was 'divided into 12,000 fully paid shares of £25 each'. Writing on this subject in 1877 he himself said:

> The relations between foremen engineers and their employers have lately become of a much more intimate character, particularly in concerns which have availed themselves of the Limited Liability Act. The foremen engineers have themselves become employers. Three years since (on 31st March 1874) I converted my business into that of a company under the Limited Liability Act, but not in the usual sense of asking the public to take shares in it. Myself, the foremen and others in the concern, 23 in number, hold 92 per cent of the shares and have practical control, while the remaining 8 per cent of the shares are held by others. In this transaction there was no goodwill to be charged for, and the plant was taken at a *low* valuation. The shares of £25 were offered, as many as could be taken, to the foremen, draughtsmen, clerks and workmen. For the workman who has not the means to buy shares, arrangements have been made that will, I think, solve some of the difficulties between capital and labour. When a workman who intends to save receives his wages he deposits with the clerk appointed what he thinks fit. This money is employed in the concern as capital, and whatever dividend is paid to the

> shareholders the workman is paid for his deposits in the shape of interest on them. It has been said that these terms are more favourable to the workmen than to the shareholders; but the shareholders provide only capital and as the workman devotes both his labour and capital the terms ought to be more favourable. If a workman, from sickness or other cause, wants to withdraw what he has deposited, he can by giving three days' notice receive a quarter, six days' notice a half and twelve days' notice the whole of what stands to his credit. When a workman leaves he must withdraw his deposit; and if he holds shares he must sell them to the company at the price he paid for them.[34]

There is no doubt his ideas were visionary – some perhaps would say delusory, in view of subsequent experience – but however the cynics may interpret his concern about the relations between capital and labour, Whitworth was thoroughly genuine in his belief that 'One Nation' industrial management was superior both from an employer's point of view and from that of a workman. To have done what he did was courageous. Not for the first time he was prepared to lead by example; not because of some Marxist reasoning but because his logic was Bacon-inspired. Six years later, he moved his factory from Chorlton Street to Ashton Road, Openshaw. It had by then grown to over 1,000 workers but when the 'One Nation' experiment was assessed in 1893, only seventy-two employees held one or more shares. Perhaps the cynics were right: although more likely the reason was probably cost; that one share represented, on average, nearly ten weeks' wages.

An analysis as to who were the real opinion formers, the directors and leading shareholders throughout this period, illustrates yet another reason why Whitworth succeeded in changing his company structure against all the hearsay and 'doubting tommies'. But the majority of those to whom he *gave* shares in the beginning were his own draughtsmen and it is this particular aspect which animates the most profound ideological doubts of Whitworth's creed. The period 1874–97, when the idea of managerial democracy spread, was almost a quarter-century when Whitworth's design staff had the talent and the freedom, the design experience and all the incentives, to elbow ahead of the world with mechanisms and machine tool designs in advance even of the American best. But what happened? Why did Whitworth's drawing office fail (with the exception of his brilliant twist drill manufacture) to continue producing machine tools capable of leading the world?

One answer could be, of course, that the drawing office knew that after the death of Whitworth (or his wife Mary) the firm would be gobbled up by Sir William Armstrong of Elswick. They were right; exactly twelve months after the death of Lady Whitworth in 1896 the firm became Sir W.G. Armstrong Whitworth and Company Ltd. But if that is considered a feasible explanation why they no longer cared it is not good enough. The unpleasant truth is that the Whitworth drawing office from 1874 onwards chose an easy life – they proved that if any great motivator is taken away from the team and the hire-and-fire man removed, the rest will settle for mediocrity and an easy but false security. All this can only be a miserable explanation even for Liberal progressives: for someone like Whitworth it would have been a devastating result of a failed belief: the joy of *collective decision making* proved neither carrot nor whip, in fact it proved to have little or no influence at all. Had he lived long enough he would have sensed what was happening and found another way. Sadly, Whitworth's democracy looks like being at least two centuries ahead of our industrial understanding.

As the *Manchester Guardian* said in its obituary on 24 January 1887: '. . . he wanted to extend the influence of reason into every department of action. The world has record of very few lives that have contributed more largely than Whitworth's towards what he conceived to be the great task of humanity – to establish the supremacy of intelligence over the material universe'.

On a much lower plane it is noteworthy that when it came to handing out company shares in 1874, Whitworth gave generously to the younger end of his family. In doing so he disproved that he was an anti-family man, giving his twenty-six-year-old nephew, Joseph Whitworth MacGowan, a considerable number of shares and a place on the Board. In 1885, he made him the Company Secretary. He also gave the same number of shares to Mary Louisa's son-in-law, J.S. Higginbotham, before going on to set another beguiling example when he appointed the young graduate William Greenwood to the Board. Greenwood was the very first Wh. Sch. and after a very short time, Manny Gledhill, the Managing Director, made him his engineering assistant mainly to help him sort out the difficulties arising from the hydraulic forging of Whitworth's fluid compression steel.

And finally, in answer to the query 'where lay Whitworth's strongest support?' the answer can only point towards his old friends and leading shareholders. It would not have happened otherwise. Apart from the company's articles of association, the directors had other legal duties under the 1862 Act. Admittedly the legal position was confused; it was an entirely new agenda and Whitworth wanted to pursue a wholly different management philosophy. Happily the Board was led by men like Edwin Chadwick, Sir Henry Cole, Professor Henry Roscoe MP and Henry Tootal Broadhurst. They were all major shareholders but also powerful advocates of Liberal democratic ideology; it was they who characteristically carried the day. It was they, and not the 'professional' politicians, who were the most supportive.

THE GREAT BENEFACTOR

'Sir Joseph Whitworth, the greatest of a group of great mechanics', died on Saturday night, 22 January 1887, at the English Hotel, Monte Carlo, 'full of years and honours'. So wrote the editor of the *Manchester Guardian* before embellishing this sad announcement with a typical aphorism, unmistakably C.P. Scott in origin: 'The great benefactors of mankind have seldom been granted that happiness which might have come from the due appreciation of their work by their contemporaries. Sir Joseph Whitworth was no exception to this rule.'

In the most remarkable way Whitworth and his wife Mary were unique philanthropists. They were exceptionally public spirited, not in any charitable sense, but because they passionately believed that if living standards were to be raised it was down to themselves to show by example how the teaching of industrial technology would vastly improve the nation's prospects. Local education boards were then virtually non-existent: money, even for the most rudimentary teaching was meagre; anything more advanced was a matter for philanthropic endowment.

Yet despite the mean treatment spooned out by both the press and the civil service regarding Whitworth's ideas, the couple's own generosity and public-spiritedness never diminished. Excluding Cecil Rhodes, Whitworth in fact was by far Britain's most generous benefactor prior to the death of Lord Nuffield in 1963. The point has a special significance particularly in regard to the way Nuffield's executors were able to fund his Foundation and professorships and how they were able to establish the Nuffield College. Whitworth's original ambition – as set out in his first will – was the funding of a self-perpetuating scheme whereby young people from about the age of fourteen in Manchester, Salford and Stockport would have had a scheme of going on to study the arts and industrial technology. However, it wasn't to be: Whitworth's scheme was five or six years ahead of legislation. The education boards, which would have made it realizable, were not then in place and on making further enquiries Whitworth's legal adviser, Mr R.D. Darbishire, persuaded him to withdraw the scheme from his will.

Having to abandon this particular ambition proved a great disappointment for both Mary and Joe; so much so, that twelve months after her husband's death, Mary Whitworth sent £10,000 to the Mayor of Stockport, Alderman Joseph Leigh, with the following letter:

> I sincerely hope that in making this gift *we* are helping effectively to serve the great cause of enabling young *women* and young men to develop their powers and increase their usefulness to themselves and others, and to those for whom in later life they may be especially responsible, by applying themselves to their work in life, whatever it may be, with intelligence and skill, with trained perseverance and educated accuracy and with an honest love of perfect workmanship.

The letter confirmed that the money was for the exclusive use of the Stockport Technical School as other monies had been earmarked for use by the Stockport Girls Industrial School quite independently.

During the eighteen months it took to collate his will Whitworth authorized four published codicils, each occasioned by a changing legal opinion as he and others explored possible alternatives. The implementation of his original scheme grew ever more complex. Various friends who were knowledgeable in these matters were invited to stay at Stancliffe but apart from family bequests the original will drawn up by Whitworth in December 1884 clearly indicated that it was his profound wish that the bulk of his estate should provide an educationists' foundation capable, as he himself put it, 'of carrying forward eligible pupils (male or female) to become superior workmen or pupil teachers, or in extraordinary cases, students of science, practical or theoretical, or both, and I desire to leave the entire management of the *income* of such respective gift . . . to the proper institution'. He then referred to his appointed trustees, his wife, Richard Copley Christie and Robert Dukinfield Darbishire, all three of whom had agreed so to act long before the will was finalized; therefore one assumes that they were in full agreement with Whitworth's intentions. Indeed, written in the will he declared unequivocally: 'I repose in them the most unlimited confidence and give to them the fullest powers in the management and disposition of my property and affairs which it is possible for me to grant'.

Why then did it become necessary for him to revoke his original wish to establish a teaching foundation? It had been his dear wish to leave behind an estimable scheme endowed perhaps with some £800,000 (£42 million at 1994 values) hoping that it would serve the twin cities of Manchester and Salford. Was it a blemished scheme?

Why was it necessary for him to issue four codicils? By doing so he had in effect wiped the slate clean, thereafter leaving his legatees absolutely free to use their own judgement as to how best his own wishes could be executed. The primary reason why Joe accepted the lawyers' advice was neither indecision on his part nor poor mental health – at eighty years of age he was as bright as a button – but what he, Christie and Darbishire clearly understood once they had concluded their discussions on possible joint funding arrangements with Manchester's Corporation officials was that the existing local government legislation would have to be considerably amended; although it had been promised by the Prime Minister, the Marquess of Salisbury, that he would be introducing a Technical Instruction Act or something similar, it would have been essential to have this enabling legislation before the Whitworth proposals would become financially feasible.

Immediately these uncertainties were recognized a further impediment frightened the lawyers; a plethora of vexatious litigation loomed ahead of them. Both Christie and Darbishire realized how vulnerable they would have been with such indefinite instructions and persuaded Joe that he should change his will and leave all his wealth without strings (except, that is, his specific legacies) to his three trustees.

The evidence suggests that Whitworth understood very clearly what was happening and proceeded, in February 1885, to completely restyle his earlier directives. In doing so, he confirmed his absolute faith in what he was doing, 'they (his trustees) being each aware of the general nature of my objectives . . . and my purpose'. It was a remarkable avowal. It testified his warm unity with the politics and opinions of the two very fine Liberals he had asked to act on his behalf. Some years later, Robert Darbishire said: 'It was a magnificent confidence – going back many years to his friendship with my own father – a confidence Sir Joseph had in his wife, his friend, Chancellor Christie and myself.'[35]

As things turned out Whitworth's decision to equally divide the residue of his estate between his trustees as a pure gift free of any conditions proved to be a masterly touch. On the occasion of the official opening of the Whitworth Institute on 29 July 1908, not many weeks before his own death, Robert Darbishire, as the sole surviving trustee, happily declared: 'The wisdom of bestowing (guardianship of the Whitworth fortune) in the way he did put it out of the power of any public body or private person to impeach such action as if it had been in any way a gift *in trust.* The wisdom of this confidence was afterwards proved when Sir Joseph's legatees successfully resisted no less than eleven distinct blackmailing suits in Chancery, for which, by the way, no single plaintiff ever paid a penny of costs.'

Of these court initiatives only two related to matters of principle; that is to say, only two plaintiffs sought to question whether or not the legatees had used Whitworth's wealth in the way he wished. Both actions were ruled out as in the opinion of the courts the legatees were free to do as they did; but more on that shortly – there was still one other court action to come. It was a case which started in 1915 and lasted until October 1921 when the plaintiff was granted leave to appeal to the House of Lords. In the end it was given short shrift, the Master of the Rolls concluding: 'this was a hopeless appeal which ought never to have been brought'.

The origins of this meddlesome case started soon after Whitworth's death. It flickered on and off as succeeding generations of Joe's distant family probed to see if they could unearth any money. In the first place his executors were threatened with proceedings by the very man Whitworth had made his company secretary, J.W. McGowan, his nephew. Apart from one or two side issues, Joe McGowan didn't like the way his mother (Sir Joseph's step-sister, Ellen) had been treated. Playing safe, the executors sensed trouble and looked for a way to protect themselves: more than anything they wanted absolute freedom to get on with their Whitworth work unimpeded. They feared that this particular case could spark off additional claims from Fanny Uniacke (Whitworth's heiress-at-law, an Australian citizen) not realizing that Fanny was already on her way to England to consult a lawyer. Once alerted, Robert Darbishire wasn't sure what the courts would do and decided to act. Fanny Uniacke accepted £25,000 having agreed to transfer back to Whitworth's executors any remaining rights she may have had under the will. Ellen McGowan was treated likewise and paid an undisclosed sum. And there, for the next twenty years, the matter rested until a Mr O'Rourke, the Uniackes' administrator, came along in 1916 to unsuccessfully ask that the deed signed by Fanny Uniacke be set aside. He then went on to challenge what he believed to be the unlawful yet still tenuous arrangements once agreed between Robert Darbishire and the two ladies.

We now know that the case which O'Rourke so tenaciously propelled into the House of Lords failed miserably; but at least it serves a good purpose here in that the most impressive aspect of the evidence given confirmed that there was overwhelming public support behind the legatees' schemes and that any remaining doubts about Whitworth's mental fragility were little more than ill-disposed gossip. One Bakewell solicitor said in evidence that he frequently saw Sir Joseph at Stancliffe Hall and that the last time he saw him he was 'absolutely brilliant'. Edwin Reed, one of Whitworth's works managers at the time, said 'I found him bodily feeble but very good mentally'. 'Indeed', said Reed, 'Sir Joseph suggested that all young men going in for engineering should have their "bumps" felt', a sure sign, thought Reed, that Joe was still in full possession of his faculties.

One convincing but often overlooked factor when journalists have considered the propriety or otherwise of the executors' work was the overseeing presence throughout the 1887–96 period of Whitworth's widow, Mary. She was constantly consulted as a well-informed person and was wholly in favour of building the Whitworth Institutes both at Darley Dale and Manchester. She fully supported the university's new buildings, its library and the new technical college quite apart from her favourite Darley projects like the hospital. She also had her own crusade in terms of education for women and quietly but firmly supported the Manchester and Salford College for Women, always insisting that women should never again be disadvantaged in any part of the university.

Evidence of the legatees' sincerity was further enhanced by the extraordinary way they themselves supplemented the Whitworth money with considerable sums of their own. Lady Whitworth, for instance, personally added to the endowment of the hospital at Darley Dale. Mr Christie himself donated generously money and books for the building of the Christie Library and the Great Whitworth Hall. Both he and Robert Darbishire gave handsomely to the creation of the Manchester Whitworth Institute. The development of the Whitworth Park and Gallery was a dominant part of their work, but quite unsung, was the legatees' purchase in 1890 of the Stanley Grove Estate, five large houses with twelve acres: one of the houses became 'The Cancer Pavilion and Home', forerunner of the now world-famous Christie Hospital. 'But for them,' wrote the *Manchester Guardian* in 1908, 'the Manchester Royal Infirmary would not now be about to enter a new era.'

But if the actual size of Whitworth's historic legacy is to be fully comprehended a simple comparison between 'then and now' money values is required. The value of today's pound is less than two pence when compared with the year of Whitworth's death, 1887, and what it would buy then. To compare a simple basket of 'then and now' rents and everyday purchases it is necessary to multiply the money Whitworth left by a factor of *fifty-three*.[36] The fact that he and his wife Mary bequeathed something like £1.8 million during their final years means that the Whitworths left about £95 million at today's values.

Even when compared with Lord Nuffield's magnificent £25 million which he left in 1963 it is still a considerable sum. But to compare like with like the Nuffield figure should itself be multiplied by a factor of *nine* – Whitworth's legacy of '£95 million' is therefore about 40 per cent of Nuffield's '£225 million' when both are considered at 1994 values.

Before leaving this matter of comparative values a further element should also be taken into account: namely the gross undervaluing of Whitworth's property. The Firs was never entered in the books at its proper value. Likewise, the valuation of the Openshaw works was considerably lowered for very good reasons: the value of the Sackville Street site was only partly included during the technical school discussions. Had these items plus a number of other significant gifts been correctly valued, the total worth of Whitworth's will would have been considerably more. Of course, most of these items would have appeared on both sides of the account but at least it would have projected a more realistic assessment of Whitworth's generosity.

Robert Darbishire, the legatees' sole survivor, was called upon twice in 1908 to give an account how he and his co-legatees had portioned out the vast sums left to them. The newspapers, generally, praised their judgement:

> It is incredible that any body of legatees should discharge such a task in a way that would seem to all critics, or perhaps to any, ideally wise . . . yet this they have done . . .

So wrote the *Manchester Guardian*.[37] But part of the legatees' initial wisdom was, in fact, to carefully consult men like C.P. Scott, William Agnew, Charles Behrens, John Ramsbottom (the railway engineer) and William Mather – a mixture of brilliance and wit. Essentially, they had started out with the wealth of one man but morally, the Owens College developments, the Manchester Institute and Art Gallery, the new Whitworth Park, the technical schools and the Openshaw Baths plus all the other benefactions were the interpretational work of partisan enthusiasts. It was to this whole team of engineers, lawyers and literary giants to whom we owe such a creatively living reminder – the Whitworth memorial.

It was, in fact, from within this galaxy of advice that the inspired decision was made to purchase Potters Field – an open space which ran alongside Oxford Road, Manchester – for it to become the historic basis of the Whitworth Institute scheme and the gallery. The credentials for doing this were impeccable as the 'Fields' were imbued with splendid Potterite history. Just ahead of the site being finally cleared, however, the one remaining house was The Grove, which was owned by John Hopkinson, grandfather of Dr John Hopkinson FRS (Whitworth's personal assistant and confidant) and his brother, Professor Alfred Hopkinson QC MP, later to become Vice Chancellor of the University. Potters Field-cum-Whitworth Park is symbolic; not only because of Sir Thomas Potter, the first Mayor of Manchester and founder of both the *Manchester Guardian* and the *Manchester Examiner*, or indeed of the Hopkinsons, but because of their inspirational links with so many engineering personalities, particularly during the later Fairbairn and Whitworth years. Dr Edward Hopkinson, the last member of the family to live at The Grove before moving out to Alderley Edge, was a wonderful case in point. In 1894, he became the managing director of Mather and Platt Ltd., celebrated engineers, before going on to become Member of Parliament and President of the IMechE following exactly in the footsteps of his mentor, Sir William Mather MP, Chairman of the company, but equally important, a sincere upholder of Whitworthian ideas.

It is difficult to summarize the influence generated by these personalities or to single out any of them for special mention but of those engineers brought together by Robert Darbishire, probably Sir William Mather was the most outstanding of Whitworth's successors. Unwavering, he wanted to get into the House of Commons to advance the cause of British engineering and to promote the state funding of technical education. He was, in fact, the most successful of all the nineteenth-century engineer MPs, persuading the Government to introduce the Technical Instruction Act 1889, and by radically amending the Customs and Excise legislation of that year he won for technical colleges half the duty collected from the sale of spirits to assist pay for their technical teaching.

William Mather was, however, much more of an internationalist than Whitworth. Like many sons of Manchester merchants he attended a college near Heidelberg as a seventeen-year-old; thus he later demanded for Britain the same advantages the Charlottenburg Technical University had given Germany. He was equally inquisitive about the Russians after the 1917 revolution and installed at Owens College a professorial chair in Russian but it was his high regard for German teaching and engineering science which animated his active interest in the Manchester Schiller Institute. He talked a great deal about European politics, believing as he did that German engineers were too intelligent to allow war with Britain. 'Britain and Germany might build as many ships as they liked – they will never go to war', he once told the 1909 annual dinner of Schiller friends. Nor did he hesitate to remind both political and engineering audiences of his profound belief that 'it is the power of organised engineering knowledge that decrees enrichment and decides a nation's destiny'.

Nowadays, the Whitworth Art Gallery ranks as one of the nation's most interesting collections with its fifty Turner watercolours, early European etchings and its Epstein sculpture. Many of the generous contributors who were responsible for its creation in 1893 were also present on subsequent occasions when Sir William Agnew, doyen among London art dealers and President of the Manchester Whitworth Institute, reported the Gallery's progress.

William Agnew was typical of the men who pioneered the Institute in that he idolized Gladstone; Agnew's son, George, was also an offshoot of this Gladstonian Manchester mania and became the Liberal MP for Salford in 1905 – and although art appreciation was part of the Agnews' rationale, they never once wavered in their tribute to Whitworth. William was gifted with an exuberant vitality – a born actor – nevertheless the superb watercolours and other pictures which he personally gave to the Whitworth Gallery illustrated not just his devotion towards Manchester but his dedication for the cause Whitworth enunciated so well: the intellectual enrichment of young people facing for the first time a technically more advanced world.

History, very often, is dramatically changed by the unexpected and the sequence by which Whitworth's legatees sought to realize his assets was indicative of the point. Indeed, much of what they did could only have been done once Lady Whitworth herself had died. The historic misadventure in this case, or – perhaps better put – the macabre fortuity of Lady Whitworth's own unexpected death in 1896 (at the age of seventy-three) only nine years after her husband, facilitated the release of the Stancliffe estate and enabled the purchase outright (in 1897) of the Sir Joseph Whitworth Company by the Sir W.G. Armstrong & Co. to go ahead. Whitworth himself would have been mortified had he suspected for one moment the identity of the only feasible predator waiting in the wings. Presumably, it was his widow, Mary, out of respect for her husband, who put off during her own lifetime the negotiations which would have enabled Sir William Armstrong, Joe's lifelong adversary, to take over his company, lock, stock and barrel. It so happened that the buy-out was itself completed only three very sparse years before the death of Armstrong himself.

It was an inevitable and sensible merging of joint interests, nonetheless the new title – Sir W.G. Armstrong Whitworth and Co. – was steeped in irony. Of the two remaining legatees, Christie and Darbishire, both were familiar with Whitworth's ambition that the Board of his company should one day become a combination of worker-directors and senior management based on a shareholding workforce. In fact, just prior to his death, Whitworth had asked Christie if he would take over the Chairmanship of the company precisely because Christie, at that time, was probably Britain's leading commercial lawyer. If anyone had the expertise to radically reconstruct the company the way Joe wished then it must have been Richard Christie. Some years earlier, in 1879, Christie had left Manchester to reside in Darley Dale. For two years or so, he was a close neighbour of the Whitworths and regularly went over to Stancliffe, often discussing the many problems associated with worker-directors and the managerial society. As Robert Darbishire recalled: 'I recollect that one of Sir Joseph's schemes which he dwelt upon over and over again but could never perfect, was to find some way or other of interesting his workmen in the success of what was practically their own work. We had many discussions of various plans for this purpose but none appeared to him perfect enough for final adoption. When the executors completed the sale of their share in Joseph Whitworth and Company – if I recollect right – no less than about £25,000 was invested by workmen of the firm in purchasing shares in the new partnership'.[38]

During the takeover discussions between the two companies, Richard Christie was in the Chair. It is inconceivable that the future of Whitworth's scheme for worker shareholdings was not discussed yet none of it survived. It was in fact fifteen years later before the company issued a superior type of brochure to update the situation. 'It must be remembered that when both Mr Armstrong and Mr Whitworth started to exploit their inventions,' the booklet stated, 'they from the first, rigidly insisted on perfection in workmanship, and the training that the original workman received from these two pioneers has been handed down as a tradition of the Works from father to son. The Openshaw Works are devoted to manufacturing armour plate, guns and mountings, projectiles, machine tools, bullet-proof plate, propeller shafting, tool steel, small tools and special alloy steels.' Obviously, by 1912, the marriage had been fully consummated; the ghosts of Whitworth past sufficiently exorcised. No mention was made of 'workers saving for shares'.[39]

But sadly the manufacture of Whitworth machine tools at Openshaw came to an abrupt end in 1928, almost a century after he had first set up his three-man jobbing business in Manchester. One of his leading competitors (from 1853) was a firm started by the formidable Craven Brothers, both the senior partners having served apprenticeships with Charles Beyer and William Fairbairn. To update the story, however, the year 1927 had been particularly bad for machine makers everywhere and Messrs Armstrong Whitworth invited Craven Brothers Ltd. to take over the machine tool section of their Openshaw business. This they did – it was in spirit almost a founders' reunion – the pioneering Craven Brothers have, in fact, stood watch throughout our chronicle here, hence it never surprised anyone when the coming together of these two powerful traditions proved a satisfactory – if somewhat rueful – conclusion to the story of Whitworth's machine tools.

But as we know, Whitworth's innermost self was never exclusively Manchester. Like his great friend William Fairbairn, he loved the London round and quietly believed that the nearer one got to the parliamentary scene the greater the chance of success. For him personally it didn't work that way; nevertheless when he first created the Manchester Rifle and Ordnance Company in 1862, he purchased from the well-known artist, George B. Potts, No. 28 Pall Mall, London, almost opposite the then Ministry of War. He made the ground floor his London office but on the first floor and above he invited Daniel Gooch MP and John Pender MP to share his newly furnished living accommodation. It very much became an 'engineering' establishment – particularly when Gooch's Vulcan Foundry took over part of the premises – and for a decade it became the venue for many an 'engineering' and parliamentary tête-à-tête. In 1874, William Cunard took over the lease of the premises on behalf of the Cunard Steamship Co., affably allowing Whitworth and his colleagues to continue their use of the place for the next two years.

By 1875, however, Whitworth and Gooch were anxious to move within 'bell' distance of Parliament and were invited by the engineers, G.R. Stephenson and George Bidder, to share the front half of No. 24 Great George Street, just off Parliament Square. The Institution of Civil Engineers already occupied the house next door, No. 25, together with the rear parts of No. 24. The fact that the membership of the Institution had long outgrown its facilities meant that they were desperate to find a more spacious headquarters: it gave them an added interest in their adjoining properties. But when the freehold of No. 24 came on to the market in 1878 it was not the 'Civils' who purchased the whole building but Whitworth himself. Why he did so remains a mystery. Soon afterwards he moved his London office nearby to Victoria Street, a place John Hopkinson found conveniently close to both Parliament and the Engineers.

The puzzle why Whitworth purchased the freehold of No. 24 Great George Street broadens out considerably in the light of subsequent events. Although he was still an active Council member he refused the later request of the 'Civils' to buy the property from him yet paradoxically in 1883 he left instructions with Robert Darbishire that in the event of his death, the 'Civils' should be offered No. 24 Great George Street for £15,000 – a 'gift' they gladly accepted in August 1887. By this time, because the Institution now owned Nos 24, 25 and 26 the Ministry of Works promised they would *sympathetically* compensate the Engineers should they, the Government, go ahead and compulsorily purchase the entire street, in preparation of their own building programme comprising of a new Treasury and a new Foreign Office. To facilitate this, their much-vaunted Westminster Improvements Bill finally went through in 1887 and after a further twenty-two years the Engineers were obliged (clutching their meagre compensation) to cross the street and commence the building of their own impressive library and new headquarters.

Although Whitworth himself left a few company shares to both the 'Civils' and the 'Mechanicals' there has been some criticism lately that his legatees did not do more. To better understand this criticism consider first the resounding call to arms originally uttered by Whitworth the campaigner – words that have been repeated many times by IMechE Presidents – 'we must try as hard as we can': yet the impoverished legacies bequeathed by engineers to the Institution have never again been remarked upon.

Whitworth's words were as he himself practised. 'The replacement wherever possible of human effort by mechanical contrivance and the attainment of ever rising living standards largely rests with the mechanical engineer'. And so it did; but if the Institutions were intended to be the professional means by which the engineer could advance his status in society, then the founding fathers – the Beyers, the Fairbairns, even Whitworth himself – laid down some pretty threadbare precedents offering little encouragement to their successors; hence the cruel whiff of censure nearly a century later.

For *him*, more important than receiving any particular honour, Whitworth strove mightily for the international recognition of his work. Too often he was honoured rather than recognized. It was this he reviled. Only the French cited his military work as being in the leadership of the world when, in 1868, Louis-Napoleon III appointed him to the Legion of Honour. During the same year he also received the Albert Gold Medal 'for the invention and manufacture of instruments of measurement and uniform standards' but Whitworth was right to be irritated for it was more than a decade before the Board of Trade finally adopted his gauges as British standards. In 1869 he was created a baronet in addition to a host of other awards and honorary doctorates. What he really longed to hear was someone in government say, 'Joe – you've given the world precise measurement, machine tool know-how and a gun system the best in the world,' but no one ever did. Grudgingly he left the world almost as quietly and as ignobly as he had entered it eighty-four years earlier.

The author has tried to present Joseph Whitworth in a true and fair light. He was indisputably an outstanding Baconian scholar but because the bulk of his learning has remained in the toolroom rather than the library his creativity has gone unrecognized. Nonetheless, his everlasting epitaph must be the far-seeing comment first written by C.P. Scott and later repeated by Sir John Coode, 'The world knows of few lives that have contributed more conclusively than Whitworth's towards what he conceived to be the great task of humanity – *the supremacy of intelligence over the material universe*'.

One final question remains: advanced knowledge and technology has undoubtedly improved the quality of life but has it made the world a happier and safer place? Probably not. Contemporary engineers and scientists have taken the world to the edge just as Whitworth wanted to do but as in all spheres of engineering technology, the old, when faced with the new, evolves and finally dies away but human happiness very much depends upon the new technology and method never becoming bigger than the person. Joseph Whitworth understood this but like most of the world's greatest engineers he seldom put a philosophical pen to paper. It's a pity. Engineers will go on changing the world – it would be nice to know whether the ensuing changes sired the sequel they intended.

Notes and References

CHAPTER ONE

1. The following is a synopsis of the false obituaries. They appeared from Heginbotham, *Stockport Ancient and Modern,* Vol. 2, 1892 to the current volume of the *DNB.* As follows: Joseph Whitworth son of private school proprietor. High class pupil boarders. Congregational Minister. Joseph was sent to Vints Academy at Idle, near Bradford. Afterwards he was placed with rich uncle, a cotton spinner in Derbyshire, where he was trained and appointed under-manager. He married a farmer's daughter. He was a *pupil* of Maudslay in London.

2. Legend has it that Whitworth kept all his personal correspondence and papers. If he did, very little survived. Ernest Paulson, Darley Dale historian, in a letter to Prof. Diamond of Manchester University, 13/11/1984, explained that his own information about the burning of Whitworth's papers came from three sources (a) Paulson's family (his great uncle was a Stancliffe estate worker), (b) the late Mrs Wooliscroft, a maid at Stancliffe Hall, and (c) some important Whitworth papers were found in an old cupboard when the Stancliffe Quarry was closed, and these indicated that a possible collection (kept elsewhere) had been destroyed.

3. John Hurst Scrapbooks, Vols 2, 3, 6, 7 and 8; correspondence between Hurst and local tradesmen; Heginbotham, *Stockport Ancient and Modern,* Vol. 2, 1892, in Stockport Central Library, Local Studies. John Hurst provided a veritable maze of information which the author and his aides researched extensively. Local newspapers in Stockport did not exist before 1822. Some small houses west of Fletchers Yard were mill accommodation. The cottages to the south were known as Market Cottages. Considerable clearance of derelict dwellings occurred during the period 1790–1810, hence the open, dirt-covered spaces around the Middle Hillgate area at the turn of the nineteenth century. Mr Slater (Stockport auctioneer and recognized student of Stockport history) told John Hurst that 'Whitworth was born at the back of 13 John Street', *Advertiser,* October 1914. Following the death of Lady Whitworth (*Cheshire Notes and Queries,* Vol. I, 1896–7, p. 98) her obituarist writes: 'there is a general belief that [Sir Joseph was born] in a place formerly occupied by a marine store dealer'. That place can only be at the top of the stone steps, Fletchers Yard.

4. Orchard Street Chapel's *Church Book* lists Charles Whitworth as a Sunday School helper, 1805–10.

5. *Church Book, op. cit.*, 3/3/1805.

6. John Hurst (of Hurst Brothers, Shaw Heath, Stockport), *op. cit.*; in addition to the talks he gave to the Lancashire & Cheshire Antiquarian Society and last reported in the *Stockport Advertiser,* 13/3/1925.

7. See note 3.

8. The Orphan Houses which preceded those on Ashley Down, Bristol, to whom Whitworth left some company shares.

9. Elizabeth Briggs, Archivist, Kirklees District Archives, West Yorks. The burial entry (ref. No. N1/S/2) for Joseph Whitworth's sister, Sarah (aged 20) is as follows: 'Sarah, daughter of Charles and Sarah Whitworth of Shelley, died 5 March, buried 8 March 1833 in the Chapel at the base of the pulpit by George Ryan'.

10. The truth is of course that it was Charles, his father, who entered Vints Academy as a student, aged 32, single, or, more truthfully, a widower. These sad family circumstances and the Revd C. Whitworth's subsequent career were brought to light only by the careful piecing together of incidental references patiently researched with the expert help of Dr Williams's Library, Gordon Square, London WC1. While the library staff are in no way responsible for the author's conclusions it is clear that no more than a smattering of evidence would have graced this part of the narrative without their guidance through largely non-indexed material. See further Revd B. Nightingale, *Lancashire Nonconformity*, Heywood, 1893; Wright Watson, *Idlethorpe*, 1950; Miall, *Congregationalism in Yorkshire*, 1868, pp. 361–2; Revd Pool, *Our Village Churches*, 1891 (Revd C. Whitworth was at Dogley Lane Chapel, Shelley, West Yorks. 1826–34); Kenneth W. Wadsworth, *Yorkshire United Independent College*, 1954.

11. Vints Academy was probably not the best choice to sustain the myth of Joseph's education but it was the only feasible option.

12. Baines' *Directories of Yorkshire*, 1816–22; *Airedale Academy Reports*, 1800–24, Leeds City Library, Local History Unit. Charles Whitworth was first listed at Airedale, Upper Chapel and School, 1816.

13. Thomas Baines, *Lancashire & Cheshire – Past and Present*, Mackenzie, London, 1867, Vol. II, pp. 153–65 (chapter written by William Fairbairn 'Mechanical Engineering in these Districts'); *Manchester City News*, 15/11/1865. Occasional references to Whitworth's apprenticeship appear in various trade journals 1845–65. Their correct sequence resolved *inter alia*.

14. James Kershaw MP was speaking at the fiftieth anniversary of the opening of the new school hall. 'Stockport Sunday School', *Stockport Advertiser*, 1855, *op. cit.*

15. See note 10 for the source references.

16. *County Union Reports*, 1815–22; *Home Missions Report and Accounts*, February 1819. See *CU Reports* concerning Woolton and Garston, near Liverpool, April 1822; Revd J. Pool, *op. cit;* Dr Williams's Library, *op. cit.*

17. Ellen Whitworth McGowan's eldest son, Joseph Whitworth McGowan, of 4 Arthur Terrace, Bishop Street, Whalley Range, Manchester (31.3.1874) became company secretary and director, J. Whitworth and Co. Obviously Joseph Whitworth thus demonstrated sympathy for his stepsister and also her son when he appointed him secretary of his company. Clearly they had some knowledge of Ellen's childhood and the circumstances.

18. Revd J. Pool, *op. cit.*

19. The absence of expected features, e.g. church, family records, tenant farmer possessions, land ownership, works against the *DNB* description of Fanny (or Frances) Ankers being a farmer's daughter from Tarvin, Cheshire. The evidence is strongest in favour of her being one of the many Ankers distributed around the canal basins between Chester and Northwich, daughter of a bargee. Their marriage was witnessed by a William Tunnicliffe, the Church Warden, which suggests that they eloped.

20. Strange that a titled lady should be buried locally without local paper comment. *Chester Chronicle*, 5/11/1870, sole reference: 'Whitworth, 28 ult., at the Forest House, Delamere, Lady Frances Whitworth, aged 70 years'.

21. Very few of the episodes which form the basis of this chapter are in themselves well documented by contemporaries (or

near contemporaries) of Whitworth. The author was satisfied, therefore, only after careful scrutiny by colleagues had established a reassuring groundwork. There was an ocean of print to search, much of it contradictory. It would have been misleading to list a convenient reference taken from an otherwise unreliable opinion even though it has been repeated down the years. In total some 300 catalogues, patents, essays, letters, reports, etc. provided sufficient factual material to make this chapter a model source for Whitworth's London experience.

22. The first mechanical calculator.

23. Samuel Smiles, *The Late Wm. Muir – Mechanical Engineer*, Rowallen edn, James Collins and Co. See also Muir's MS sketchbook.

24. *The Engineer*, 6/6/1856.

25. Sir J. Emerson Tennent LLD, FRS, *The Story of the Guns*, Longmans, Green, 1864, p. 23.

CHAPTER TWO

1. Marsden and Walker and W.J. Crighton and Co. were leading textile machinery makers in Manchester prior to 1824.

2. J.P. Kay, *The Moral and Physical Condition of the Working Classes Employed in Cotton Manufacturing in Manchester*, 1832.

3. Edwin Chadwick, *Inquiry into the Sanitary Conditions of the Labouring Population of Gt. Britain*, 1842.

4. For relevant comparisons between Bodmer, Beyer, Nasmyth and Whitworth see Manchester Association of Engineers, 1856–70; also Doan, *Some Episodes in the MEA*; Manchester Institute of Engineers, *Proceedings* (1860s); Manchester Scientific and Mechanical Society *Reports* (1870s), ICEng, *Trans.*, Vol. 28 (1868–9), pp. 573–608; cf. *The Engineer*, 23/5/1856. It is sometimes claimed that Bodmer preceded Whitworth in the matter of gauging. Study of contemporary work however will show Bodmer's gauging to be simple feeler, profile and depth gauging. For a resolution of this question study the poor quality of early textile machinery and locomotive building before 1850. See also later notes.

5. See J.G. Bodmer's patents and comments on the 'Manchester pitch'. Interesting archival material: Manchester Museum of Science and Technology and Local History Unit; D. Brownlie, 'J.G. Bodmer. His Life and Work', *Newcomen Society Trans.*, Vol. 6 (1925–6); Roe, 'Interchangeable Manufacture', *Newcomen*, Vol. 17, 1936–7; J.W. Roe, *English and American Tool Builders*, Yale, 1916.

6. D.K. Clark, *Railway Machinery*, London, 1854; Z. Colburn, *Locomotive Engineering and the Mechanism of Railways*, Collins, 1871. See also Beyer Peacock archive, MMST.

7. See note 6. Also James W. Lowe, *British Steam Loco Builders*, Goose and Sons, 1975.

8. James Nasmyth, *Autobiography*, Murray, 1883. See also the Patricroft Collection.

9. Ibid., see also G.S. Messinger, *Manchester in the Victorian Age*, MUP, and R.H. Kargon, *Science in Victorian Manchester*, MUP. Kargon's book particularly, if read alongside Messinger, provides a detailed backcloth and source material for this chapter.

10. Ibid., see also Edward Tootal obituary notice, *The Times*, 24/9/1873. Nasmyth, *op. cit.* (E. Tootal's will). See histories, L.N.W. Railway and Tootal Broadhurst Lee and Co.

11. *Manchester Historical Recorder*.

12. Patent No. 6926, 1835 and later, an improved model Patent No. 11504, 1846.

13. *John Bright's Diary*, Cassell and Co. Ltd, London, 1930.

CHAPTER THREE

1. Following his critical examination of Whitworth's machinery and drawings and other contemporary machines the author turned to the following sources for eye-

witness opinion: William Muir (1806–88), MS papers and sketchbooks (Muir was employed by Whitworth July 1840–June 1842 as chief draughtsman and works manager); Charles F. Beyer (1813–76) diary and sketchbooks; Robert Mallet InstCE, FRS, *Practical Mechanics Journal* 1859 & 1862; D.K. Clark, Superintendent, Machinery Dept, South Kensington, and convenor of Exhibition Jurors.

2. Patent No. 6566, 27/2/1834.

3. Patent No. 6850, 1835.

4. Confirmation of Whitworth's planing machine programme see: Chorlton Street inventory, 31/12/1837, IMechE; Charles F. Beyer notebooks (Beyer archive); contemporary trade magazines, e.g. *Engineer* and *Practical Mechanics*. See further Chapter 7.

5. The figure £6,720 is Whitworth's own 1837 valuation of some 34 machine tools (IMechE archive). The update figure is based on an auction catalogue (1988); total cost for a 'similar' collection of simple second-hand machine tools (£1.3m); cf. other value-of-money comparisons in this book.

6. 1862 Exhibition edn, *Mechanics Magazine.*

7. J.G. Moon, addressing the Junior Institution of Engineers in 1914. (Maudslay, Sons and Field finally closed down 30/4/1899. For the purpose of auction all Maudslay's original machine tools were photographed. *Engineering,* 18/1/1901, and Poplar Public Libraries/GLC collection.)

8. *Manchester Collectanea* – Harland newspaper cuttings, Manchester Central Library, Local History Unit; *Manchester Examiner and Times*; final reference in *Manchester City News,* 26/12/1925; the *City Lantern* and other ad-hoc cuttings.

9. Ibid.

10. Local History Unit, Manchester. There exists a myriad of casual cross-references to the period 1835–75 concerning the Bright–Cobden (Manchester School) and Potter families and their political devotees. What could be described as a Potterite myriorama sets out how the paths and daily activities of men like Whitworth and Chadwick and the Potterites crossed and re-crossed during the period. Political judgements being spreadable the source of Whitworth's political sympathies are axiomatic; likewise his friends.

11. Whitworth shared his London accommodation at 28 Pall Mall with Daniel Gooch and other parliamentarians.

12. Patent No. 7453, 2/11/1837.

13. Ibid.

14. cf. Nicholson and Wordsell compounds, IMechE library.

15. Charles Beyer (1813–1876) and John Ramsbottom (1814–97) were arguably Britain's best locomotive designers during the 1850s and 1860s. Beyer particularly, consistently called upon locomotive engineers to appoint many more talented draughtsmen. He believed that good loco design was the key to Britain maintaining world leadership in steam engineering.

16. John Ramsbottom, locomotive superintendent LNWR, received salary of £500 p.a. in 1849, advanced to £5,000 p.a. from 1/1/1864 on becoming general manager LNWR. See Brian Reed, *Crewe Locomotive Works and its Men,* David and Charles, 1982.

17. Much of this reasoning persuaded Fairbairn to appoint W.C. Unwin (1838–1933) his personal assistant in 1861. Prof. Unwin later became Engineering Dean, Imperial College.

18. Sir William Fairbairn FRS, *The Life* (ed. William Pole), Longmans, Green, 1877.

19. Robert H. Kargon, *Science in Victorian Manchester,* MUP, 1977. Kargon's research is prodigious. His meticulous dredging of Manchester records provided leads without which the author would not have tracked many of Whitworth's activities. See also Gary S. Messinger, *Manchester in the Victorian Age,* MUP.

CHAPTER FOUR

1. Isambard Brunel, *Life of Isambard Kingdom Brunel*, Longmans, Green, 1870.
2. Patent No. 2894, 1876.
3. *Life of William Fairbairn FRS* (ed. Wm Pole), Longmans, Green, 1877.
4. L.T.C. Rolt, *Tools for the Job*, Batsford, 1965, p. 120.
5. Ibid., p. 125.
6. Whitworth Misc. Papers on Mechanical Subjects Part 1, 1882, p. 62.
7. *Manchester City News*, 25/11/1865.
8. This account is repeated in several of Whitworth's obituaries. It probably originated *Manchester Courier* after the *Manchester Guardian* article, 9/12/1840.
9. James Nasmyth, *Autobiography* (ed. Samuel Smiles), Murray, 1883.
10. Prof. F.C. Lea IMechE, monograph, *Whitworth*, British Council, 1946, p. 5.
11. *Report* of the British Association for the Advancement of Science, August 1840. Printed in full in Whitworth pamphlet, *On Plane Metallic Surfaces*, 1841. Also see Misc. Papers 1858.

CHAPTER FIVE

1. P.J. Booker, *History of Engineering Drawing*, Chatto and Windus, 1963.
2. *Engineering*, 18/1/1901.
3. Nasmyth, *Autobiography* (ed. Samuel Smiles), 1883.
4. 1854 Weights and Measures Bill. Select Committee evidence.
5. Ibid. Whitworth was examined on 6–8 June 1855.
6. 'Report of Committee on Standards and Gauges', *Trans. ASME*, Vol. IV, Engineering Societies Library, NY; Prof. J.W. Roe, *English and American Tool Builders*, Yale, 1916.
7. George M. Bond, 'Standard Measurements', *Trans. ASME*, Vol. II.
8. Henry J. Chaney, *Standard Weights and Measures in Use in the British Empire*, 1897; Misc. papers quoted by Chaney and others – House of Lords library; Select Committee evidence and reports; Measurement legislation, House of Commons Library and Board of Trade (Record of Standards – Measurements).
9. NWML correspondence with author, 26/11/1991. The Armstrong-Whitworth Company (1900) donated to the NPL a special lathe claimed to be capable of cutting and correcting lead-screws to within 0.0002 in. This machine is currently stored at Wroughton Airfield, Swinton.
10. T.M. Goodeve and Prof. C.P.B. Shelley, *The Whitworth Measuring Machine*, Longmans, Green, 1877.
11. Ibid.
12. All Whitworth's papers on measurement commencing with *Inst. CE Proceedings* 1841 – *IMechE Proceedings* 1857 inclusive and reprinted in his *Miscellaneous Papers*, 1858.
13. Goodeve and Shelley, *The Whitworth Measuring Machine*, Longmans, Green, 1877.
14. *The Times*, 11/6/1855, p. 7.
15. Ibid.
16. Ibid.
17. The Jefferson correspondence, Smithsonian Institution.
18. At least two reports commissioned by the US Congress (1828 & 1853) referred to tolerances as 'wide' and 'close'. The 'close' tolerance referred to in the first report was probably around ± 0.001 in: not good enough for dependable interchangeability even if attainable. See also Fitch, *Report on Manufactures of Interchangeable Mechanism*, US Census, 1880, in Engineering Societies Library, New York.
19. The Brown and Sharpe Manufacturing Company of Providence, USA, in 1877 possessed both a metre and a 'yard standard'. (Copies of the official standards held in Washington.) In July 1877 they wrote to the Coast Survey Office, Washington, as follows: 'Taking 39.370 as the standard, there is only 0.00023 ins in the metre different in our comparison,

which perhaps is as close as may be expected. We shall now consider your comparison of our steel bar with the standard at Washington as correct, and in our comparisons with it shall be able to detect errors as small as 0.000025 ins.' In 1893, an order was issued by Congress defining the US yard in terms of the metre at 20°C. *ASME Trans,* Vols II to V, Engineering Societies Library, NY; Prof. J.W. Roe, *English and American Tool Builders,* Yale, 1916. (Author's note. To modify the Brown and Sharpe correspondence: please note that the first 'millionth' comparator was made at NPL in 1918.)

20. Ibid; George M. Bond, 'Standard Measurements', *ASME,* Vol. IV; also his lectures on measurement, Franklin Institute, Philadelphia, 1884.

21. Whitworth slip-gauges (1870) ± 0.0001 in (The 'Enfield inch' standard made by Whitworth in 1860 when measured in 1966 was 0.99985 in). Today's slip-gauges (reference std) are guaranteed ± one micro-inch at 20°C.

22. John Fernie IMechE, Chairman, Clarence Iron Works, Leeds (1858–71), recognized nineteenth-century authority on history of measurement, delivered a paper to Inst. Mechanical Engineers, 26/1/1865. He included the following definition. 'The length of the metre was consequently defined in 1798 by Borda . . . by giving 0.99385 metre' (the ten-millionth part of the Earth's polar quadrant passing through Paris).

23. Kenneth J. Hume, *A History of Engineering Metrology,* MEP Ltd, 1980.

CHAPTER SIX

1. Edwin Chadwick (1800–90), environmental health reformer, voluminous writer of pamphlets, first Sanitary Commissioner 1839, became partner of Whitworth concerning street cleaning and sewage disposal. Many of his ideas (which he shared with Whitworth in the 1840s) can be seen in the plans he made for Cawnpore (south of Lucknow), India, to improve its defective (army) sanitation. This work was done at the behest of Gladstone in 1871.

2. Dr John Leigh, medical man and chemist. One of the greats in the history of environmental health. Campaigner for clean air. Baconian scholar. Close to Chadwick. Described by *Manchester Guardian* as 'brilliant scientist'. His two papers (October 1844) on 'Respiratory Disease' and 'History of Cholera' were reported in the *Manchester Guardian,* 5/5/1849.

3. *Manchester Guardian,* 9/10/1844.

4. Patent No. 8475 (1840) and Patent No. 9433 (1842) Machinery for cleaning roads.

5. See Manchester Council Minutes, reports and Whitworth–Chadwick correspondence; 'Extract from the Fourteenth Annual Report of the Lamp, Scavenging Committee', Manchester, 1842; Chadwick Papers and correspondence, University College, London University Library.

6. Letter from Whitworth to Chadwick, 15/3/1846 *op. cit.,* and Birmingham Council. For report of the Manchester Guardian's Council, see *Manchester Guardian,* 24/1/1852.

7. Jane Carlyle, *Letters* (ed. Alexander Carlyle), 1903, Vol. 1, Letter No. 78.

8. Letter Whitworth to Chadwick, 14/11/42.

9. Ibid.

10. Very little information exists as to Whitworth's ideas for a mass-production foundry. Obviously conveyor belt systems would be required if local authorities adopted Chadwick's plans for street drainage: cf. note 1.

11. Daniel Broadhurst (1789–1859) was appointed Treasurer of the Borough on 5/12/1842, at an annual salary of £300. Married Mary Tootal 1825.

12. Jenny Uglow, *Elizabeth Gaskell,* Faber, pp. 555–6.

13. *The Engineer,* 6/6/1856 and 14/12/1866, pp. 445–6.

14. Ibid. See also Charles Beyer, Diary, 8/7/1842 and 8/12/1853; *Manchester City News,* 25/11/1865.
15. Beyer, Diary, 8/12/1853.
16. *The Engineer,* 6/6/1856, p. 305.
17. 'Uniform System of Screw Threads', ICEng, *Proceedings* 1841, pp. 157–60 and *Miscellaneous Papers,* 1858 (pamphlet).
18. Charles Beyer disseminated very clear views on why it was necessary to define the meaning of (professional) *engineer.* The profession has since paid a heavy price for ignoring his advice.
19. Samuel Smiles, 'Brief Memoir of the Late William Muir', *Mechanical Engineer* (1888).
20. Ibid.
21. Muir left Whitworth on 22/6/1842 to partner a man named Thomas Edmondson. It was Whitworth however who fixed an appointment for Muir to see Edmondson on 28/4/1842. Also consider that Henry Goss (Whitworth's chief draughtsman) openly advised Muir, particularly in regard to patents.
22. John Hetherington (John Hetherington and Sons Ltd), machine tool builder, Manchester, trained with Muir at his Britannia Works, Strangeways, Manchester. In 1890, Hetherington marketed an outstanding radial-arm drill (14 different controls grouped together on the saddle) but graciously later acknowledged that the original radial arm was Whitworth rather than Muir: cf. D.K. Clark, *The Exhibited Machinery of 1862* (1864), V & A Library; T. Baker, *The Elements of Practical Mechanism and Machine Tools,* 3rd edn, 1867.
23. See picture of Whitworth's early development of universal borer (1865), the first of its kind.
24. *Jurors Reports (Machine Tools)* 1862.
25. Nasmyth, *Autobiography.*

CHAPTER SEVEN

1. William Muir (Diary Notes 1840–43) and Charles F. Beyer (Diary Notes 1842–6). The detailed notes and drawings of Whitworth's early work. Note 9 and beyond.
2. The foundation upon which Whitworth progressed to the next stage (sometimes referred to as Whitworth's machine inheritance) has been established by the author using the following route: (a) examination of 1840s and 1850s machine tools and textile machinery and the possible machine shop procedures available to the constructors at that time, (b) corroboration of these factors by reconstructing the methodology on the drawing board, and (c) close examination of patent drawings, catalogues, photographs and exhibition write-ups.
3. Charles F. Beyer, Diary Notes, 8/7/1842.
4. *The Engineer* 23/1/1863. This triggered a correspondence mostly critical of Whitworth's machines. See *The Engineer,* 30/1/1863, 6/2/1863, 13/2/1863 and 20/2/1863. Despite these criticisms all the leading engineering establishments (Maudslay, Crewe Railway, Sharp Stewart, Beyer Peacock, etc.) continued to install Whitworth's machines, particularly planers. For the reader to make a personal judgement compare the general arrangement shown in fig. 1 with the only alternative available, i.e. simple rack and pinion systems.
5. Typical of the eulogies, Robert Mallet FRS, *The Practical Mechanics Journal,* February 1864: 'The result has been such tools as undoubtedly the work never saw before, and which to this hour stand at least unsurpassed in general excellence of design and perfection of execution'; see also D.K. Clark, *The Exhibited Machinery of 1862* (1864) pp. 128–39; John Ramsbottom, *Improved Methods of Metal Machining,* 1864, Crewe.
6. Following the 1862 Exhibition competing machine makers criticized Whitworth's machines, *The Engineer,* 13/2/1863. Francis Wise, former

Whitworth chief draughtsman, defended Whitworth vying with William Collier and Company of Salford. Collier's dubious claim to have built 'considerable numbers' of 40 ft planers (80 ft overall) seriously flaws the correspondence.

7. 'Beyer and Peacock's Graduating Engine', *The Engineer*, 20/6/1856, pp. 332–4.

8. J.W. Roe, *English and American Tool Builders*, Yale, 1916, pp. 202–4.

9. W. Steeds, 'The Evolution of Engineering Series', *Chartered Mechanical Engineer*, June 1964, p. 325. This machine was made at the Chorlton Street factory, 1878, and presented to the NPL, 1901. Unfortunately, the NWML press office (28/11/1991) were unable to establish the current whereabouts of the machine.

10. J.W. Roe, *op. cit.*, pp. 206–7.

11. This was one occasion when Whitworth apparently deserted his Baconian principles.

12. Whitworth's so-called self-acting 'power' indexation arrangement failed to take account of 'backlash' problems, hence the machine failed correctly to locate the gear blank.

13. J.W. Roe, *op. cit.*

14. J.W. Roe, *op. cit.*

15. 'Practical Essays on Mill Work', 1841, pp. 393–418.

16. House of Commons Select Committee on Small Arms, 12/5/1854.

17. Edward T. Bellhouse, IMechE (1816–1881) (E.T. Bellhouse & Company, Eagle Foundry, Manchester), was the father of modern hydraulic presswork. Richard Ormerod (Ormerod and Sons, St George's Foundry, Manchester) probably developed the Benjamin Hick hydraulic press in association with Whitworth.

18. Nasmyth, *Autobiography*; see also Iron Armour Select Committee, 1847, for detailed reports; Bessemer, *Autobiography*, p. 162.

19. A.S.E., Manchester No. 3 Branch, July 1852.

20. ICE, *Proceedings*, 20/2/1894, Ralph Hart Tweddell; see also ICE, *Proceedings*, Vol. 98, 1889, W.H. Greenwood.

21. Sir Henry Bessemer (1808–98) *Autobiography*; see also *The Times*, 14/8/1856.

22. Ian McNeil, MA, Hydraulic Power Transmission, 'Engineering Heritage', IMechE.

23. Sir Edward Carbutt, see ICE, *Proceedings*, 20/2/1894, p. 93.

24. *Op. cit.*, note 20.

25. *Op. cit.*, note 20. Tweddell said, 'Haswell's press . . . was not a forging – but a stamping press'. Tweddell then went on to quote Haswell's own description of his stamping press from 'The Manufacture of Locomotive Details by Pressure: Haswell's System', by R.L. Haswell.

26. F.C. Lea, *Sir Joseph Whitworth*, Longmans, Green, 1946, and his Sheffield papers.

27. See Chapter 9, 'Fluid Compression Steel'.

28. Evidence, Ordnance Select Committee, 1862–3; see also (Cast Iron) Select Committee, 1863; evidence given to Ordnance (Expert) Special Committee, WO, 1863.

29. See Chapter 9.

30. Evidence, Iron Armour Select Committee, 1862–6, and relevant Admiralty papers.

31. WO 33/20, Abstract of Proceedings (Artillery Committee minutes) 1868, pp. 867–9, 1869, pp. 287–90, 433–7, *Reports and Miscellaneous Papers*; Whitworth, *Mechanical Subjects – Guns and Steel –* Longmans, Green, 1873; Whitworth, Pressing, Shaping and Forging Metals, Patent No. 3064, 1874; *E.S.C. News*, 1957–8, Part III, pp. 6–7; R. Hart Tweddell, 'Hydraulic Machine Tools', IMechE, *Proceedings*, 1872. *Mechanics Magazine* 6/9/1861, see pp. 145–7, 'Admiralty gets £2.5 million for 5 frigates'. The magazine claimed that the science of armour plating had, by then, improved beyond the techniques used for HMS

Warrior. Not so. The basic reason why the vessels were phased-in over four years (according to the Admiralty) was the hope that by 1865 full armour plating would be possible the whole length of the ship. Confidential papers, Iron Armour SC.

CHAPTER EIGHT

1. The Paxton Palace of Hyde Park.
2. From an engineering gossip point of view there is no satisfactory single volume on the Great Exhibition, so Whitworth's Exhibition activities can only be gleaned piecemeal. See *Official Catalogue*, London, 1851; Hobhouse, *1851 and the Crystal Palace*, 1937; engineering journals; *The Times* and the *Manchester Guardian.* In regard to all these matters (1851–5) see Prof. G.S. Emmerson's *John Scott Russell*, Murray, 1977, by far the best digging-out of the most penetrating material.
3. Wendy Hinde, *Richard Cobden*, Yale; John Morley's *Cobden*, 1881.
4. This chronological narrative and analysis of the 1852 engineering lock-out is, in the main, derived from two sources: (a) *Account of the Lock-out of Engineering 1851–52* by Thomas Hughes, Barrister-at-Law, commissioned by National Association Social Science, and (b) *Masters and Workmen* (with analysis of Select Committee evidence) by William Newton, published by A.S.E., 1856. Additional information cited by the press and indicated by date and title.
5. *London Coffee House*, 24/12/1851; Thomas Hughes, *op. cit.*
6. Manchester 3rd to District Committee March 1861.
7. William Allan, General Secretary A.S.E., issued a statement 2/2/1852 explaining the piecework system. 'If a man's ordinary wages at day work [i.e. flat rate] be 30 shillings a week, the employer, no matter how hard the man works . . . will never pay more than £2 5*s* 0*d*' [i.e. 30 shillings at time-and-a-half]. London average wage (ASE), July 1852, was £2 3*s* 6*d* for 'skilled' men on 'full rate'. The A.S.E. Manchester District Schedule, 8/7/1876, gave the 'skilled' flat rate as 33*s* 4¾*d* per week plus average bonus 11*s* 6*d*. Consolidated rate (skilled) average £2 10*s* 0*d* for 54 hours (September 1876). Col. H.T. Arbuthnot (Digest of Evidence) Army Manufacturing Departments *Report*, 1887. Toolroom wages at RSAF, Enfield, varied little between 1857 and 1887. Arbuthnot gave toolroom weekly average wage (1887) £2 12*s* 6*d*., gaugemakers £2 14*s* 6*d*.
8. October 1852, the first Australian A.S.E. branch founded with 27 members, *AEU Centenary Statement.*
9. Thomas Hughes QC, *op. cit.*; *The Times*, 14/1/52.
10. Ibid.
11. The first meeting demanding piecework for the semi-skilled, held People Institute, Heyrod Street, Manchester, 19/1/1852, fully reported *Manchester Guardian*, 21/1/1852. The wider piecework argument reported *Manchester Guardian*, 24/1/1852, likewise *The Times*, 21–8/1/1852.
12. Whitworth personally declined to give evidence on these particular points to the House of Commons Select Committee on 'Masters and Operatives', 1856. Written submissions were made representing Manchester Masters Federation, thought to include Whitworth & Co.
13. See 'Advice When Ordering Machines' attached to Whitworth & Co. catalogues, 1862.
14. See Edward Vansittart Neale QC, *May I not do what I will with my own?*, Bezer, 1852 (pamphlet); Parliamentary Select Committee on the Trade Unions, 1868–9; Masters and Operatives, *op. cit.*, 1856.
15. *Op. cit.*, note 14. Vansittart Neale quoted Lord Cranworth quoting Whitworth. Cranworth took a great interest in 'capital–labour' affairs during the 1850s. In

correspondence with the press and others he quoted Whitworth being in favour of each workman being treated as an individual, e.g. not being paid the 'rate for the job' but the 'rate to which the man is entitled'.

16. A.S.E. quarterly returns from Manchester branches 1852–62. Unfortunately much of this material was destroyed during a clear-out at Manchester and at Peckham Road, London.

17. Left England SS *Britannia* 4/1/1842, arrived Boston 22/1/42.

18. Letter from Boston, 21/11/1867.

19. New York Industrial Exhibition, Special Report of Joseph Whitworth, House of Commons, 6/2/1854.

20. Ibid.

21. Ibid.

22. Marx, *Foundations of the Critique of Political Economy*, 1857–8. Marx laid stress on the artistic-scientific education of individuals during the 'free time' created by machines.

23. Marx, *Capital*, Vol. 1 and 'Wages, Price and Profit', SW., Vol. 1. Marx misconceived the idea of 'self-acting' machines to mean the replacement of men. In the event, wages and employment moved upwards.

24. In reply to Lord Panmure. *Report* by Sir John Anderson (May 1856) on the situation at Enfield RSAF.

25. 'The First 80 Years', an account of the Enfield Lock Branch (founded 1855). The Enfield District Committee (AUE and F) researchers could find no evidence either in Branch Minutes or Reports of any opposition to 'American machinery or methods'.

26. This John Hetherington was the Manchester machine tool manufacturer.

27. Reported in *The Engineer*, 22/2/1856.

28. Ibid.

29. Report to Lord Stanley, Board of Trade, August 1855.

30. William Fairbairn, *Useful Information for Engineers*, Third Series, 1866. Fairbairn alluded to excellent European loco design 11/12/1866 when speaking of the need for a professorial chair in engineering at Owens College.

31. IMechE, *Proceedings*, 25/6/1857.

32. 13/7/1857.

33. Fred J.F. Wilson and Douglas Grey, *A Practical Treatise upon Modern Printing Machinery and Letterpress Printing*, Cassell, 1888; *The History of* The Times, *1841–1884*, published *The Times*, 1939.

34. Charles T. Porter, *Engineering Reminiscences*, London, 1908.

35. Ibid. For an entirely different eye-witness account see *Manchester City News*, 25/11/1865; see also *The Engineer*, 6/6/1856 and 14/12/1866. The trade press generally (home and overseas) applauded Whitworth's machine tools during the period 1863–7.

36. Following the South Kensington Exhibition of 1862, Whitworth employed more draughtsmen than ever – though still not enough.

37. About 1872, Tom Pemberton became associate editor of *The Technologist*, New York.

38. Porter, *op. cit.*

CHAPTER NINE

1. *The Times*, 23/4/1857.

2. *Edinburgh Review*, 1859, p. 515.

3. Annual Lecture, United Services Institute, November 1859.

4. Minutes of Evidence, Whitworth examined 20/3/1854. Select Committee on Small Arms.

5. Whitworth correspondence quoted throughout this chapter is to be found MOD Library, PRO Kew (W.O. Series and confidential 'A' Papers, see note 18) and House of Commons library (Select Committee Minutes and Confidential Papers). Cross-references and the continuity of correspondence is extraordinarily difficult to trace. In the event the author is wholly indebted to the immense research and superb bibliography set out by Dr C.H. Roads MA, *The British Soldiers Firearm 1850–1864*,

Jenkins, London, 1964. His work is an indispensable piece of scholarship. Students working on Whitworth's 'small arms' period, 1855–65, should first concentrate on Roads's bibliography.

6. *Op. cit.*, note 4.

7. *Observations upon Small Arms*, 1843, pamphlet issued by Birmingham Gunmakers, Enfield RSAF Collection.

8. *Op. cit.*, note 4, p. 149.

9. RSAF Records. See Confidential 'A' Papers 146½, 1861, re Fox, Henderson and Company contracts.

10. T. Greenwood, IMechE, *Proceedings*, 1862, pp. 328–39 and drawings.

11. HofC Library. Misc. papers. Rebuilding work, 1846–56.

12. *Op. cit.*, note 4.

13. *Op. cit.*, note 4; see also W.W. Greener, *The Gun and its Development*, Bonanza Books, New York, 1881.

14. Ibid., pp. 630–31; also HofC Army Estimates, 1857.

15. *Op. cit.*, note 4.

16. Bessemer, *Autobiography.*

17. HofC Debate, 25/6/1861.

18. *Op. cit.*, note 5. See especially PRO, WO Confidential Papers 046½, 'A' Paper 117 of 1860. 'A Selection of Official Documents Relating to the Experiments on Rifled Arms Carried on by Mr Whitworth on Behalf of the Government, 1854–57'. Confidential 'A' Paper 16 of 1857. (Note. Westley Richards, born 1815, Royal Gunmaker of 178 New Bond Street, London and 82 High Street, Birmingham.)

19. HofC Select Committee on Ordnance, 1863 – see evidence given by Whitworth 20/4/1863, 23/4/1863 and 7/5/1863 in regard to the origin of polygonal system and I.K. Brunel. See also correspondence etc. privately circulated by Isambard Brunel (son of I.K. Brunel) with Introductory Statement. RSAF Archive.

20. Whitworth Collection. University of Padua, Italy.

21. *The Times*, Foreign Correspondent, 15/11/1859. Also Whitworth references, Musée de l'Armée, Hôtel National des Invalides, 75007, Paris.

22. Experimental results filed under 'Curtis and Harvey' and Colonel Boxer, Superintendent of Royal Laboratory, using Nitro cellulose, RSAF Record; see also Longridge (and F.A. Abel), *Mechanics Magazine* 11/5/1860, p. 310.

23. Dr Harold Edgerton (1903–90), Massachusetts Institute of Technology.

24. RSAF Archives.

25. DeWitt Bailey, *Guns Review*, March 1969.

26. *Op. cit.*, notes 5 and 18.

27. J. Whitworth FRS, *Mechanical Subjects*, Part II, Rifled Small Arms.

28. Ibid.

29. The barrel of this rifle was probably drilled in July 1859 using a twist drill some 20 in long. See also Jack Rigby of Dublin, *Practical Mechanics Journal* (Great Exhibition 1862) p. 467, 'Drilled from Solid'. In 1963 Mr Roy Jordeson (Engineering Dept, Manchester University) together with the author experimented by reproducing the exact difficulties experienced by Whitworth drilling deep holes when using a plate-drill. By twisting the drill as Whitworth had done and by using a manual feed we found it was then possible to drill a straight hole.

30. At the time of the 1862 Exhibition, Whitworth supplied rifle barrels drilled from the solid and finished hexagonally broached in steel, price £3 4*s* 4*d* – double the price of forged barrels. See evidence 14/2/1868, Special Committee of Breech-loading Rifles. Whitworth stated, 'I think they might now be made at about 25 shillings each if made in great numbers and in steel' (Minute 1327).

31. See evidence given by General Peel setting out Armstrong's position. HofC Select Committee on Ordnance, 1863.

32. Ibid. See official documents.

33. Whitworth charged the American Confederates (Invoices filed under 'Fraser,

Trenholm and Company', National Archives, Washington DC, microfilm M346) (20/12/1862), £700 each for a 70-pounder field gun plus £150 for the carriage. These prices were fixed in 1860. Compare this with his offer to supply the War Office, London, with 100 70-pounders at £275 each plus £150 for the carriage etc. (10/9/1869) as against a 64-pounder made at Woolwich for £245 12*s* 0*d* each. See PRO, WO 33/20 (Director-General Ordnance) p. 434, 6/11/1869 (Minute 27484). This matter of Ordnance and gun prices went back to Cabinet, March 1864, and Palmerston advised that the matter be left open. For the third time Palmerston acted in Whitworth's favour.

34. Hansard, 17/6/1862. Cabinet Papers, June 1862.

35. Thomas Greenwood, ex-chief draughtsman, Greenwood and Batley Limited, Albion Works, Leeds. See also the J.H. Burton correspondence, Burton Papers, Yale University, in addition to Burton's evidence to the Special Committee on Breech-loading Rifles, 7/2/1868, pp. 27–8, Appendix 1.

36. *The Engineer*, 3/7/1857, also the *Manchester Examiner* and *The Times* of the same date.

37. Evidence to Special Committee on Breech-loading Rifles, Lt.-Col. H.C. Fletcher in the chair, 7/2/1868.

38. *Op. cit.*, note 35. For results see Southport Trials report. 4/6/1857.

39. Sir J. Emerson Tennent, *The Story of the Guns*, Longmans Green, 1864, and *Manchester Guardian*, 26/7/1860.

40. *Mechanics Magazine*, 2/3/1860; 'Statement on Cast Iron', *Spectator*, 7/3/1860; 'Statement on Gun Trials', 21/2/1860; Whitworth's letter to *The Times*, 28/2/1860; Whitworth, *Misc. Papers, Mechanical Subjects, Guns and Steel*, 1873.

41. Ibid.

42. Tennent, *op. cit.*

43. *Mechanics Magazine*, 2/3/1860.

44. *The Times*, 25/9/1862 and 14/11/1862.

45. Prof. F.C. Lea, Whitworth Monograph. See also his Sheffield papers, 1946, on Whitworth and steel. When Lea became Dean, Faculty of Engineering, Sheffield University, he consulted steelmen extensively about the usefulness or otherwise of Whitworth's 'fluid compression' methods, therefore his opinion on this must carry some weight.

46. Undoubtedly Whitworth knew his guns were being supplied (via his agents in Liverpool) to both sides. In the main he kept silent. In answer to questions, 14/2/1868, the only meaningful answer he gave was '. . . I understand my guns were subject to the most harsh conditions and . . . if my own projectiles were used . . . my guns proved a good record'.

47. Griffiths, *'Rally Once Again' Battle Tactics of the American Civil War*, Crowood Press.

48. Bibliography (section on American Civil War), p. 327. The American Civil War is excellently researched and referenced. The following sources constitute the bulk of this section: (a) *'The War of the Rebellion': Official Record of the Union and Confederate Armies*, Series III Vol. 1, (b) Richard I. Lestor, *Confederate Finance and Purchasing in Great Britain*, University Press, Virginia, (c) Alexander L. Holley, *A Treatise on Ordnance and Armour*, 1865, (d) Hazlett, Olmstead and Hume Parks, *Field Artillery Weapons of the Civil War*, University of Delaware, and (e) Warren Ripley, *Artillery and Ammunition of the Civil War*, Van Nostrand Reinhold, New York.

49. J. Whitworth, *Misc. Papers on Mechanical Subjects*; see also letter to *The Times* 9/9/1870. Whitworth wrote: 'There is nothing so likely to shorten the duration of war and to prevent the resort to war, as the horrible effect of destructive power at long distances.'

50. J. Whitworth, *op. cit., Misc. Papers.*

51. J. Scott Russell, 'Into Versailles and Out', *Macmillans Magazine*, Vol. 23, 1871.

52. James P. Joule (1818–89) was actively

associated with both St Ann's Church and Cross Street Chapel, Manchester.
53. James P. Joule, MSS, UMIST, St Ann's Church discourse.

CHAPTER TEN

1. Joseph was accompanied by Fanny for the unveiling of a portrait, Manchester Infirmary, 22/2/1855, *Manchester City News*, and at a foundation stone ceremony, St Mary's Hospital, 3/9/1855, but not afterwards. Significantly, Fanny was not present either with or without her husband at the opening of the hospital on 10/10/1856 nor at any subsequent Manchester event.
2. Katherine Chorley, *Manchester Made Them*, Faber, 1950.
3. Jane Welsh Carlyle, *Letters and Memorials*, Vol. I, 1903, No. 78.
4. Vice Chancellor's 'Firs' File, Manchester University, also 'Firs Estate' documents; see Mrs W.C. Williamson, *Sketches of Fallowfield and the Surrounding Manors, Past and Present*, 1888; 1850 Ordnance Survey Map; Local History Unit, relevant documents.
5. Letter, Sir William Mansfield Cooper to Dr N. Pevsner, 21/8/1967.
6. See note 36 for the value of money, then and now, 1850–1990.
7. The architect Whitworth engaged in 1872 to do the alterations was Prof. T. Roger Smith of University College, London, followed by E.M. Barry in 1879.
8. Edmund Yates, *The World*, June 1877.
9. *The Gardeners' Chronicle*, 27/12/1884, pp. 807–8.
10. *Op. cit.*, *The World*.
11. Stockport Library, Local History, *Stockport Ancient and Modern*, Vol. II; *The Hurst Collection*, Vol. II, Mayors of Stockport, 1836–1896; *Stockport Advertiser*, January 1849, Newspaper File S/41, D62.
12. Edward Tootal (obituary notice, *The Times*, 24/9/1873), founder of Atkinson Tootal. His nephew, Henry Tootal Broadhurst (1822–96), became Whitworth's brother-in-law following his second marriage to Mary Louisa Broadhurst, 12/4/1871. See *Dictionary of Business Biography* Vol. I, 1984, and the company's own record, *Growth of the Tootal Organisation*. Daniel Broadhurst, father of Mary Louisa, was appointed Treasurer of Manchester 5/12/1842. See family obituaries 1850–1950 for a wider synopsis of the family.
13. *Op. cit.*, note 9.
14. Terence Kilburn BSc, MA, ARHist.Soc., *Joseph Whitworth – Toolmaker*, Scarthin Books, Cromford, Derbyshire, 1987, p. 53.
15. Deputy Registrar, Royal Archives, Windsor Castle, confirmed, in answer to query from author '. . . the Prince Consort's diary has not survived, and that very few of his private papers seem to have been preserved'. Letter 1/12/1989.
16. *Op. cit.*, Kilburn, note 14.
17. C.T. Porter, *Engineering Reminiscences*, New York, 1908.
18. Edmund Yates, *op. cit.*, note 8.
19. *The Architect*, 25/4/1872, p. 269.
20. J.G. Crace (1809–89), extremely versatile designer – from ships' saloons for J. Scott Russell to Pugin and the House of Commons. Pictures of Abney Hall, Stockport Library and the 'V & A Album'.
21. Katherine Chorley, *op. cit.*, note 2.
22. Chadwick (Whitworth) correspondence, University College, MSS.
23. Oddly enough, *The Times* gave Whitworth greater support over his lifetime than did Scott and the *Manchester Guardian*.
24. William Fairbairn, *Autobiography*.
25. Joseph Thompson, *The Owens College: Its Foundations and Growth*, Manchester University Press, 1866. For committee proceedings see Minutes of Trustees' Meetings (Education Purposes).
26. Evidence to Parliamentary Select

Committee on Scientific Instruction, 1868. This report is an invaluable background to campaigns for science education.

27. Letter to Disraeli, 18/3/1868.

28. *Op. cit.*, note 25.

29. The Bill (cited as the Department of Science and Art Act, 1875 No. 283) was sent from the Lords to the Commons, 3/8/1875, for the purpose of 'taking over lands and property'.

30. A.C. Magian MD, *The History of Owens College*, 1931.

31. ICEng, Special Report, William Pole, Part III, 21/2/1889; House of Commons debate, March 1871; W.H. Armytage, *A Social History of Engineering*, Faber, 1961, p. 235; *The Hornsey and Finsbury Park Journal*, 19/9/1881.

32. John Menassah Gledhill, 181 Upper Brook Street, Manchester. When the company moved to Openshaw, 1/2/1881, Gledhill became Chairman and moved house to Hazeldene, Fallowfield, Manchester.

33. Articles of Association, 31/3/1874; PRO, Ref. BT 31/2027/8791, 1874–1888; BT 31/4134/26647, 1888–1897.

34. J. Whitworth, Miscellaneous Papers, 1877. *Manchester Guardian*, 24/1/1887, p. 6. During the period 1875–80 occasional references 'for and against' appeared in the press and trades union journals, but no assesssment of its managerial value.

35. *Manchester Guardian*, 30/7/1908. The Whitworth Institute, pp. 4–6.

36. To compare the value of money in 1887 (the year of Whitworth's death) with 1994 is difficult for the following reasons: (a) essential cost-of-living indices throughout the period are not comparable; (b) the degree of labour intensity, methods and materials, varies enormously (historically) between different industries, e.g. new property bequeathed in 1887 would cost today a lot more than the index if a similar replacement were constructed. If modern transport, medicine and TV, say, are excluded from these comparisons, the £ in 1887 is today worth about 2p or one-fiftieth. If average wages (job for job) are considered, machine toolmakers in 1887 earned £2 8*s* 0*d* for 54 hours compared with £394 today, or times 164. (Whitworth paid his top gaugemakers 5.5 new pence per hour in 1863. Today's average contract-toolroom rate is £9.00 per hour or times 164.) The construction costs of new buildings over the same period represents a factor of about 128 or more. Using Department of Employment 'Historical Abstract' statistics and CSO tables together with Deane and Cole, *British Economic Growth* figures, a (weighted) comparison between Whitworth's 1880s and today would seem to be a factor of 53 or 54 (excluding, that is, tax and insurance). The comparison between the 1860s and the 1990s is not a great deal different, i.e. about times 54.

37. *Op. cit.*, note 35.

38. Ibid.

39. Armstrong Whitworth, *From Battleships to Tool Steel and Small Tools*, Palethorpe and Cond, Birmingham, 1912.

Appendix

British Patents Issued to Joseph Whitworth

Patent No.	Date	Title
6566	1834	Machinery for cutting screws
6813	1835	Machinery for spinning & doubling cotton, flax, wool, silk and other fibrous substances
6850	1835	Tools/apparatus for turning, boring, planing & cutting metals and other materials
6926	1835	Machinery for knitting & producing a fabric similar to that of knitted stockings
7095	1836	Machinery for spinning & doubling cotton wool & other fibrous substances
7226	1836	Machinery for spinning & doubling cotton wool & other fibrous substances
7332	1837	Tools/apparatus for turning, boring, planing & cutting metals and other materials (Not submitted)
7441	1837	Tools/apparatus for turning, boring, planing & cutting metals and other materials
7453	1837	Locomotive & other steam engines
8188	1839	Tools/apparatus for turning, boring, planing & cutting metals or other substances
8475	1840	Apparatus for cleaning & repairing roads or ways: applicable to other purposes
8705	1840	Tools/apparatus for cutting & shaping metals and other substances
9433	1842	Machinery for cleaning roads: applicable to other purposes
11504	1846	Machinery for knitting
12907	1849	Machinery for cutting metals; machinery applicable to agricultural & sanitary purposes
1349	1853	Machinery for cutting & harvesting corn, grass and other crops
1350	1853	Machinery for perforating or punching paper cards & other materials

Patent No.	Date	Title
2525	1854	Cannons, Guns & Fire-arms
903	1855	Ordnance, fire-arms, projectiles; machinery for the manufacture thereof
2410	1855	Artillery & Fire Arms
1645	1857	Ordnance, fire-arms & projectiles; Machinery employed in their manufacture
2329	1858	Guns, gun-carriages & ammunition
1959	1859	Ordnance, fire-arms & ammunition
2990	1859	Projectiles; machinery for their manufacture
2104	1861	Improvements in sights for small arms & ordnance and in fitting apparatus used with small arms (with W.W. Hulse)
510	1862	Improvements in manufacturing & preparing projectiles and in apparatus to be used for those purposes
1663	1862	Improvements in shells
51	1863	Ordnance (with W.W. Hulse)
2743	1863	Treatment & application of steel and homogeneous metal
261	1864	Projectiles
2856	1865	Preparing the ammunition or charges for rifled ordnance & rifled fire-arms
3018	1865	Improvements in casting iron & steel and in apparatus employed for this purpose
2416	1866	Cartridges for ordnance
2522	1866	Improvements in casting iron & steel and in apparatus for this purpose
963	1867	Breech-loading fire-arms & cartridges
1745	1870	Improvements in fire-arms & ordnance and in rifled projectiles & machinery for the manufacture of the same
2149	1871	Ordnance
782	1872	Wheels for railways & roads
1298	1872	Gun-carriages
3062	1874	Compressing fluid metal
3063	1874	Standard surface plates
3064	1874	Pressing, shaping & forging metals
2096	1875	Ordnance
2894	1876	Wheels for carriages
4937	1876	Steel crank axles
1743	1877	Armour for ships & forts
1171	1878	Armour for ships & forts
2869	1878	Crank axles

Select Bibliography

In addition to the general works cited below the most informative sources for all phases of Whitworth's work can be found in his published 'Miscellaneous Papers on Mechanical Subjects', Parliamentary Select Committee Reports and Minutes, War Office Special Committee Proceedings, Institution of Mechanical Engineers and the Civil Engineers *Proceedings* together with *Transactions of the Newcomen Society.*

The main Select Committee Reports are: Artizans and Machinery, 1824; Masters and Operatives, 1856; Cause of Strikes, 1856; Trade Unions, 1867–68; Small Arms, 1854–64; Ordnance, 1854–64; Armour Plate, 1859–64; Weights and Measures, 1855; Export of Tools and Machinery, 1825; Exportation of Machinery, 1841; Machinery of the USA, 1854–55. Records of the BSA Company, 1861–1900, courtesy of Herbert Woodend, MOD Pattern Room, Royal Ordnance plc, Nottingham.

Great Exhibition 1851, *Official Description and Illustrated Catalogue* (3 vols and supplement) London 1851, also *Jury Reports* and *Illustrated Catalogues*, South Kensington Exhibition, 1862.

Place of publication is London, unless stated otherwise.

Berriman, A.E., *Historical Metrology*, Dent, 1953.

Booker, P.J., *A History of Engineering Drawing*, Chatto and Windus, 1963.

Bright, Philip, *The Diaries of John Bright*, Cassell, 1930.

Brunel, Isambard, *Life of Isambard Kingdom Brunel, Civil Engineer*, Longmans, Green & Company, 1870.

Chaloner, W.H. and Henderson, W.O., *Engels as a Military Critic*, Manchester University Press, Manchester, 1959.

Chorley, Katharine, *Manchester Made Them*, Faber, 1950.

Emmerson, George S., *John Scott Russell*, John Murray, 1977.

Fairbairn, William, *Autobiography* (ed. William Pole), Longmans, Green & Company, 1877.

Gash, Norman, *Reaction and Reconstruction in English Politics, 1832–1852*, Greenwood Press, Connecticut.

Goodeve, T.M. and Shelley, C.P.B., *The Whitworth Measuring Machine*, Longmans, Green & Company, 1877.

Greener, W.W., *The Gun and its Development*, Bonanza Books, New York, 1881.

Hartog, Sir P.J., *The Owens College: A Brief History of the College*, MUP, Manchester, 1900.

Haslett, J.C., Olmstead, E. and Hume Parks, M., *Field Artillery Weapons of the Civil War*, Associated University Press, USA, 1983.

Hinde, Wendy, *Richard Cobden*, Yale, 1987.

Hogg, Ian, *The Weapons That Changed the World*, Ebury Press, 1986.
Hume, Kenneth, *A History of Engineering Metrology*, MEP, 1980.
IMechE, *Engineering Heritage*, Vol. 1, Heinemann, 1963.
Kargon, Robert H., *Science in Victorian Manchester*, MUP, Manchester, 1977.
Kilburn, Terence, *Joseph Whitworth Toolmaker*, Scarthin Books, Cromford, 1987.
Lea, F.C., *Sir Joseph Whitworth*, British Council.
Lestor, Richard I., *Confederate Finance and Purchasing in Great Britain*, University Press of Virginia, Charlottesville, USA.
Magian, A.C., *The History of Owens College*, MUP, Manchester, 1931.
Messinger, G.S., *Manchester in the Victorian Age*, MUP, Manchester, 1970.
Mills, W. Haslam, *The Manchester Guardian, A Century of History*, 1921.
Nasmyth, James, *Autobiography* (ed. S. Smiles), John Murray, 1883.
Nicholson, J.T., *Lathe Design for High and Low Speed Steels*, Longmans, Green & Company, 1908.
Porter, Charles T., *Engineering Reminiscences*, Lindsay Publications Inc., 1985 reprint.
Prentice, Archibald, *Historical Sketches and Personal Recollections of Manchester* (1851), new edn, Donald Reed, 1970.
Rennie, George, *Practical Essays on Millwork*, John Weale, 1841.
Ripley, Warren, *Artillery and Ammunition of the Civil War*, Van Nostrand Reinhold, New York, 1970.
Roads, C.H., *The British Soldiers Firearm, 1850–1864*, Herbert Jenkins, 1964.
Roe, Joseph W., *English and American Tool Builders*, Yale, New Haven, 1916.
Rolt, F.H., *Gauges and Fine Measurement* (2 vols), Macmillan, 1929.
Rolt, L.T.C., *Tools for the Job*, HMSO, 1986.
Rose, Joshua, *Machine Shop Practice*, 1880.
Simon, Sheena D., *A Century of City Government; Manchester, 1838–1938*, 1938.
Smiles, S., *The Lives of Engineers* (2 vols), Murray, 1861.
Steeds, W., *A History of Machine Tools, 1700–1910*, Oxford, 1969.
Stewart, Cecil, *The Stones of Manchester*, 1956.
Treatise on Service Ordnance, 7th edn, HMSO, 1909.

Index

JW = Joseph Whitworth.
Numbers in *italics* refer to illustration captions.